$600

D1107581

EQUIPMENT IN THE HOME

HARPER'S HOME ECONOMICS SERIES

Under the Editorship of HELEN R. LE BARON

DEAN, DIVISION OF HOME ECONOMICS
IOWA STATE COLLEGE

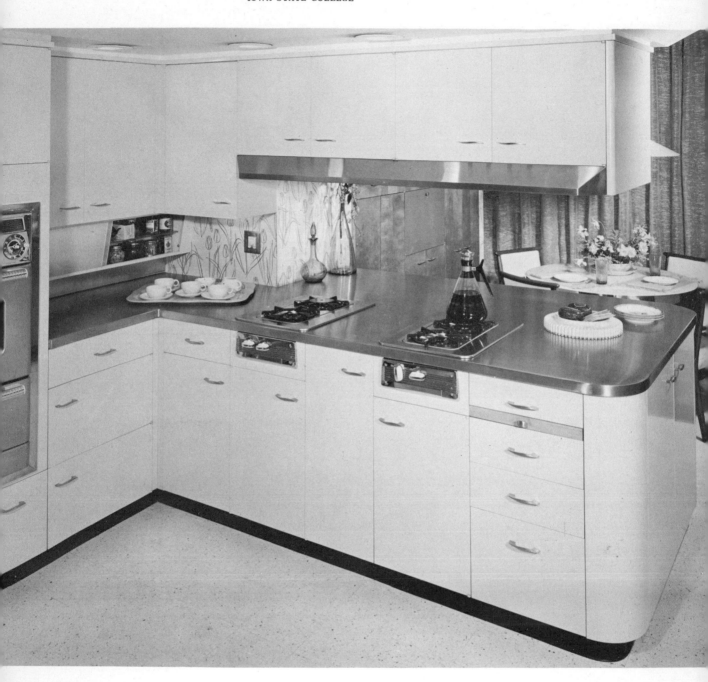

EQUIPMENT IN THE HOME

APPLIANCES, WIRING AND LIGHTING, KITCHEN PLANNING

Florence Ehrenkranz

PROFESSOR, SCHOOL OF HOME ECONOMICS
UNIVERSITY OF MINNESOTA

Lydia Inman

ASSOCIATE PROFESSOR, HOUSEHOLD EQUIPMENT DEPARTMENT
IOWA STATE COLLEGE

HARPER & ROW, PUBLISHERS — NEW YORK, EVANSTON, AND LONDON

Contents

Editor's Introduction

The rapid technological advances of recent years have produced an increasing variety of equipment designed for the home. Annual changes in design and improvements in conventional items such as ranges, refrigerators, and washing machines are taken for granted by both industry and the consumer. New and different types of equipment and appliances to ease and change the routines of housekeeping are developed at frequent intervals. We know that even more revolutionary changes can be expected in the years ahead.

Some equipment items are considered as a part of the house itself, others as furnishings for it. In both cases, they represent a large portion of the family's investment for housing.

Equipment for the home has become of such major importance that it is now considered as a separate area of study for college students of home economics. A homemaker trained in home economics is expected to be an intelligent consumer and user of equipment; she must understand the principles underlying its operation, its expected performance, its intelligent selection, and its efficient use.

The professional home economist employed in industry, in the instruction of high school students and adults, or in extension programs must have this same basic training to guide her as she works with families on problems of housing and equipment.

Related subjects such as wiring and lighting for the home, materials used for interior surfaces, and kitchen planning are included in this text. It is apparent that the home economist should be acquainted with recent research findings in relation to each of these subjects, and should understand their appropriate use in the home.

Both authors are experienced teachers of college classes in household equipment and have participated in the planning and development of courses in this area. Dr. Ehrenkranz is recognized also for her many contributions to research on household equipment.

HELEN R. LE BARON

vii

Preface

Equipment in the Home is planned as a textbook for college courses and a reference source for homemakers and their husbands, home economists, and business people in the home appliance industries.

Principles and practical considerations involved in kitchen and laundry planning and in selection, use, and care of appliances are one field of home economics. The teaching experience of the authors suggests that the material in this book can be useful as a textbook for an introductory course of one quarter, one semester, or two quarters, and as a reference text for advanced courses in refrigeration equipment, cooking equipment, and laundry equipment.

The outlines of experiments at the ends of most of the chapters are intended to emphasize relations between theory and practice. Also, it is our belief that students who are not specializing in the field of equipment may be pleased to find that only one book is required for their equipment course or courses.

Credit is given to the St. Charles Manufacturing Co. and Suter, Hedrich-Blessing for use of the frontispiece illustration. It is a pleasure to acknowledge the courtesy extended by many home economists and many manufacturers in supplying technical information and photographs.

FLORENCE EHRENKRANZ
LYDIA INMAN

EQUIPMENT IN THE HOME

CHAPTER 1

Electricity in the Home

Familiarity with some terms and a few elementary principles will help in understanding many factors associated with the use of electricity in the home. The material in this chapter covers some of the basic concepts needed for understanding *why* different recommendations are made for particular circuits in the home, for interpreting information given on nameplates of electric appliances, for estimating costs of operating different types of appliances, and so on.

Electricity used in the home is not a stored quantity. Rather, whenever a path for the flow of electric charge is completed, as by closing a switch, small electric charges known as electrons move along the completed path or circuit, provided the circuit includes a source of electric energy. The source of electric energy used in the home is the electric generator in the city or rural power plant that serves the home.

As electric charges move in a wire, certain effects occur that are utilized in household appliances. One effect is generation of heat. Heating appliances, such as hand irons and surface units on electric ranges, are designed to use the heat associated with the motion of electric charges.

Another effect is a magnetic field around the wire created by the movement of electric charges in the wire, by means of which the wire can be made to rotate under appropriate conditions. In motor-driven appliances, such as mixers, washers, motors of electric refrigerators, and so on, part of the wire in which the electric charges move is coiled on a shaft that is in turn mounted in bearings, and a magnetic field, provided by another coil in the motor, exerts force on the wire coiled on the shaft and thus causes the shaft to rotate in its bearings. The rotation of the shaft causes beaters of mixers to rotate, agitators of washers to oscillate, pistons or cams of electric refrigerator compressors to operate, and so on.

Electric dryers, ironers, and rotisseries utilize both the magnetic field and the heating effect associated with moving electric charges.

A. Basic Concepts

Some terms or words used in a discussion of electricity have a quantitative aspect; so many *amperes* are required by an appliance, or an appliance is rated for a given number of *volts*. Other terms do not have a quantitative aspect but nevertheless need to be defined; examples are *electric circuit, open circuit, short circuit*.

An *electric circuit* is a complete or closed path for the flow of an electric charge. An *open circuit* is a circuit that is interrupted or broken at one or more points; the electrons in the circuit wire on one side of the break do not cross the break and continue along the circuit. A *short circuit* is a circuit in which at least part of the moving electric charge traverses a smaller portion of the circuit than it should. This may happen when two parts (two wires or a wire and a switch, for example) that should not make electrical contact do make contact. A short circuit or a "short" is usually accidental; sometimes, however, an electrician shorts part of a circuit purposely in testing.

1–1. CURRENT, RESISTANCE, AND VOLTAGE

Electric current is a flow or motion of electric charges in a definite direction. The electric current in a wire that is part of an electric circuit is actually a motion in a definite direction of the loosely bound or "free" electrons of the atoms of which the wire is made. Thus when we turn on an electric appliance, we do not wait for electrons from the generator at the power plant to reach the appliance; rather, the free electrons in the circuit and in the wire of the appliance start moving almost instantly.

The practical *unit of electric current* is the *ampere*. The number of amperes flowing in a circuit depends on the electrical resistance of the circuit and the voltage applied to the circuit.

Electrical resistance is a physical property of materials. It is, as the name implies, the opposition or resistance that materials offer to a flow of electric charge. The *practical unit of electrical resistance* is the *ohm*.

For most household applications, three factors determine the number of ohms of electrical resistance of materials. One is the material itself. Copper, a good *conductor* of electricity, has a relatively low electrical resistance. Other materials, for example porcelain and Bakelite, have a high electrical resistance and are therefore called *insulators*. The second factor is the length of the material. Electrical resistance is directly proportional to length. For house circuits the material used is copper wire. If house circuit A is twice as long as house circuit B and both use wire of the same diameter, the electrical resistance of circuit A is twice the electrical resistance of circuit B.

The third factor is cross-sectional area. The electrical resistance of a given material is *inversely* proportional to the cross section available for flow of electric charge. If the diameter of the wire used in house circuit C is twice that used in house circuit D and the lengths of the two circuits are the same, the resistance of circuit C is one-fourth that of circuit D.

The *voltage difference* or *potential difference* between two points in an electric circuit is the work done when one unit of electric charge moves from one of the points to the other. The practical *unit of potential difference* is the *volt*.

Potential difference is often likened to water pressure. Indeed, potential difference is sometimes described as the "electrical pressure" required for the flow of electric charge. In some cases this analogy is fruitful. For example, it suggests correctly that electric charges will always move when a potential difference exists between two points connected by a conductor. Also, electric charges will not move between two points of a conductor when there is no potential difference between the two points. In an electric circuit, of course, the potential difference is due to a source of electric energy such as a battery or a 115-volt supply.

Ground or a good connection to ground is arbitrarily assumed to be at zero volts. The potential difference between ground and a circuit wire is either plus or minus—for example, plus 115 volts or minus 115 volts. Good connections to ground in the home include water supply lines and water drain lines.

1–2. OHM'S LAW

Ohm's law states that the current that flows through an electrical resistance is equal to the potential difference divided by the resistance.

$$\text{amperes} = \frac{\text{volts}}{\text{ohms}}$$

$$\text{ohms} = \frac{\text{volts}}{\text{amperes}}$$

$$\text{volts} = \text{amperes} \times \text{ohms}$$

The application of Ohm's law to household appliances is direct. Assume that a hand iron with a resistance of 13 ohms is connected to a 115-volt supply. Assume also that the resistance of the wires in the house circuit to the hand iron is negligible. (This last assumption is not completely valid, as is shown in the third example below, but it is a reasonable one for the present illustration.) According to Ohm's law, the amperes that will flow through the iron equal volts divided by ohms, and 115 divided by 13 is approximately 8.8 amperes.

As another example of Ohm's law, consider that the nameplate of an electric roaster indicates 10 amperes, 115 volts. The resistance of the coil in the roaster is volts divided by amperes, and 115 divided by 10 is 11.5 ohms.

As a third example, Ohm's law can be used to compute the *voltage drop* in a house circuit. Assume that an outlet in which we are interested is 100 feet from the electric service entrance in the basement where electricity is "delivered" to the house at 115 volts. Assume that 9 amperes actually flow through a small appliance plugged into this outlet. Then 9 amperes also flow through the two wires between the service entrance and the outlet.

To determine the voltage drop between the electric service entrance and the outlet, we must know the total resistance of the wires between the service entrance and the outlet. Wire used for small-appliance circuits in the home has an approximate resistance of 0.16 ohms per 100 feet. Applying Ohm's law, the voltage drop in each of the two wires between the service entrance and the outlet is amperes times ohms, or 9×0.16 which is 1.44. The total voltage drop in the two wires is 2×1.44 or 2.88 volts. Therefore the voltage at the outlet into which the appliance is plugged is not 115 volts; rather, it is 115 minus 2.88 or 112.12 volts.

1–3. POWER, ENERGY, AND COST OF ELECTRIC ENERGY

Electric power in a circuit or any part of a circuit is the rate at which work is done or energy is given up. The practical *unit of electric power* is the *watt*. Another unit often used is the *kilowatt,* 1 kilowatt being equal to 1000 watts.

In circuits that contain resistances only, such as those of heating appliances, watts equal volts times amperes. For example, one model of a nonautomatic coffee maker uses 4.4 amperes at 110 volts. Since the coffee maker is a heating-type appliance, the electric power it uses is 110×4.4 or 484.0 watts (0.484 kilowatts). As another example, we can return to our two 100-foot lengths of wire and the outlet for a small appliance. If the small appliance plugged into the outlet is a heating appliance, the power used by it is 112.12×9 or 1009.08 watts. The power used in *each* of the 100-foot lengths of wire is 1.44×9 or 12.96 watts. The power used in the entire circuit is 115×9 or 1035 watts.

Electric energy is the work done or the energy expended in a circuit or part of a circuit in a given time. Electric energy is power times time, and this is true for any kind of electric circuit. One unit is the *watt-hour.* Most simply, watt-hours are watts times hours. For example, when a 100-watt lamp is turned on for one hour, the lamp uses 100 watt-hours and in two hours it uses 200 watt-hours. A 1000-watt automatic toaster that is on for three minutes ($\frac{3}{60}$ of an hour) uses 1000 times $\frac{3}{60}$ or 50 watt-hours. A 300-watt refrigerator that is on for 15 minutes uses 300 times $\frac{1}{4}$ or 75 watt-hours.

A *kilowatt-hour* is 1000 watt-hours. Thus the 100-watt lamp uses 100 watt-hours or 0.1 kilowatt-hours per hour. The same lamp uses 0.2 kilowatt-hours in two hours. The 1000-watt automatic toaster uses 50 watt-hours or 0.05 kilowatt-hours in three minutes.[1]

[1] Some students have difficulty distinguishing between kilowatts and kilowatt-hours because they think kilowatt-hours simply *must* be more involved than kilowatts times hours. If you are such a person try to exercise a little faith and accept the idea that kilowatt-hours are exactly what their hyphenated name implies.

The *cost* of operating appliances and our monthly electric bills are calculated by multiplying kilowatt-hours by cost per kilowatt-hour. Cost per kilowatt-hour varies in different communities. In the city in which this text is being written, electricity for residences at this time costs five cents per kilowatt-hour for the first 100 kilowatt-hours and two cents per kilowatt-hour for all over 100. Thus if a family in this city uses 120 kilowatt-hours per month, the cost that month is 100×5 cents plus 20×2 cents or $5.40.

The number of kilowatt-hours used per month is obtained by "reading the meter," actually a kilowatt-hour meter, at the beginning and end of the month and subtracting the initial reading from the final reading.

The cost of electricity in most communities is "scaled"; the first 60 or 100 kilowatt-hours cost more than the second, and the second 60 or 100 may cost more than the third. Thus no single figure is accurate for determining how much it costs to operate a particular appliance for a given length of time. A figure around 2.8 cents per kilowatt-hour is often used at present as an average for the United States. At this rate, the operating cost of a 100-watt lamp for one hour is 0.28 cents. Operating cost of a 1000-watt automatic toaster for three minutes is 0.14 cents.

1–4. ALTERNATING CURRENT, INDUCTANCE, AND POWER FACTOR

Direct current—current that flows in one direction only—is supplied by dry cells and batteries and is little used in homes. *Alternating current* varies in magnitude and reverses in direction. The alternating current now commonly supplied in the United States is *60-cycle* current, though 50-cycle current is supplied in some areas. In each cycle, the current increases from a value of zero to a maximum value; then decreases to zero; increases again to a maximum value, but this time in the opposite direction; and decreases once again to zero. The cycle repeats 60 times per second for 60-cycle current or 50 times per second for 50-cycle current (Fig. 1–1).

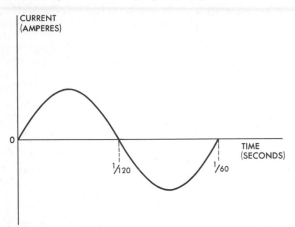

Fig. 1–1. Variation of 60-cycle alternating current during one cycle.

During one-half of each cycle, electrons are moving in one direction along a wire; during the other half of the cycle they move in the opposite direction. At the instant the motion reverses, the current is zero.

a. Inductance, Inductance-Type Motors, and Universal Motors

The *inductance* of a circuit or part of a circuit is the opposition offered to a change in magnitude of electric current. The mechanical analog of inductance is inertia—opposition to change in motion, such as starting or stopping.

Inductance is relatively unimportant in heating appliances, but it is of considerable importance in some motor-driven appliances. Coils of wire are used in motors of motor-driven appliances; they usually are wound on cores of iron or other magnetic material. Such a coil may offer a significant opposition to a change in magnitude of current. And alternating current definitely changes in magnitude.

Motors used in most motor-driven household appliances either are *inductance-type* or *universal* motors. Inductance-type motors are used in washers, dishwashers, electric refrigerators, freezers, dryers, fans, and room air conditioners, and in some other appliances. Universal motors are used in mixers, blenders, and in a few other appliances. Inductance-type motors are intended to be used at the *frequency* specified on the nameplate, for example 60 cycles per second. Universal motors may be rated to operate at any frequency from zero cycles per second (direct current) up to 60 per second.

The power developed in inductance-type motors is *not* equal to volts times amperes. Rather, it is equal to volts times amperes times a number which is different for different designs of inductance motors, but is always less than one. This number is the power factor of the motor.

b. Power Factor

An explanation of the physical basis for a power factor is beyond the scope of this text. It is given in texts on electricity. *Power factor* may be defined, however, as the number obtained when actual (observed) watts are divided by the product: volts times amperes.

The power factor of motor-driven household appliances is not stated on the nameplate. (For room air conditioners it is sometimes included on the specification sheet.) Measurements made by students in classes of the senior author have indicated power factors from 0.2 to 0.7, approximately, for different inductance-type motors used in household appliances and from 0.9 to practically 1.0 for universal motors used in household appliances.

The actual or approximate value of the power factor may be needed for estimating power and energy indicated on the nameplates of household appliances with inductance-type motors. For example, the name-plate on one model of a wringer-type washer specifies 5.5 amperes and 110 volts. Actually, this washer uses 272 watts rather than the 605 watts calculated from volts $\times$ amperes (110 $\times$ 5.5). The washer motor draws 5.5 amperes at 110 volts, but because the power factor of the motor is approximately 0.45, the power used is 110 $\times$ 5.5 $\times$ 0.45 or 272 watts. In other words, the electric energy used per hour by the washer is 272 watt-hours.

This answer on electric energy used by the washer is of course quite different from that which would be estimated from nameplate data if the power factor were not taken into account.

It is of course not necessary to know the power factor to calculate watts if the nameplate specifies the watts.

1–5. TRANSMISSION AND DISTRIBUTION OF ELECTRICITY

Electricity is transmitted by high-voltage wires from the power plant where it is gen-erated; the actual value of the high voltage depends on the area in which the electricity is transmitted. In rural and suburban areas where there is a generator or a substation, a transmission voltage of 6600 volts is common. If a generator or substation is located within a city, a transmission voltage of 2400 volts may be used within the city. The electric current transmitted is alternating current.

A three-wire transmission system is usual, and the three wires are connected to *step-down transformers* at many locations. In cities one or two transformers on poles often serve for one city block. In some farm areas one transformer per farm is usual. The trans-former decreases or steps down the high volt-age used for transmission to the voltage used in homes.

From the low voltage side of a transformer, two or three wires enter a house through a kilowatt-hour meter (Fig. 1–2). If a house has a two-wire supply, one wire is at a nominal 115 volts and the other is at zero volts; that is, the other wire is connected to ground or is grounded. If a house has a three-

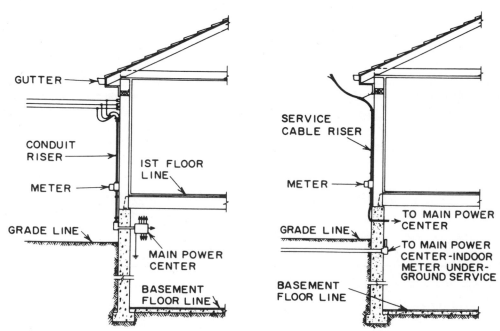

Fig. 1–2.   Three types of electrical service installations for homes. ("Live Better Electrically")

wire supply, one wire is at nominal plus 115 volts, one wire is grounded, and the third is at nominal minus 115 volts.[2]

From the kilowatt-hour meter the wires go to a main power center or to a switch and fuse control box. The fuse box is wired so that separate electrical circuits will be available in the house. The separate electric circuits are called *branch circuits*. For example, one branch circuit which starts at the fuse box may serve lighting and convenience outlets for a bedroom and living room, two other branch circuits may serve outlets for small appliances in the kitchen, and so on.

Branch circuits have two or three *current-carrying wires*. The circuits in the home that have two current-carrying wires are 115-volt circuits, except those for electric water heaters and some power tools which are 230-volt circuits. The circuits that have three current-carrying wires are always 230-volt circuits. These are used for electric ranges and for electric dryers.

A 115- or 230-volt circuit with two current-carrying wires is fused with one fuse or one circuit breaker. A 230-volt circuit with three current-carrying wires is fused with two fuses or two circuit breakers.[3]

Figure 1–3 is a schematic illustration of a kilowatt-hour meter, disconnect switch and fuse or circuit breaker panel. All branch circuits need not start at a main power center. Instead, the six sets of fuses and switches marked for appliances on Figure 1–3 could be

[2] The expression "nominal 115 volts" is used to indicate that the voltage is not exactly 115; also the voltage does not have a constant value. The actual voltage delivered to a house depends on several factors, one of which is the variable demand for electricity from other houses served by the same transmission system.

[3] Some 115-volt circuits have two current-carrying wires and one noncurrent-carrying wire. The wire that is not connected to the power supply is grounded, as is one of the current-carrying wires. The extra grounded wire is, of course, a special safety provision, and 115-volt circuits with three wires are used at present for special applications only. For example, electric dishwashers are now connected in such a circuit.

part of a separate or subcontrol center. And, in fact, some homes are now wired for *feeders* and one or more subcontrol centers between the main power control and different areas of the house. When one subcontrol center is provided, Figure 1–3 might show some branch

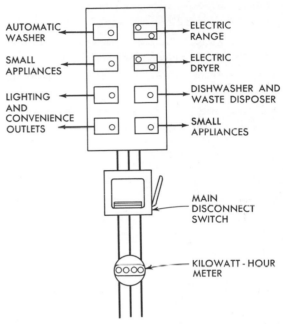

Fig. 1–3. Kilowatt-hour meter and main power center for branch circuits in the home.

circuits controlled at the main center and relatively large feeder wires to one subcontrol center. From this subcontrol center, smaller wires would lead to outlets that are parts of other branch circuits. This practice permits improved voltage throughout the house.

1–6. HEATING EFFECT AND OVERLOAD PROTECTION

When an electric current I flows through a resistance R for t seconds, the heat developed is proportional to the square of the current times the resistance times the time; that is, the heat developed is proportional to I^2Rt. As stated at the beginning of the chapter, this heat is utilized in heating appliances.

Also, since heat is developed wherever electric current flows through a resistance, heat is developed in the wires leading to the outlets into which appliances are plugged. The wires that lead to the electrical outlets in a house are installed where we do not see them. They are likely to be attached to the framing of the house and to pass through plaster. Clearly, if enough current flows through them, the wires *could* become sufficiently hot to be a fire hazard. This is the reason for overload protection, in the form of fuses or circuit breakers, in the separate circuits in a house.

Fuses and circuit breakers are rated in amperes. The ampere rating of the fuse or circuit breaker used in a circuit depends on the size of the wire used in the circuit.

The metallic alloy in fuses melts when current above the rated value of the fuse, 15 amperes, 20 amperes, 30 amperes, etc., flows through it. When the alloy melts, or the fuse "blows," the circuit is open and current no longer flows through it. Thus when a fuse of proper rating is used in a circuit, excessive heat will not develop in the hidden wires in the house, and the house is protected from a fire due to overheating of these wires. The protection is lost when an unwise or uninformed person replaces a "blown" fuse with one whose ampere rating is too high for the size wire in the circuit.

A circuit breaker is similar to a fuse in that it "trips" and opens a circuit when excess current flows. A circuit breaker can be reset manually. A blown fuse must be replaced.

Special characteristics of fuses and circuit breakers are discussed on page 13.

1–7. EFFECTS OF LOW VOLTAGE

Earlier in this chapter, Ohm's law was used to calculate the voltage drop in a resistance. In the discussion on distribution of electricity in the house, the value of one or more sub-controls in improving voltage throughout the house was noted. These considerations should suggest strongly that low voltage is something to be avoided in branch circuits.

Low voltage has undesirable effects on the performance of heating appliances and motor-driven appliances. As indicated earlier, the quantity of heat developed when a current I flows through a resistance R for a time t is proportional to I^2Rt. The reader may verify by use of Ohm's law that I^2Rt is equal to V^2t/R, where V is voltage. Therefore, a heating appliance rated to deliver a certain amount of heat in a given time at 115 volts will clearly deliver less than the rated amount when the appliance is used on 105 or 110 volts.

Suppose an iron rated at 115 volts is used at 105 volts to iron linen. The heat developed will be proportional to 105 squared instead of 115 squared. The iron will require a longer time to reach the linen setting than it was designed to require, and it may not deliver the heat output appropriate to the linen setting during ironing. Thus, for heating appliances, low voltage causes slow heating, and in some cases failure to deliver the designed heat output.

The undesirable effect of low voltage on motor-driven appliances comes when the motor starts or tries to start. If the voltage is low, an inductance-type motor may "labor" on start and its moving part may not reach operating speed. If the labored start is prolonged, excess heat develops and a thermal overload protective device, when one is provided in the motor circuit, opens the circuit. If a protective device is not included, the motor may burn out. Thus, the effect of low voltage can be more harmful for motors than for heating appliances.

Design voltage for electric appliances is given on the nameplate of the appliance. Design voltage for incandescent lamps is often marked on the lamp.

B. Nameplates and Underwriters Laboratories Seal of Approval

The previous section dealt with basic physical principles of branch circuits and electrical appliances. Nameplates are considered separately in this section, partly in order to emphasize their importance.

1–8. NAMEPLATES

Nameplates on heating appliances—irons, toasters, and so on—usually indicate watts and volts or amperes and volts. Some heating appliances use different wattages at different settings. A nonthermostatically controlled surface unit of an electric range, for example, uses different wattages at different settings. The wattage given on the nameplate for such appliances is the wattage used at the highest setting.

Nameplates on motor-driven appliances indicate cycles per second, volts and amperes or cycles per second, and volts and watts. Again, the highest operating wattage is given for appliances which have settings that use different wattages.

Horsepower is specified on nameplates of some motor-driven appliances. One horsepower equals 746 watts. By convention, the horsepower indicated is nominal *output* whereas wattages on nameplates are *input* wattages.[4] Thus a nameplate marked ⅓ horsepower states that the appliance will deliver approximately 250 watts. The wattage input will always be higher since the efficiency (the ratio of the output to the input) is always less than one.

Fuses, outlets, switches, and other wiring

devices are usually marked for amperes and volts.

1–9. UNDERWRITERS LABORATORIES SEAL OF APPROVAL

Underwriters Laboratories, Inc. maintains and operates laboratories for the examination and testing of devices, systems, and materials in their relation to life, fire, and casualty hazards, and crime prevention. The organization is chartered as a nonprofit organization. Underwriters Laboratories, Inc. issue "listings" of articles that are submitted by the manufacturer and that meet the laboratories' standards with respect to absence of hazards.

In addition, articles that are checked under a follow-up program may carry the label or seal. This program involves frequent inspections at the factory in which the products are manufactured. In many cases, tests are also conducted at a central laboratory on samples purchased on the open market of products carrying the label.

Labels are attached to products in different ways. A fuse, for example, may have the expression "Underwriters Laboratories, Inc. Inspected" marked on top of it. Often the abbreviation UL, enclosed in a circle, is used on a nameplate or elsewhere on the housing of a part or a complete piece of equipment. Wires that are UL approved may carry a paper ring so marked. In other cases the UL seal may be on the spindle from which a length of wire is cut.

Since the UL seal indicates that the article has been tested for safety, it is wise to look for it when purchasing equipment and electrical parts.

---

[4] The horsepower rating of some canister and tank vacuum cleaners is an input rating. This is an exception to the general rule that horsepower ratings refer to output.

C. Safety Considerations

It is well known, of course, that electricity can be harmful to both persons and property. Since effective precautions in home use of electricity must be based on knowledge of possible hazards, some of these hazards are considered here.

Reference has already been made to the fire hazard caused by overfusing. Where extension cords are used, they should be out of the way of floor traffic to prevent walking on wires and possible shorts. Frayed appliance and extension cords should be repaired or replaced.

Probably the three most important precautions to follow in using electrical appliances are these: (1) Never handle at the same time an electrical appliance or wiring device such as a switch and a good connection to ground such as a water faucet. (2) Handle only one electrical appliance or wiring device at a time. (3) Do not handle electrical appliances or wiring devices with a wet or even a damp part of the body.

These three precautions are stated categorically in order to aid the reader in remembering them.

While it is probably true that more people are killed annually by 115 volts than by any other voltage, it is fortunately also true that fatal accidents usually require an unusual set of circumstances. For example, a person can violate the first precaution and handle an electrical appliance and a good connection to ground safely, *provided* the appliance is in good condition. But if the insulation in the appliance between the live wire and the housing is defective and a person touches the housing near the defective insulation and a good ground at the same time, he has placed himself across 115 volts. In the same way, one can handle two electrical appliances safely *if* both appliances are in good condition, but it is not predictable when insulation inside an appliance will become defective.

In case a person has accidentally contacted a live wire and is unable to pull away, a rescuer should, if possible, first disconnect the source of power before trying to aid the victim. If this is not practical, the rescuer should use an insulating material such as a dry wood stick or dry clothing to separate the victim and the wire. If he fails to do this, he can himself make contact with the live wire through the victim. Next, if necessary, the rescuer should call a physician and start artificial resuscitation while waiting.

D. Experiment on Nameplate Inspection

Locate nameplates on heating appliances, motor-driven appliances, combination heating and motor-driven appliances, wiring devices, and fuses.

For all appliances, wiring devices, and fuses note the following:

1. Manufacturer's name and address.
2. Model number.
3. Underwriters Laboratories seal.
4. Electrical quantities stated: voltage, watts, current, cycles.

For motor-driven appliances, such as electric refrigerators, note whether horsepower rating is given in addition.

For combination appliances, such as ironers and rotisseries, note whether separate nameplates are used for the motor and the heating unit or for the motor and the entire appliance.

Note any additional information given on the nameplate. The nameplate on one electric dryer, for example, specifies the minimum capacity of the fuse to be used in the dryer circuit.

Organize your observations so that you may draw inferences on the following:

1. Wattage or current used by thermostatically controlled versus nonthermostatically controlled heating appliances—for example, controlled versus noncontrolled toasters, coffee makers, surface units of electric ranges.

2. Wattage or current used by heating appliances versus wattage or current used by motor-driven appliances.

3. Motor-driven appliances that have a power factor of one versus those that have a power factor of less than one. (The nameplate on motor-driven appliances that have a power factor less than one will usually specify 50 to 60 cycles or 60 cycles only.)

Electrical Parts and Home Wiring

The electrical parts used in home wiring include cables, wires, fuses, circuit breakers, outlets or receptacles, switches, and other devices. These parts are described and illustrated in the first part of this chapter. Outlets and switches for different areas of the home and service entrance equipment and branch circuits for adequate wiring are discussed in the second part. Recommendations for adequate wiring are changing with the increasing use of electrical appliances. The discussion in this chapter summarizes the currently accepted recommendations for present and anticipated future electrical needs.

A. Electrical Parts

2–1. CABLES, WIRES, FUSES, AND CIRCUIT BREAKERS

As an electrical part, a *cable* is an assembly of two or more insulated conductors enclosed in a sheath of metal or nonmetallic material such as a plastic material, braided cotton, or treated paper. When metal is used for the sheath, the cable is described as *armored* cable. Both armored and nonmetallic cables may be constructed to be flexible.

A moisture- and corrosion-resistant type of

nonmetallic cable or conduit is commonly used between a kilowatt-hour meter located outside the house and the main power center in the house (see Fig. 1–2). The wiring between the main power center and the various outlets in the house may be one of several types, such as nonmetallic cable, armored cable, knob-and-tube wiring, and flexible conduit. At present nonmetallic cable is accepted as a good practical choice from the point of view of cost and time required for installation. Flexible conduit may be more convenient for adding additional circuits.

Knob-and-tube wiring was at one time almost always used for homes and is still used for wiring new homes in some areas. In this type of branch-circuit wiring, the conductors are supported by knobs and tubes made of an insulating material, usually porcelain, mounted at intervals of about 4½ feet in hollow spaces of walls and ceilings.

The diameter of the wire used for the conductors in the cable is measured by a device known as an American Standard Wire Gauge and is expressed as an AWG number. The diameters for the AWG numbers listed below were taken from a wire gauge manufactured by the Starrett Company.

AWG (number)	Diameter (inches)
0	0.325
1	0.289
6	0.162
8	0.128
10	0.102
12	0.081
14	0.064
16	0.051
18	0.040

Note that diameter decreases as gauge number increases. Since diameters for different gauge numbers apply to solid, uninsulated wire, the diameters cited above for different gauge numbers do *not* apply, for example, to insulated and stranded lamp cord wire.

Plug fuses are standard or tamper resistant. The standard type of fuse is made so that fuses rated at 15, 20, 25, or 30 amperes may be used interchangeably in a single fuse socket. This type permits an uninformed person to use a fuse with a higher rating than the circuit should have. Tamper-resistant fuses have adapters which restrict the possibility of overfusing.

Standard fuses and tamper-resistant fuses that are made with a time-delay feature provide a short time allowance for overloads due, for example, to starting of motors. With continued overload or with excessive instantaneous load, the fuse blows.

Circuit breakers are thermal, electromagnetic, or thermal-electromagnetic. A thermal breaker includes a bimetallic element that expands and flexes when heated by the current in the circuit. With enough heat, the flexing of this element opens the circuit contacts. The thermal type thus depends on current and time, since the heating effect of electric current depends on current and time.

An electromagnetic breaker is essentially a switch operated by an electromagnet. When the current through it reaches a predetermined value, the breaker opens the circuit. The electromagnetic type thus depends on current only.

A thermal-electromagnetic breaker utilizes both thermal and electromagnetic actions. The thermal part depends on current and time; the electromagnetic part depends on current alone. The thermal part provides the time-delay feature needed for the instantaneous, somewhat-high, starting currents of electric appliances. (A circuit breaker that tripped every time a refrigerator started, for example, would be rather a nuisance.) The electromagnetic part provides for instantaneous tripping of the breaker due to the very high currents characteristic of short circuits, and this of course is desirable.

Sometimes different ratings are recommended for a circuit breaker versus a fuse in a particular circuit. For example, it is suggested that an automatic washer be installed in a circuit protected by a 15-ampere time-delay fuse or a 20-ampere circuit breaker. (From the discussion just given can you figure out *why* different ratings might be reasonable?)

Fuses or circuit breakers of proper ratings provide overload protection. The choice of which to use depends partly on cost versus convenience. It is easier to reset a circuit breaker than to replace a fuse, but circuit breakers are more expensive to install initially than fuses.

2–2. WIRING DEVICES

Wiring devices include outlets and switches.

A *lighting outlet* is a means by which house wiring is connected to fixtures, portable lamps, light sources in valances, etc. A *convenience outlet* is a plug-in receptacle used for portable electric appliances, radios, and other electric housewares. A *split-wired,* duplex, convenience outlet, as the name implies, is connected to two circuits.

A *special-purpose* outlet is a point of connection to the wiring system of a particular appliance, and normally the outlet is reserved for the exclusive use of that appliance. Special-purpose outlets used for dishwashers, ranges, and dryers are installed in walls. Special-purpose outlets for electric water heaters, fuel-fired furnaces and built-in space heaters may be part of the equipment; in this case the equipment is permanently connected to the house wiring system.

Available outlets include standard duplex and triplex convenience outlets, floor outlets, weatherproof outlets with protective caps, hanger outlets for clocks and fans, outlets that provide a grounding connection, lock-type outlets, raceways with convenience outlets spaced relatively close together, and special-purpose outlets. Some of these outlets are illustrated in Figures 2–1 through 2–9.

A standard duplex outlet is illustrated in Figure 2–1. A triplex or even a quadruplex outlet is advantageous in a bedroom. The

WIRING DEVICE CHART

 **Standard Duplex**—"U" slot devices recommended to permit grounding. Split-wired receptacles permit switching of one outlet.

 Weatherproof outlet—single or duplex devices have screw-on caps to keep out moisture.

 Dryer outlet—30A-250V receptacle may be flush mounted in std. box. Also suitable for work bench power outlet.

 Cover-Mounted outlets—several types of receptacles can be obtained mounted on covers for use with exposed boxes in basement and garage.

  Range outlet—3 wire—50-amp, 250-V polarized receptacles available for flush or surface mounting.

Fig. 2–1.   Wiring devices. ("Live Better Electrically")

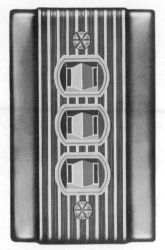

Fig. 2-2. Triplex convenience outlet. (The Bryant Electric Company)

Fig. 2-3. Floor outlet with protective cover. (The Bryant Electric Company)

Fig. 2-4. Recessed hanger outlet. (The Bryant Electric Company)

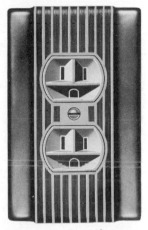

Fig. 2-5. Grounding convenience outlet. The outlet has two current-carrying contacts and one grounding contact. (The Bryant Electric Company)

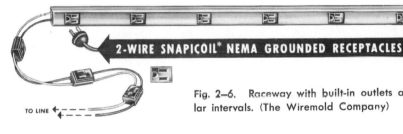

2-WIRE SNAPICOIL* NEMA GROUNDED RECEPTACLES

TO LINE

Fig. 2-6. Raceway with built-in outlets at regular intervals. (The Wiremold Company)

Fig. 2-8. Interchangeable device consisting of two switches and a receptacle. (The Bryant Electric Company)

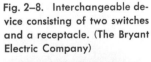
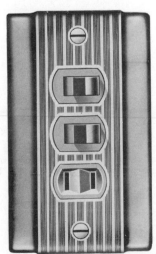

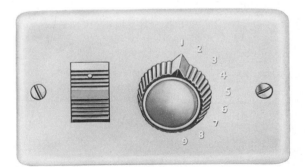

Fig. 2-9. Master selector switch. (The Bryant Electric Company)

Fig. 2-7. Range outlet. (The Bryant Electric Company)

former is illustrated in Figure 2–2. A floor outlet under a dining table set away from a wall eliminates trailing wires; a special cover closes the outlet when it is not in use (Fig. 2–3). A weatherproof outlet is useful outside the house for decorative lighting, outdoor cooking, and electric garden tools (Fig. 2–1). A threaded cover may be included to provide a weatherproof seal. A recessed hanger outlet for an electric clock or fan eliminates long wires (Fig. 2–4).

Outlets that provide a grounding connection are desirable for appliances used in the basement, for automatic washers wherever used, and for electric dishwashers. Different types are available. The one illustrated in Figures 2–1 and 2–5 is for use in a three-wire, 115-volt circuit. The plug on the appliance cord must of course be appropriate for the outlet.

Lock-type outlets require a partial turn of the plug to complete the circuit. Such outlets are especially desirable for freezers since they prevent accidental disconnection of the freezer. Again, the plug on the appliance cord must be appropriate for this outlet.

Raceways with outlets at frequent intervals permit flexibility in placement of lamps, radio, television set, etc., in the living room when the raceway is installed in the baseboard (Fig. 2–6). They are useful in workshops when installed above the counter. Raceways are available with different types of outlets, such as standard duplex or grounding outlets.

The special-purpose outlets for electric ranges are three-wire, 50-ampere, 250-volt, polarized receptacles (Figs. 2–1 and 2–7).

(A polarized receptacle is one in which a plug can be installed in only one way.) The special-purpose outlets for electric dryers are usually rated at 30 amperes.

The straight toggle switch is probably the most common switch in the home. However, various special types are available. *Interchangeable devices,* for example, are combinations of one, two, or three switches, pilots, and receptacles (for appliances) that fit into one box. The interchangeable device shown in Figure 2–8 consists of two switches and a receptacle. An interchangeable device for a night light may consist of a box with a cover plate, a night light, and two switches—one to control the night light and the other to control hall or room lighting. Such a device is useful, for example, in a bathroom to prevent groping for a switch in the dark.

A *multicontrol light switch* is one which controls one or more lights from more than one point. A three-way switch controls one light from two separate points. One use of a three-way switch is to control a garage light from both house and garage. A four-way switch provides control from three separate points. They are called three-way and four-way switches because the electrician must connect them three or four ways.

A *multicontrol master switch* is somewhat complex in wiring, unless a *low-voltage control* is used. Such a switch in the master bedroom, for example, may be wired to control outdoor lights and indoor lights in selected areas of the house, bathroom heater, and other equipment (Fig. 2–9).

B. Home Wiring

The basic requirements for home wiring are safety and adequacy for present and anticipated electrical needs. A discussion of recommended practice must almost necessarily be in terms of wiring for a new home, though the same recommendations hold when new wiring is installed in an existing house.

A family may quite reasonably prefer to use its money for purposes other than rewiring for adequacy, thus making the decision to accept the limitations associated with inadequate wiring: (1) Only certain appliances will be used at the same time. (2) The idea of buying a room air conditioner may be given up. (3) Lights may dim each time the refrigerator motor starts. (4) Heating appliances may heat at a slower rate than the manufacturer specified and may never deliver specified heat output.

However, it is unreasonable for a family to accept the hazards involved in *unsafe* wiring. Wiring should be repaired when a person gets a nonstatic shock from a switch, outlet, fixture, or water pipe. An example of a static shock is the shock one gets sometimes on touching a switch after walking across a carpet. A nonstatic shock might come from touching a defective switch in a basement that has a concrete floor.

2–3. SAFETY AND ADEQUACY OF HOME WIRING

a. Safety in Home Wiring

Safety in home wiring is obtained by using wiring materials that carry the label of the Underwriters Laboratories and by installing materials in accordance with requirements of the National Electrical Code and local codes. When no local code is imposed, as may be the case in some rural areas, the power supplier is usually willing to aid in interpreting applicable provisions of the National Electrical Code.

b. National Electrical Code

The National Electrical Code is a standard of the National Board of Fire Underwriters for electric wiring and apparatus. It is revised periodically to conform with developments in wiring methods and in equipment. The purpose of the code is "the practical safeguarding of persons and of buildings and their contents from the hazards arising from the use of elec-

tricity."[1] The introduction to the code also states that "compliance therewith and proper maintenance will result in an installation essentially free from hazard, but not necessarily efficient, convenient, or adequate for good service."

An example of an application of the code in the home is: "For the small appliance load in kitchen, laundry, pantry, dining-room and breakfast-room of dwelling occupancies, one or more 20-ampere branch circuits shall be provided for all receptacle outlets (other than outlet for clock) in these rooms and such circuits shall have no other outlets."[2]

c. Adequacy of Home Wiring

Adequacy of home wiring is obtained for most families by following recommendations which are set up to meet present and anticipated needs in terms of lighting facilities and electrical appliances already widely used.

2–4. OUTLETS AND SWITCHES FOR DIFFERENT AREAS

The material in this section on outlets and switches and in the following section on service entrance equipment, branch circuits, and special wiring is adapted from the *Residential Wiring Handbook*.[3]

Some general recommendations apply for many areas in the home. For example, with a few exceptions that will be noted, convenience outlets should be of the duplex or mul-

[1] *1953 National Electrical Code,* National Board of Fire Underwriters, Introduction.

[2] *Ibid.,* Article 210.

[3] The *Residential Wiring Handbook* was prepared by the Industry Committee on Interior Wiring Design, 420 Lexington Ave., New York, in 1954. Sponsoring organizations include American Home Lighting Institute, Edison Electric Institute, National Association of Home Builders, and other organizations. Endorsing organizations are the American Society of Electrical Engineers, American Society of Agricultural Engineers, and the Illuminating Engineering Society. Several of the sponsoring organizations of the *Handbook* also sponsor the National Adequate Wiring Bureau.

tiple type and should be located approximately 12 inches above the floor. Also, convenience outlets should be located near the ends of wall space rather than near the center to reduce the possibility that they will be concealed by furniture. For many areas in the house the recommendation on spacing is that enough convenience outlets should be provided so that no point along the floor line of a usable wall space will be more than 6 feet from an outlet. (This recommendation is equivalent to a 12-foot spacing of outlets only when doors or other architectural features do not cut into the wall space.)

Wall switches for lighting outlets should usually be located at the latch side of doors and within the room or area where the lighting outlet is located. An exception is the control of exterior lights from indoors. Generally, if wall switches are required in an area that has more than one entrance, such as a living room, multiple switches should be used at each main entrance to the room, except when such main entrances are less than 10 feet apart. Wall switches usually are mounted at a height of approximately 4 feet from the floor.

Recommendations for particular areas are summarized below.

Exterior entrances. One or more wall-switch-controlled lighting outlets should be at each entrance.

A weatherproof convenience outlet, preferably near the front entrance, should be located 18 inches or more above grade and controlled by a wall switch inside the house. Any additional outlets along the exterior of the house for decorative lighting or electric garden tools should also be controlled by a wall switch.

Living room. There should be wall-switch-controlled lighting outlets for ceiling and wall fixtures used for general illumination. If general illumination is provided by portable lamps rather than fixtures, two wall-switch-controlled convenience outlets or one plug position in two or more split-receptacle con-

venience outlets are recommended. Outlets are also suggested for use of an electric clock, radio, decorative lighting, etc., near built-in shelves or at other appropriate locations.

Convenience outlets should be placed so that no point along the floor line in any usable wall space is more than 6 feet from an outlet. Where windows extend to the floor, this recommendation may be met by floor outlets.

A convenience outlet flush in a mantel shelf is desirable if construction permits. A *single* convenience outlet in combination with the wall switch at one or more of the wall-switch locations is desirable for use with vacuum cleaners and electric floor polishers.

A heavy-duty, special-purpose outlet is needed for a room air conditioner.

Dining area. At least one wall-switch-controlled lighting outlet is necessary.

Convenience outlets should be placed so that no point along the floor line in any usable wall space is more than 6 feet from an outlet in that space. If the table is to be placed against a wall, one of the outlets should be installed at the table location just above table height. Also, if a counter is to be built in, an outlet above counter height is convenient for portable appliances.

Kitchen. Wall-switch-controlled lighting outlets are necessary for general illumination and for lighting at the sink. Local switch controls should be within easy reach for lighting fixtures under wall cabinets.

There should be one convenience outlet for an electric refrigerator and one for each 4 linear feet of work-surface frontage, with at least one outlet for each work surface, placed approximately 44 inches above the floor line. If a planning desk is to be installed, an outlet should be near it. Also, a convenience outlet is recommended in a wall space if an iron or electric roaster might be used near that wall.

One special-purpose outlet each is suggested for an electric range and a ventilating fan, if both are used. There should also be an outlet or outlets for a dishwasher and/or food waste disposer, if appropriate plumbing facilities are also installed, provision for an electric clock in the kitchen, and a special-purpose outlet for a freezer either in the kitchen or in some other convenient location.

Laundry area. At least one wall-switch-controlled lighting outlet is essential. (*All* laundry lighting outlets should be wall-switch controlled if more than one is provided.)

In addition, there should be at least one convenience outlet for a hotplate, sewing machine, etc., and one special-purpose outlet each for an automatic washer, an iron or ironer, and an electric clothes dryer, if these appliances will be used in this area.[4]

Requirements for an electric water heater, if one is to be used, may be obtained from the local power supplier.

Bedroom. There should be wall-switch-controlled outlets for general illumination purposes and a multicontrol master switch in the master bedroom for large homes (p. 16).

Convenience outlets should be located within 3 to 4 feet of the center line of the probable locations of each bed. Because of the increasing popularity of radios, bed lamps, and electric bed covers, triplex or quadruplex convenience outlets are suggested. Additonal outlets should be installed so that no point along the floor line in any other usable wall space is more than 6 feet from an outlet in that space. In addition, it is recommended that a receptacle outlet be provided at one of the switch locations for a vacuum cleaner or other portable electric appliance.

A heavy-duty, special-purpose outlet is required for a room air conditioner.

Bathroom. *All* lighting outlets should be wall-switch controlled. There should be outlets to provide illumination on both sides of the face at mirrors, and a ceiling outlet or outlets for general room lighting and for combination shower and tub. If an enclosed shower stall is planned, the outlet for the vaporproof luminaire in the stall should be controlled by a wall switch *outside* the stall. A switch-controlled night light may be desirable.

There should be a convenience outlet near the mirror, 3 to 5 feet above the floor, and one in any wall on which a mirror might be placed, for use when shaving with an electric razor.

Hall. Wall-switch-controlled lighting outlets should provide for appropriate illumination of the entire area.

At least one convenience outlet is needed for each hall with a floor area greater than 25 square feet. For long halls, the recommendation is one outlet for each 15 linear feet, measured along a central line. Also, it is recommended that a convenience outlet be provided at one of the switch outlets for a vacuum cleaner.

Closet. One outlet is suggested for each closet unless shelving makes installation of lights within the closet impracticable. Use of wall switches near the closet door or door-type switches is recommended.

Stairway with finished rooms at both ends. Lighting outlets with multiple-switch controls should be located at the head and foot of the stairway. *No* switch should be located so that a fall might result from a misstep while reaching for it.

A convenience outlet is recommended at intermediate landings of a long stairway.

Recreation room. Wall-switch-controlled lighting outlets are recommended for general illumination purposes.

Convenience outlets should be installed so that no point along the floor line of any usable wall space is more than 6 feet from an outlet in that space. Outlets for radio, television set, slide projector, and the like, should be near the places where these devices will be used.

---

[4] A convenience outlet serves for a hand iron or ironer. The convenience outlet becomes a special-purpose outlet in this case when installed at a height that normally would be used only for an iron or ironer.

Utility space and basement. Lighting outlets are needed for the furnace area and work bench, if one is planned. In unfinished basements the light at the foot of the stairs should be wall-switch controlled near the head of the stairs. For stairways of basements with finished rooms or with garage space, the stairway lighting recommendations apply.

A convenience outlet should be located preferably near the furnace or work bench. A special-purpose outlet for a freezer may be provided here or in the kitchen.

Accessible attic. One wall-switch-controlled outlet at the foot of the stairs is recommended for general illumination. If stairs are not installed, a pull-chain-controlled lighting outlet over the access door is recommended.

In addition, a convenience outlet is recommended for general use, and a special-purpose outlet, multiple-switch controlled (attic and downstairs), may be desirable for an attic fan.

Porches and breezeways. A wall-switch-controlled lighting outlet is necessary if the floor area is more than 75 square feet. Multiple-switch control is recommended when the area is used as a passageway between the house and garage.

At least one convenience outlet is desirable if the area is planned for informal eating.

Exterior grounds. Lighting outlets for floodlights placed on the exterior of the house or garage or on posts may be desirable. Such outlets should be switch-controlled from within the house.

2–5. SERVICE ENTRANCE, BRANCH CIRCUITS, AND SPECIAL WIRING

The *service equipment* is the main power center (switch and fuses or circuit breakers and their housings and other accessories) located near the point of entrance of the electrical supply to the house. The *service entrance conductors* are the portion of the supply conductors between the service equipment (main power center) and the meter for overhead supply, or between the service equipment and the point outside the home where the supply conductors are joined to the street mains for underground supply (Fig. 1–2).

The size of the service entrance conductors and the rating of the service equipment should be adequate for the total electric load—that is, for lighting, for portable electric appliances, and for the fixed electrical equipment that will be used in the house.

A three-wire, 230-volt supply to the service equipment is desirable even when no 230-volt appliance is to be installed. The three-wire service permits wiring 115-volt circuits across each half of the supply. However, good wiring *can* be obtained with a 115-volt supply.

Service equipment rated for 60 amperes and 230 volts is sometimes suggested as minimum. Such equipment allows for simultaneous use of 13,800 watts (230×60). Service equipment rated for 100 amperes and 230 volts is adequate for lighting, for portable electric appliances, and for the following "fixed" electric appliances: range, automatic washer, dryer, dishwasher and food waste disposer, water heater, fuel-fired heating equipment, and one additional "fixed" appliance such as a room air conditioner.[5] For homes larger than 3000 square feet in floor area or homes which may use additional appliances, such as a built-in electric bathroom heater or electric work bench equipment, service equipment with a rating higher than 100 amperes probably will be necessary.

Common wiring practice usually has all the separate circuits in a house controlled at the service equipment. However, as indicated on p. 7, improved voltage is obtained, especially in a house that has many circuits for appliances, when one or more subcontrol centers served by relatively heavy feeder lines

[5] *Residential Wiring Handbook, op. cit.,* p. 30.

are used between the service equipment and one or more different areas of the house.

a. Disconnecting Means at Service Entrance

The National Electrical Code prescribes that with certain exceptions buildings shall be supplied through only one set of conductors; one exception is buildings of multiple occupancy.[6] The code also requires that the service entrance conductors be provided with *a readily accessible means of disconnecting all conductors* from the source of supply. The disconnecting means must be manually operable. It may consist of not more than six switches or circuit breakers in a common enclosure.

The broad, general requirement is that no more than six hand operations shall be necessary to disconnect all conductors. This requirement can be met, of course, by installation of one master switch.

b. Branch Circuits

Branch circuits were defined earlier as the separate electric circuits in a house. Three types of branch circuits are considered in the recommendations for adequate home wiring.

General-purpose circuits supply lighting outlets throughout the house and some convenience outlets. Recommended practice calls for at least one 20-ampere, general-purpose circuit for each 500 square feet of floor space.[7] The wire size recommended is number 12. The "capacity" of a 20-ampere, 115-volt circuit is 2300 watts (115 × 20).

Small-appliance circuits supply convenience outlets for small electric appliances and for an electric refrigerator. Recommended practice calls for at least one three-wire 115/230-volt circuit with split-wired outlets or two two-wire, 115-volt, 20-ampere circuits to service the

kitchen, dining area, and laundry area. The wire size again is number 12.

Two 115-volt, 20-ampere circuits will carry a total of 4600 watts. Each circuit will serve for simultaneous use of two, high-wattage, small appliances such as a 1000-watt automatic coffee maker and a 1200-watt electric frypan. A third appliance in either circuit usually will blow the fuse.

Individual-equipment circuits, as their name implies, are separate circuits for individual pieces of equipment. Such circuits are recommended for the following appliances: automatic washer; home freezer; room air conditioner; electric dishwasher and food waste disposer (one circuit serves both); electric range; electric water heater; electric clothes dryer; fuel-fired heating equipment (gas or oil); summer-cooling attic fan; electric equipment for work benches. Individual-equipment circuits are 115-volt or 230-volt, according to the equipment served.

A blown fuse or tripped circuit breaker may cause less inconvenience when rooms are served by two circuits. The same circuits may, of course, serve several rooms.

A total of 12 or more branch circuits is sometimes suggested for adequate wiring. For a house with an area of 1200 square feet, these might be the following: three general-purpose circuits; two small-appliance circuits; individual-equipment circuits for freezer, automatic washer, room air conditioner, fuel-fired central heating unit; and three individual-equipment circuits for additional appliances that might be added at a later time. If 12 or more branch circuits are planned, the service entrance equipment will need to have a capacity of 100 amperes or more.

c. Special Wiring

Special wiring may be planned for electric entrance signals (usually a transformer will be needed), intercommunication devices between

---

[6] *1953 National Electrical Code, op. cit.,* Article 2351.

[7] Recommended practice for branch circuits meets, and may exceed, requirements of the current edition of the National Electrical Code.

rooms, telephone outlets at several locations, and other uses.

2–6. ELECTRICAL SYMBOLS AND HOUSE WIRING PLANS

The symbols shown in Figure 2–10 include symbols from the American Standards Association Standard ASA Z32.9–1943 and symbols that have been proposed for the next revision of the standard. Familiarity with the symbols is helpful in checking a wiring plan for a room or for a complete house.

Armin suggests six steps for checking the wiring plans for a house:

1. Know the electrical symbols.
2. Take one room at a time in order to be able to concentrate on the individual symbols that apply to that room.
3. Consider the activities carried out in the room or area under consideration. For example, if the room is a recreation room or family living room, are convenience outlets properly placed for use of a slide projector, a television set, or any other piece of equipment the family plans to use in that room? Are the lighting facilities appropriate for the activities that will be carried out in the room?

4. Note location of outlets relative to doors and windows. In particular, note on which side a door will be hinged to be sure the wall switch for general lighting in the room is on the latch side of the door. Check that a convenience outlet is not planned for wall space that will be occupied by a window.
5. Check electrical connections systematically. Locate the fixed lights, ceiling or wall, and the switches which control them. Are there enough convenience outlets and are they correctly placed? Are special-purpose outlets provided for anticipated electrical needs? For example, is an outlet provided for a kitchen clock so located that the clock will be visible from most parts of the kitchen?
6. Check that a statement is made on the house wiring plan or in the house specifications on the following points: rating of service entrance equipment, number of branch circuits, wire size and fuse rating of the circuits, and areas to be served by the different circuits. A seemingly large number of outlets will be convenient only if the outlets are served by enough branch circuits to permit use of the outlets as the family wishes.[8]

[8] Frances Armin, "How to Read a Wiring Layout," *What's New in Home Economics,* April, 1948, pp. 61, 146, 148.

C. Wiring Plan Exercises

1. Check the wiring plan for the 18 × 23 foot living room shown in Figure 2–11. Assume the wall space at the right of the outlet on wall with staircase is occupied by floor-to-ceiling book shelves. Are the switches for the valance lighting properly placed?
2. Check the wiring plan for the kitchen shown in Figure 2–11. Is any additional information needed to know whether the wiring in this kitchen is adequate?
3. Check the wiring plan for the three-level house shown in Figure 2–12.
4. Find a house wiring plan in a shelter-type magazine or elsewhere and check the plan.

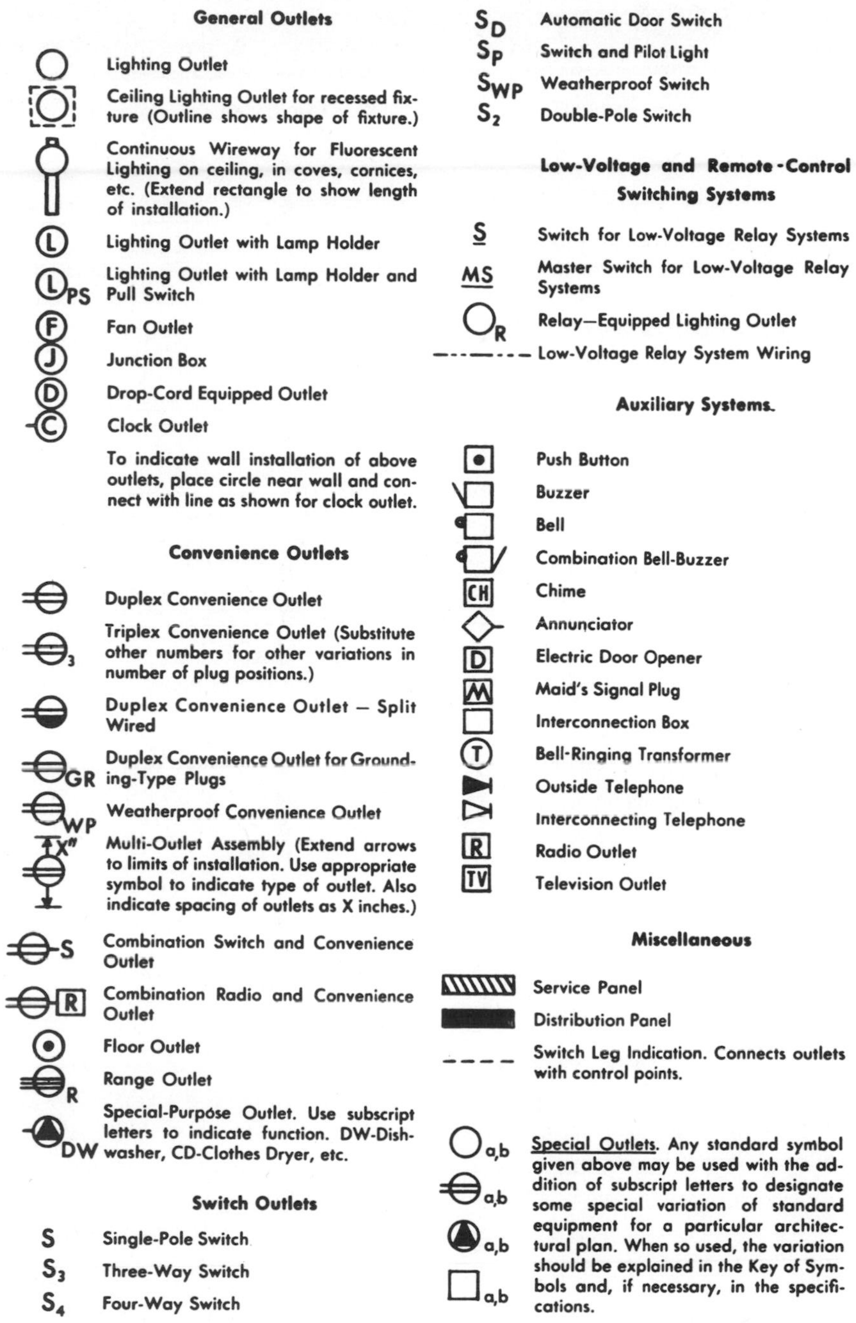

General Outlets

O — Lighting Outlet

[Ō] — Ceiling Lighting Outlet for recessed fixture (Outline shows shape of fixture.)

— Continuous Wireway for Fluorescent Lighting on ceiling, in coves, cornices, etc. (Extend rectangle to show length of installation.)

(L) — Lighting Outlet with Lamp Holder

(L)PS — Lighting Outlet with Lamp Holder and Pull Switch

(F) — Fan Outlet

(J) — Junction Box

(D) — Drop-Cord Equipped Outlet

–(C) — Clock Outlet

To indicate wall installation of above outlets, place circle near wall and connect with line as shown for clock outlet.

Convenience Outlets

⊖ — Duplex Convenience Outlet

⊖3 — Triplex Convenience Outlet (Substitute other numbers for other variations in number of plug positions.)

⊖ — Duplex Convenience Outlet — Split Wired

⊖GR — Duplex Convenience Outlet for Grounding-Type Plugs

⊖WP — Weatherproof Convenience Outlet

↑x" — Multi-Outlet Assembly (Extend arrows to limits of installation. Use appropriate symbol to indicate type of outlet. Also indicate spacing of outlets as X inches.)

⊖-S — Combination Switch and Convenience Outlet

⊖R — Combination Radio and Convenience Outlet

⊙ — Floor Outlet

⊖R — Range Outlet

◆DW — Special-Purpose Outlet. Use subscript letters to indicate function. DW-Dishwasher, CD-Clothes Dryer, etc.

Switch Outlets

S — Single-Pole Switch

S3 — Three-Way Switch

S4 — Four-Way Switch

S_D — Automatic Door Switch

S_P — Switch and Pilot Light

S_{WP} — Weatherproof Switch

S_2 — Double-Pole Switch

Low-Voltage and Remote-Control Switching Systems

S — Switch for Low-Voltage Relay Systems

MS — Master Switch for Low-Voltage Relay Systems

OR — Relay—Equipped Lighting Outlet

— · — · — · — Low-Voltage Relay System Wiring

Auxiliary Systems

[•] — Push Button

[⎍] — Buzzer

[⎍] — Bell

[⎍] — Combination Bell-Buzzer

[CH] — Chime

◇ — Annunciator

[D] — Electric Door Opener

[M] — Maid's Signal Plug

[☐] — Interconnection Box

(T) — Bell-Ringing Transformer

▶ — Outside Telephone

◁ — Interconnecting Telephone

[R] — Radio Outlet

[TV] — Television Outlet

Miscellaneous

▨ — Service Panel

▬ — Distribution Panel

– – – – — Switch Leg Indication. Connects outlets with control points.

Oa,b
⊖a,b
◆a,b
☐a,b

Special Outlets. Any standard symbol given above may be used with the addition of subscript letters to designate some special variation of standard equipment for a particular architectural plan. When so used, the variation should be explained in the Key of Symbols and, if necessary, in the specifications.

Fig. 2–10. Graphical electrical symbols adopted by the Industry Committee on Interior Wiring Design from the American Standards Association Standard Z32.9—1943. (Residential Wiring Handbook)

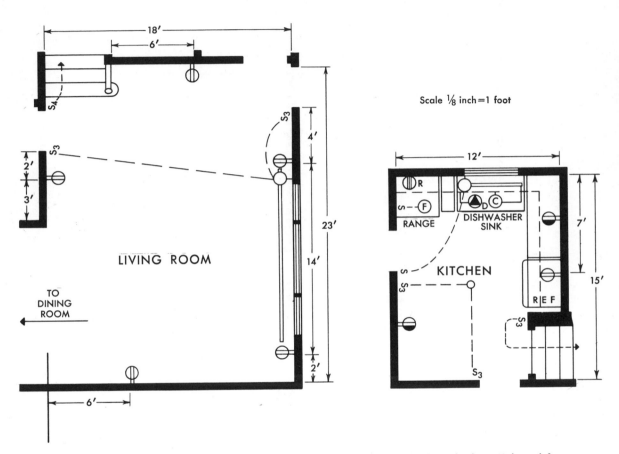

Fig. 2–11.   (Left) Wiring plan for a living room. (Right) Wiring plan for a kitchen. (Adapted from the Residential Wiring Handbook)

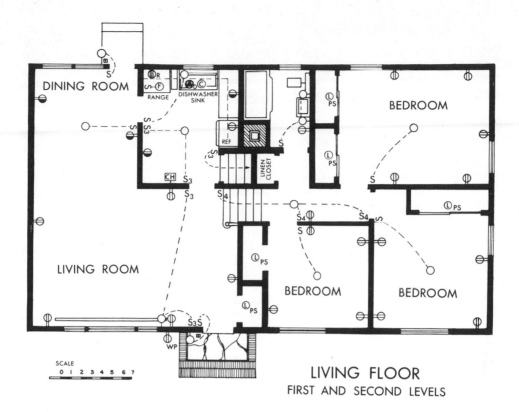

DINING ROOM

RANGE

DISHWASHER
SINK

REF

LINEN
CLOSET

CH

BEDROOM

LIVING ROOM

BEDROOM

BEDROOM

WP

SCALE
0 1 2 3 4 5 6 7

LIVING FLOOR
FIRST AND SECOND LEVELS

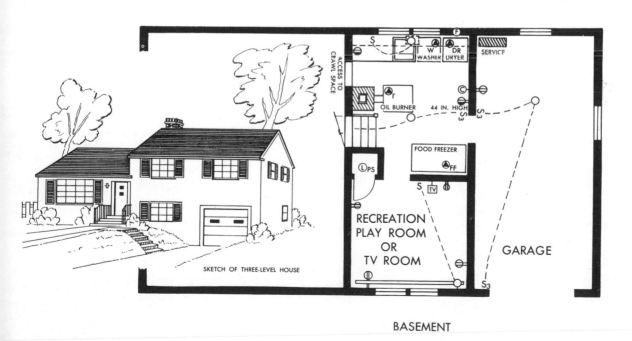

ACCESS TO
CRAWL SPACE

WASHER DRYER

SERVICE

OIL BURNER

44 IN. HIGH

FOOD FREEZER

SKETCH OF THREE-LEVEL HOUSE

RECREATION
PLAY ROOM
OR
TV ROOM

GARAGE

BASEMENT

Fig. 2–12. Wiring plan for a three-level house. (Adapted from the Residential Wiring Handbook)

CHAPTER 3

Home Lighting

A. Light, Luminaires, Improvement of Existing Conditions

Light is essential for seeing. Poor lighting can cause eyestrain and good lighting can enable many individuals with poor sight to see more clearly. Good lighting is an aid in making working conditions safer, decreasing fatigue and nervous tension, improving sitting posture, and making the home a more pleasant and interesting place.

The objectives in home lighting are good lighting for visual activities in the home and coördination of the lighting sources with the decorative scheme. Good lighting for visual activities is achieved by having enough light and light of desirable quality. Coördination with the decorative scheme is achieved by selection of appropriate fixtures and portable lamps and good placement of the fixtures and lamps.

3–1. QUANTITY OF LIGHT

The quantity of light necessary for seeing is influenced by the size of the object or material, the amount of contrast between the object and its background, and the time allowed for the eyes to focus on the object.

If the print on a page of a book is very small, more light and more time will be needed to read it than if the print is large. If the print is small the tendency is to bring the print closer to the eyes. It is common knowledge that one of the essentials in advertising is to make a sign large enough and with enough contrast so that it will be easily seen.

If black letters are printed on a stark white page, the print will stand out and be quite easily seen. Less light will be needed than if the print were grayed and the page an off-white color. In other words, the contrast between the object viewed and its immediate background influences how much light is needed.

If an object must be seen in quite a short time, more light is needed than if viewing time is longer. If there is more time for the eyes to focus and it is possible to look at the object long enough, the eyes often can see detail that at first escapes the view. It is harder to see at dusk than in broad daylight—and this is one of the reasons more care should be taken while driving a car during the twilight hours of the day.

3–2. QUALITY OF LIGHT

The quality of light depends primarily on how much light surfaces emit or reflect and the ratio of the amount of light associated with the surfaces to the amount of light in the surrounding area of space. From a practical point of view, a good quality of lighting is achieved by minimizing glare.

a. Glare

Glare has been defined as "light out of place." When the amount of light is such that it is uncomfortable for the eyes, interferes with the process of seeing, or is in any way annoying, the light is said to be glaring. Glare can be caused in a number of ways. Sources of light of very high intensity are a cause of glare. Even though the eyes may not be focused directly on the source, the light may be so bright that it causes glare when it falls on other surfaces. Light from a gooseneck study lamp falling on a book often causes glare this way.

Glare occurs when the source of light is exposed. This is true when a lamp is not shaded, when the shade is too small for the lamp, or the lamp is incorrectly placed in relation to its use. The lamp may be so placed that the user cannot help but see the bright lamp or diffusing bowl inside the shade, from a sitting or standing position.

Glare may be caused by contrast. If a white paper is laid on a dark desk, the difference in values of the two surfaces will cause glare. Bright red, bright blue, and other intense colors seem to be popular for use as desk blotters in some students' rooms at college. From the standpoint of seeing, it would be much better to introduce color into the room in some other fashion and choose for a blotter a grayed color of less intensity. The dark wood of many desk tops may be a source of glare when papers are on it. When this wood, dark or light, is highly polished or covered with

glass, another source of glare has been introduced.

Glare occurs while the eyes are adapt-
ing to a change in seeing conditions. When an
intense light is turned on in a dark room, the
eyes experience glare until they adapt to the
surroundings. This same adaptation is necessary if reading is done with a restricted source
of light in a darkened room. Every time the
eyes move away from the printed page, this
adaptation must take place. It is impossible
for the eyes not to look away even though a
person might vow he does not look away.
Lamps such as some bed lamps and some desk
lamps, that shed light only on one surface, are
not good for the eyes, if this light is the only
source of light in the room. Authorities say
there should be one-tenth to one-fifth as much
general light in the room as is provided for
any specific seeing task.

3–3. REFLECTED LIGHT

Light is reflected by direct reflection, spread
reflection, or diffuse reflection (Fig. 3–1). In
direct reflection, the angle of incidence equals
the angle of reflection. In spread reflection, the
source of light is only partially mirrored.
Spread reflection takes place when light falls
on enameled surfaces in kitchens. It is sometimes possible to see the reflections of objects
on these surfaces, though not as clearly as if
one were seeing them in a mirror. Light which
falls on mat surfaces is spread equally in all
directions; this is diffuse reflection. Since this
type of reflection is easy on the eyes, wall surfaces should preferably be of a mat finish.
Enameled wall finishes, such as are often
found in kitchens and bathrooms, give a more
glaring type of light.

3–4. MEASUREMENT OF LIGHT

Light at the source (luminous intensity of
the source) is measured in *candle power*. For
many years the composition of a standard or

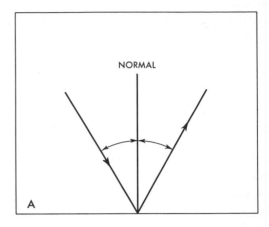

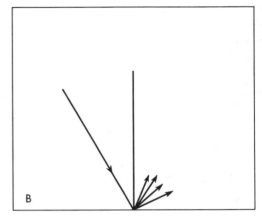

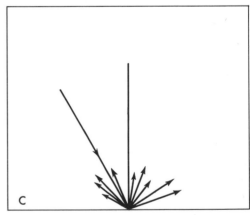

Fig. 3–1. Types of reflection. A. direct (angle of incidence = angle of reflection); B. spread (light is
scattered); C. diffuse (light is scattered in all directions).

international candle that would have a total
light output of 1 candle power was specified
by international agreement. This standard has
been replaced, but the term candle power

has remained as a unit for light output. For example, a 100-watt tungsten lamp has a light output of about 125 candle power.

Light sources and the light they emit are also described in *lumens,* which are units of light energy. If one imagines a point source of light placed inside a sphere, it would be easy to visualize that the inside of the sphere would be lighted by the source. The amount of light from a source of 1 candle power on each square foot of the inside surface of this sphere is called a lumen. The surface area of a sphere is found by the formula $4\pi r^2$, so the area of a sphere with a 1-foot radius would be 12.57 square feet. A 1-candle power source, then, is equivalent to 12.57 lumens. A 125-candle power source, such as a 100-watt lamp, has a light output of approximately 1570 lumens.

a. Inverse Square Law

The amount of light that falls on a unit area of a surface is measured in *foot-candles*. If a piece of paper is placed 1 foot from a point source of 1 candle power, the amount of light on 1 square foot of the paper is 1 foot-candle. If the paper is placed 1 foot from a 40-candle power source, the amount of light on 1 square foot of the paper is 40 foot-candles. Candle power divided by the square of the distance of the source of light from a surface equals the number of foot-candles of light on that surface. For a given point source of light the level of illumination decreases as the square of the distance from the source.

Units used for the light energy emitted or reflected by a surface are foot-lamberts, candles per square centimeter, and candles per square inch. A *foot-lambert* is the amount of light energy reflected by a surface which diffuses light equally in all directions when the surface is illuminated with 1 foot-candle. One candle per square inch equals 452 foot-lamberts. White[1] gives the luminance of a fluores-

[1] Harvey E. White, *Modern College Physics,* D. Van Nostrand Company, Inc., 1948, p. 378.

cent lamp as 2 c/cm^2, a frosted mazda lamp as 5 c/cm^2, and the sun as 50,000 c/cm^2.

Light sources and illuminated surfaces are described subjectively in terms of *brightness,* and brightness is actually a subjective measure of the light energy coming from a surface. Brightness of light is produced in three ways: it may come from the source of light itself, it may come from an object which transmits light, or it may be a result of reflection of light. Objectionable brightness may result from any one of these methods. An unshaded light bulb is an example of the first, light shining through a very translucent diffusing plate would be an example of the second, and light from a shiny page of a book would be an example of the third.

3–5. NATURAL AND ARTIFICIAL LIGHT

Natural light or daylight may be very pleasant and comfortable, or it may be just the opposite. It is difficult to control because the day may be cloudy, sunny, or fluctuating from one to the other with great rapidity. The amount of light next to a window may be quite different from the amount a few feet away. The amount of light is influenced by screens on the windows, cleanliness of windows, and use of window shades and draperies.

Natural light adds beauty to the home and makes a room a more cheerful and pleasant place in which to live. Good light in the home is a result of wise use of natural light and discriminative, selective use of artificial light.

Artificial sources of light used in the home are incandescent and fluorescent lamps.

a. Incandescent Lamps

The incandescent lamp bulb has a tungsten filament. In most lamp bulbs the tungsten filament is a coiled wire that has been recoiled. The coil is so tight and the wire so tiny that to the naked eye it may look like a straight wire. Lamps are either vacuum or gas filled.

Those of 40-watt size and larger are filled with an argon-nitrogen gas mixture. The inside of lamp bulbs is frosted by flushing out the bulbs with an acid solution that etches the inside surface. Some lamps have the inside coated with a silica coating to improve the diffusion of the light.

After incandescent lamps are used for a time the tungsten filament becomes thinner, the bulb darkens, and less light is produced. If operated at higher than rated voltage, lamps wear out sooner but give more light. The average life of an incandescent lamp is approximately 750 to 1000 hours, depending upon the individual lamp and how it is used.

As stated previously, a 100-watt lamp has an

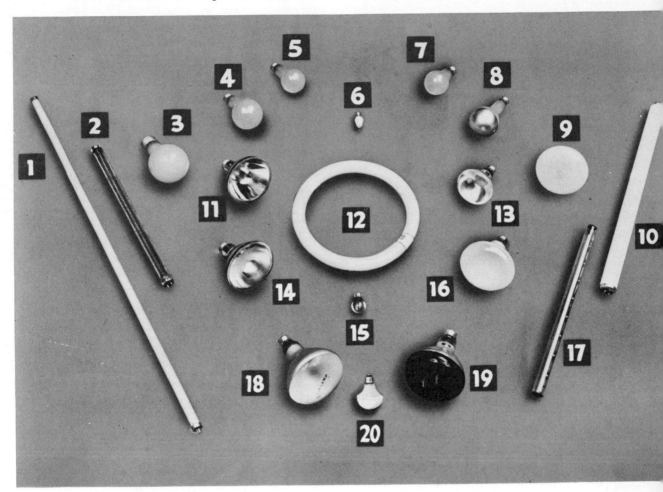

Fig. 3–2.   Lamp bulbs for use in the home. (Photo courtesy Better Light Better Sight Bureau)

1. Slimline fluorescent tube.
2. Germ-killing lamp.
3. 100-200-300-watt, three-lite bulb.
4. 50-100-150-watt, three-lite bulb.
5. 30-70-100-watt, three-lite bulb.
6. Night-lite bulb.
7. Standard inside-frosted bulb.
8. Silvered-bowl bulb.
9. R-40 white indirect-lite bulb.
10. Standard fluorescent tube.
11. Projector flood lamp.
12. Circular fluorescent tube.
13. R-30 75-watt spot or flood lamp.
14. Projector spot lamp.
15. Ozone lamp.
16. Reflector spot or flood lamp.
17. Lumiline lamp.
18. Sun lamp.
19. Infrared heat lamp.
20. Lamp for ceiling fixtures that use bare lamp bulbs.

output of 1570 lumens or 15.7 lumens per watt. The efficiency is slightly lower for smaller wattage bulbs and higher for larger bulbs. A great number of kinds and types of lamp bulbs are manufactured for home use. Some of these are shown in Figure 3–2.

b. Fluorescent Lamps

The fluorescent lamp consists of a sealed glass tube that contains small amounts of mercury and argon gas and has an electrode at each end. The interior of the glass tube is coated with fluorescent chemicals known as phosphors. When an electric current is sent through the tube, the mercury vapor emits an ultraviolet light which is converted to visible white light by the phosphors on the inside surface of the tube.

The older and perhaps more common type of fluorescent lamp is known as the preheat starting type. A few seconds after the light switch is turned on, the light comes on. The circuit for this type of lamp includes a ballast and a starting switch as shown in Figure 3–3.

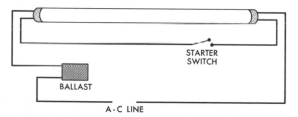

Fig. 3–3.   Preheat start fluorescent lamp circuit.

The starter switch may be either manually operated or automatically controlled. An example of a manually operated starter switch is the one on many desk-type fluorescent lamps. The starter switch on fluorescent lamps used in ceiling luminaires usually is automatically controlled. There are several types of automatically controlled starter switches.

When the starter switch is closed, electricity flows through the terminals and heating coils at one end of the lamp, through the starter switch to the heating coils and terminals at the other end of the tube, and through the ballast. When the heating coils become hot enough, the mercury within the tube is vaporized and the ends of the lamp light. The operator then releases the starter switch. The magnetic field of the ballast collapses when the starter switch is released, and this collapse gives a momentary high voltage which starts the lamp arc.

The ballast serves to limit the size of the current within the lamp and hence to protect the life of the lamp. It consists of a coil of insulated copper wire around a laminated iron core. The layers of thin iron stampings have a tendency to hum. This hum can be reduced in varying amounts by impregnating the core and coils with a special compound. Ballasts are rated according to the amount of hum they make. In industrial uses where the noise level may already be high, ballast hum is unimportant. In a home which is relatively quiet, a slight hum may be noticeable. Not all ballasts have a hum. The way in which the ballast is installed within the fixture also influences the amount of hum. Ballasts are made for the specific lamp size and type as shown on the label of the ballast. Several hundred different types of ballasts are available.

In determining the cost of operation of a fluorescent lamp, the wattage of the lamp and the ballast should be added together. This is also true when computing the efficiency of lamps—lumens per watt.

Fluorescent lamps may be operated without separate starter switches. The instant-start type of lamp has the advantage of having no momentary delay while waiting for the light to come on. A wiring circuit for this type of lamp is shown in Figure 3–4. Instant-start lamps are not preheated. Ballasts are specifically designed for use in this type of circuit, and the lamps are made differently from preheat-type lamps. No cathode preheating is required, so only one terminal is needed at each end. This is the characteristic feature of slimline lamps.

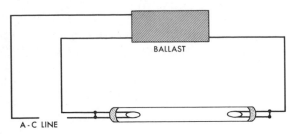

A-C LINE

Fig. 3–4. Instant-start fluorescent lamp circuit. (Adapted from General Electric Lamp Bulletin LD–1)

Instant-start lamps have a specially designed socket. Both ends of the lamp must be in place before voltage can be applied to the lamp terminals. This is a safety precaution necessary because of the high voltage required to start these lamps.[2]

New ballasts for preheat-type lamps have been developed which will also give a very quick start. Higher ballast voltage is used to start the lamps when preheat starters are not used.

With a few exceptions, most fluorescent lamps of 15 watts and above have a rated lamp life of 7500 hours. Ratings are made on lamps operated for three hours per start. A 60 percent longer life can be expected for lamps operated for twelve hours per start.[3]

Seventy to 80 lumens per watt is the *realized* efficiency of higher wattage lamps. Low wattage lamps have an efficiency of 25 lumens per watt. There are a number of reasons why the *realized* efficiency is lower than the theoretical efficiency. It appears that fluorescent lamps are near their limit of efficiency unless some new principle, at present unknown, should be discovered.[4]

The material with which fluorescent tubes are lined is not harmful. Except for some lamps manufactured before 1949, the usual precautions in disposing of broken glass are sufficient. Presumably few if any of these lamps would still be in use.

[2] C. E. Weitz, *General Electric Lamps,* General Electric Company, 1956, p. 69.
[3] *Ibid.,* p. 65.
[4] *Ibid.,* p. 62.

Fluorescent lamps get darker as they are used. Because this darkening is usually quite even over the entire lamp, it is seldom noticeable until a new lamp is compared with one that has been used for quite a long time. This darkening is, however, the main cause for depreciation of light output during the life of the lamp.

As a general rule, when a lamp begins to flicker either it or the starter should be replaced. Other reasons for flickering are low circuit voltage, low ballast rating, low temperature, and cold drafts. Working under a flickering light is very irritating to many people.

Fluorescent lamps sometimes cause radio interference, which can often be eliminated by moving radio and lamp further apart. Radio interference filters can also be installed to minimize this interference. Filters may be placed in various locations, depending upon the specific cause of the interference. A filter may be placed at the radio or at each panel box feeding fluorescent lamp circuits.

Fluorescent lamps, like incandescent lamps, should be shaded. The louvered type of reflector has proved quite satisfactory. Light from a lamp without proper shading or diffusing may be uncomfortable for the eyes, particularly when doing close work such as reading or sewing.

3–6. Luminaires and Portable Lamps

A complete lighting unit that is installed permanently is technically a *luminaire*. The more familiar term is a lighting fixture. The luminaire should harmonize with the decorating scheme and at the same time give good-quality light. A ceiling luminaire is often used for general overall lighting, but it may be used for localized light, as over a dining table or work bench. Wall luminaires are often used for special seeing purposes. Luminaires should be kept clean; they should be washed occasionally with a detergent and rinsed well.

Portable lamps, as the name implies, may be moved from one place to another. A portable lamp may be used to give general overall light, localized light, or both. Every home ought to have at least one good portable lamp—floor lamp, table lamp, or wall lamp—to be used for reading, sewing, studying, and similar seeing tasks.

a. Diffusers

Diffusing bowls and reflectors help to spread light and eliminate glare. Diffusing bowls are of two main shapes. Types 2 and 4 in Figure 3–5 are used in CLM lamps. The material of

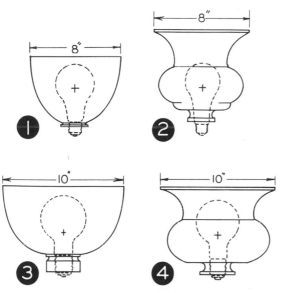

Fig. 3–5.   Diffusing bowls. (General Electric Company)

a diffuser should allow light to pass through easily, but its source should not show through. Glass and plastic are used for diffusers. The material of the diffuser should not be a source of glare.

Plastic ceiling reflectors or diffusers of a satisfactory type can be purchased relatively inexpensively. They usually clip on to the lamp bulb and hence can be used where a permanent installation is not feasible. Care should be taken to choose a pleasing color, as the light that shines through takes on that color.

b. Lamp Shades

Shades for lamps should be deep enough to cover the lamp socket and also to allow a diffuser to be used on the lamp. Shades should have a white or off-white lining. Colored linings reflect light the same color as the lining. Not only do they make seeing more difficult, but they may also make the furnishings in a room look rather odd. The shade should have a wide opening at both bottom and top, so light can go upward and give some general overall light in the room, as well as illuminate the surface of the seeing task (Fig. 3–6). The shade should be translucent but not transparent. A shade that transmits too much light is uncomfortable for the eyes. Translucent shades should be light in color—white, off-white, eggshell, or cream. A poor shade for a reading lamp is shown in Figure 3–7. Note that the book pages are in shadow.

Opaque shades are not as desirable as translucent shades but are far better than no shade at all. An opaque shade should be used if the shade "must" be a dark color. Light shining through a dark translucent shade tends to cast a dark-colored glow over all surfaces on which it falls.

c. The CLM Lamp

At the present time one of the best types of lamps for reading, sewing, and studying is one that carries a tag of approval by the Certified Lamp Makers commonly called the CLM label (Fig. 3–8). The CLM lamp is manufactured by at least 12 different manufacturers. However, all the lamps by a certain manufacturer may not be made to CLM specifications.

CLM specifications are concerned with the performance of the lamps, not with style, and good light for seeing purposes is therefore available from many designs of lamps. Lamps can be chosen that will harmonize with modern, conventional, colonial, or other types of

Fig. 3–6. A good shade for a reading lamp. (General Electric Company)

Fig. 3–7. Reading material is in shadow with a shade poorly designed for reading purposes. (General Electric Company)

furnishings. CLM lamps must not only meet performance tests but also many construction specifications for all parts of the lamp including base, socket, cord, plug, switches, shades, etc. The specifications also cover the construction and performance of parts usually made by suppliers of accessory parts.

The Beauty-plus label is also used on lamps designed to give good light. The specifications are somewhat less comprehensive and detailed than for lamps that carry the CLM label.

Lamps that do not meet CLM specifications may be very good if care is taken to choose wisely. A good lamp may be expensive, but when considered in relation to the value of good eyesight, it is not costly. A poor lamp may be just as expensive in monetary value and much more expensive when the effect on eyesight is considered.

3–7. IMPROVING EXISTING LIGHTING CONDITIONS

Existing lighting situations can often be improved immensely with a little ingenuity. The source of light should not be directly visible to the eyes; therefore put shades and diffusers on bare lamp bulbs. Light should be diffused instead of falling directly on a surface. Many lamps, some very expensive, have only a bulb under the striking shade. If a diffuser is added to the lamp, it will be improved for seeing purposes, provided the shade is of a reasonably good design.

Fig. 3–8. The CLM label on a portable lamp indicates compliance with the specifications of Certified Lamp Makers. (Certified Lamp Makers)

The use of diffusing bowls is not so important in dressing table lamps.

The source of light should not be too close to the seeing task. Many desk lamps are too short, and glare is caused because the source of light is too bright for its distance from the seeing task. Study lamps can be made taller by placing them on books, glass bricks, or wood platforms. End table lamps can be raised in the same manner or put on taller tables. A clever person can probably think of other ways to raise the height of a lamp.

Many times the placement of the lamp is poor. For reading, it does not matter whether the lamp is placed to the left or right of the reader, provided he has reasonably good sitting posture. For writing, the lamp should be placed at the right of a left-handed writer and at the left of a right-handed writer.

Consider the background for the lamp. Dark walls, dark draperies, and dark rugs absorb light. Light colors reflect light. Mat surfaces diffuse light; shiny surfaces reflect light in a more glaring fashion. Choose the furnishings of a room and fittings for a desk with these facts in mind.

Lamps may be dirty and hence much of the light emitted from them may be lost. If the shades and the diffusers are covered with dust, the user pays for electricity that is being wasted. Shades can be cleaned with the dusting attachment on the vacuum cleaner, and diffusers and lamp bulbs can be washed. Care should be taken not to subject the diffusers to extremes of temperature; sockets of lamp bulbs should never be placed in water.

As incandescent bulbs get old, they darken on one end, depending upon which end has been in the higher position. Because heat rises, it is the upper part of the lamp bulb that will turn dark. If it is the large end that darkens and not the socket end, the amount of light may be cut down considerably as the bulb ages. It is good practice to put these old bulbs in less critical seeing positions, such as hallways, storage rooms, and basement rooms, and to use new bulbs in lamps used for reading, sewing, and other detailed work.

Light for seeing can be improved by making sure the right size bulb is being used. It is false economy to use too small a bulb, and it may be just as bad to use a bulb that is much too large. The former results in a lack of light and the latter in glare.

B. Recommended Practice for Home Lighting

3–8. GENERAL CONSIDERATIONS[5]

The decision on the type of lighting to be used in a room depends on the type of activities carried on in the room, which of course varies from one family to another. A few general guides may serve to make home lighting more useful as well as pleasing.

[5] The material in this section has been adapted in part from *Recommended Practice of Home Lighting,* Illuminating Engineering Society, prepared by Subcommittee on Recommended Practice of Home Lighting Committee on Residence Lighting, 1947; and from *See Your Home in a New Light,* 2nd ed. The light-conditioning recipes were developed by the Lighting Laboratories of General Electric Company Lamp Division.

There should be at least one light in a room that can be controlled by a switch at the entrance. This should give sufficient illumination to enable a person to walk into the room safely. If there is more than one entrance and the entrances are more than a few feet apart, the light should be controlled at each entrance. It should not be necessary to retrace one's steps in the dark when leaving a room.

In general, ceilings should be light in color but not glossy. A glossy ceiling tends to make the reflections of light glaring. Dark ceilings create a contrast between the light and the ceiling and also absorb the light. Quite generally, dark colors and dark furnishings absorb light. Artificial light that has been quite adequate in a room with pastel furnishings may be totally inadequate if the room is redecorated in darker colors.

3–9. Considerations for Specific Areas

a. Kitchen Lighting

Good light in the kitchen is a composite of two sources. Overall lighting is obtained from a well-placed, not necessarily centered, luminaire or luminaries in the ceiling and from local light sources at the counter surfaces, range, and sink (Fig. 3–9).

The general lighting should be shaded and well diffused. It should light the room adequately for all tasks except special tasks carried on where local light sources are available. Many different luminaires are acceptable, but some people have a preference for the totally enclosed lighting luminaire, believing it is somewhat easier to keep clean. Glass globes should be of a frosted or translucent finish. More than one ceiling luminaire may be needed, especially in a large room. Concealed lighting in the ceiling should be planned for before a house is built.

Lights over the sink and range should be so placed that direct light does not shine into the eyes of a person working there. Light over the sink can often be concealed behind a wood or curtain valance or even cupboard space. When planning for incandescent lights, remember that these lights get hot, and allow adequate space around them for air circulation. Fluorescent lights also need some air space, but they do not get as warm as incandescent lights.

Lights placed under cupboards to light counter space should be placed far enough back so that the eye cannot see the direct light; preferably, however, they should not be placed flush against the wall. Light sources at the counter, sink, and range permit a worker to work in an area free of shadow. This is not possible with general lighting in the room, because the best general lighting cannot avoid the situation where a worker is in her own shadow when she stands between the light and the work space.

Some shadows make a room more attractive and pleasant, but care should be taken that these shadows do not interfere with seeing. Forty foot-candles of light at the sink, range, and work counters and 10 foot-candles of general illumination in the kitchen are recommended.

If fluorescent light is used in the kitchen, care should be taken to choose colors that will make foods look the most natural. The regular fluorescent lamp brings out greens and blues and generally dulls reds and yellows. The *deluxe warm* lamp or *standard warm* lamp enhances the warm colors of the spectrum.

b. Laundry Area Lighting

Although the laundry center may be located in the kitchen, it is also found in the basement, porch, and utility room. Good light here makes it easier to remove spots from clothing and to see when clothing needs special attention in cleaning. It also makes ironing easier and helps in doing a better job. Forty foot-candles of light over the ironing center and laundry tubs are recommended. The light should be placed so that it falls on the material being ironed and does not cast glare into the eyes. Ironing in front of a window may often be undesirable because of glare.

c. Dining Room Lighting

Light should be provided above the table so that the table settings will be highlighted and people at the table can see each other easily. A luminaire that fits close to the ceiling, a hanging luminaire, or a ceiling spot can be used. The light should be diffused as well as ample in quantity if sewing, writing, or games are to be carried on here (Fig. 3–10).

Cove lighting is attractive in the dining area

Fig. 3–9. A well-lighted kitchen. (General Electric Company)

and helps to avoid excessive contrasts in the amounts of light in different parts of the room. A lighted wall bracket may be used to give general illumination in the room and add a feeling of spaciousness.

d. Living Room Lighting

Soft background light may be achieved by cove lighting, valance lighting, or by a ceiling luminaire. If this light is adequate, there is greater flexibility in the use of the room and less need for moving portable lamps. The upward light from portable lamps also serves to increase the general lighting in a room.

Care must be taken in the installation of cove lighting. The lamp should be placed far enough from the ceiling so the light can spread, and the trough must be wide enough so that the wall does not get too warm when the lights are on for long periods. Direct-indirect cove lighting is pictured in Figure 3–11.

Cove lighting provides good background light for television viewing, because the light is not reflected from the television screen and at the same time enough light is provided so that the eyes are not strained by the extreme difference in room lighting and screen lighting.

Fig. 3–10. Valance lighting and direct and indirect lighting with portable lamps and a ceiling luminaire create a pleasant atmosphere in this dining-living room. (General Electric Company)

It is an extremely bad practice to watch television in a totally darkened room.

Portable lamps should be so placed that the light in the room is not spotty. The bulb or the diffuser should not be in line with the eyes of a person sitting on a davenport, in a chair, or at a desk. For casual reading, 20 to 25 foot-candles of light should be supplied; for longer periods of reading, for sewing, and for similar activities a minimum of 40 foot-candles is recommended.

e. Bedroom Lighting

General lighting in the bedroom makes it easier to clean the room and see into dresser drawers, and provides enough light for many purposes. It may also make the room more usable for a study or sitting room.

Additional lighting should be provided for reading in bed and putting on make-up. A bed lamp should give some general light as well as light directed toward the pages of the book. One-tenth to one-fifth as much general light should be available in the room as is supplied for the specific task of reading. Too often bed lamps direct all the light on the specific reading task and the rest of the room is in total darkness. Either a table lamp, wall lamp, or bracket light may be quite satisfactory for a bed lamp.

A general rule to follow in choosing lamps to be used on a dressing table is that the light through the center of the shade should be shining on the face. Colored shades should be avoided as the face color may be distorted by their use. Light should be provided for each side of the face.

f. Bathroom Lighting

Bathroom lighting should be controlled by a wall switch—one that cannot be reached while standing at the sink or in the tub or

Fig. 3–11.   Luminous cove lighting with well-designed portable lamps enhance the beauty of this living room. (General Electric Company)

shower. Mirror lighting may often be the only lighting if the room is small. Light should shine on the face, not on the mirror. A circular fluorescent lamp around the mirror provides ideal lighting for shaving and putting on make-up. Two fluorescent wall lamps on either side of the mirror and one above also make especially good lighting. If incandescent lights are used, they should by all means be shaded. It is fairly satisfactory to use fluorescent lamps unshaded for lighting at a bathroom mirror.

A center luminaire is desirable if the room is large. If a bathroom is compartmentalized with enclosed toilet space, stall shower, and dressing table unit, each area should have a

wall or ceiling luminaire. A stall shower should have a vaporproof ceiling unit.

g. Study Center Lighting

The study center in the home or college room should be well planned. Poor posture, eye strain, nervous fatigue, as well as poor grades, may result from a poorly planned, poorly lighted study center. The top surface of the desk should have a nonglossy finish of a light or medium color. The desk should not face a window; it is better to place it at right angles to the window or against a wall. The wall should have a mat finish in a light color. There should be no reflected glare, and the wall should be light enough in color so that useful light is not absorbed by a dark surface. If the wall is finished with a highly patterned paper, it is wise to cover this with a mat-finished wallboard approximately 36 inches high and as long as the desk. Books and papers should be propped up at an angle, as this makes seeing easier. The chair should be comfortable and so designed that the eyes are at least 14 inches above the desk top.

The type of lamp, its placement, and its height are most important. Figure 3–12 shows one good arrangement for a study lamp. Forty foot-candles of light over the central portion of the desk are recommended. There should be no dark shadows on the desk.

h. Entrance Lighting

Lighting at the entrance of a home should serve to make the entrance more attractive and should provide illumination so that a person coming to the house can see where he is going and those in the home can see who is approaching. Care should be taken to locate the luminaire so that light is not cast into the eyes of either the visitor or the occupant of the home. Luminaires should have frosted or other diffusing glass. Clear glass is a source of glare.

Metal parts of the luminaire should be of nonrusting material, and the luminaire should

Fig. 3–12.　Good lighting for the study desk. (General Electric Company)

be made in such a manner that it can be easily taken down for cleaning.

It is well to consider how house numbers are lighted. The light should be placed so the illumination will fall on the numbers and not blind the eyes of those who may be looking for the number.

C. Experiments

Experiments 1 and 2 can be done without any special equipment, but experiment 3 requires special equipment.

Experiment 1. *The Effect of Different Color Blotters on the Ease of Seeing*

Pull the shades, if possible. Use a recommended study lamp. Place it on a blotter, 19 × 24 inches, of neutral color. On this place a sheet of ordinary notebook paper. Turn all room lights off and turn the study lamp on. Look at the notebook paper for ten seconds. Then substitute other blotters such as bright red, bright blue, and yellow.

1.　Which blotter showed the least glare by contrast?
2.　What would you expect the effect to be over a longer period of viewing?

Experiment 2. *The Effect of Different Heights of Lamps and of Large and Small Shades on the Light Falling upon the Study Area of a Desk*

Place a light mat-finish blotter, about 19 × 24 inches, on a table. On this place a lamp in the recommended position for a study lamp. Use a lamp shorter than that recommended for a study lamp. It should have a small decorative shade with a diffusing bowl. Use a 100-watt lamp bulb. Pull the room shades and turn off all room lights. Turn on lamp and measure foot-candles of light in at least five positions—near the corners and at the center of the blotter. Record readings.

Raise the height of the lamp so that it meets the recommendations for a study lamp. Again take the readings and record.

Raise the height of the lamp so that it exceeds the recommendations by 3 or 4 inches. Again take the readings and record.

Substitute for the small shade a shade recommended for study lamps. Repeat readings as above and record.

1. Why does the recommended height give more effective light?
2. What effect does the size of shade have on the amount of light on the blotter?
3. What effect does the size of shade have on the spread of light?

Experiment 3. *Effect of Voltage on Light Output of a Lamp*

Connect a study lamp with a three-way lamp bulb to a source of electricity in which the voltage can be controlled.

Turn off all artificial lights in the room. Close the blinds or pull the shades. Using the 50- or 100-watt setting, take foot-candle readings at the center of the work area when the voltage is at 125, 120, 115, 110, 105, and 100 volts. Repeat at the 150-watt or 300-watt setting.

Connect a fluorescent study lamp and repeat the experiment at the various voltages.

Draw a graph depicting the effect of voltage on light output.

CHAPTER 4

Materials

A. Base Materials

Materials considered here are those from which the frame, the article itself, or various parts of the appliance are constructed. Some of these materials are used for many articles of household equipment and others have more limited uses. The material from which an appliance is constructed greatly influences the consumer's eventual satisfaction with it. Much greater satisfaction would result from many purchases if the consumer knew what he was buying and at the same time realized the limitations of the materials used and the care required. As in most other areas there is no one perfect material, and wise selection involves choosing the one best suited to an individual's needs. When labels are provided they should be studied for the information that they contain.

4–1. ALUMINUM

Aluminum in both cast and sheet metal form is used for household equipment. Cast utensils are made by pouring molten metal into a mold; articles from sheet metal are pressed or stamped into shape. Sheet metal that has been cold rolled is very hard and durable. Annealing makes the sheet metal more ductile and hence more easily shaped.

Pressure saucepans, skillets, and griddles are

usually made of cast aluminum or a very heavy gauge of sheet aluminum. Saucepans are made of several gauges of sheet metal and of cast aluminum. Refrigerator shelves and ice cube trays, baking pans, gelatin molds, and measuring cups are a few of the many articles made from this sheet metal.

Aluminum is light in weight. Sheet aluminum does not break upon impact, but can be dented. Cast aluminum may be broken by a severe impact. Aluminum does not rust but it is affected by food acids and alkalies. The alkalies leave the pan dark. This darkening can be removed by cooking acid foods, such as tomatoes, in the pan, or a solution of vinegar and water or cream of tartar and water can be boiled in the pan. How long this process will take and how strong the solution must be depends upon how much darkening has taken place. The darkening does not harm foods, and tomatoes or other foods that remove the darkening are not harmed when cooked in darkened pans.

Because aluminum is a very good conductor of heat, it is sometimes used on the exterior bottom of stainless steel pans to improve their heat conductivity. When these pans are new it is difficult—sometimes almost impossible—to tell where the aluminum plating ends, but after some use the line of demarcation shows plainly.

Cast metal is more porous than sheet metal, and for this reason pans will sometimes pit if hard water or foods stand in them for periods of time. Lack of thorough drying may also cause pitting. Pitting is minute or very tiny pin prick holes which are usually observed in the bottom of the pan. Theoretically this could become a problem when cleaning pans. Actually it is not a serious problem, since pitting of utensils does not seem to become excessive even after several years of use. Sheet metal is much more resistant to pitting.

Thickness of sheet metal is measured by its gauge; for cooking utensils too thin a gauge is not desirable. Ten-, 12-, or 14-gauge metals are fairly heavy and are used for cooking utensils. Eighteen- and 20-gauge metals are also used but are thinner. Aluminum is a good conductor of heat, and in the thinner gauges this heat transfer takes place so quickly that sticking may become a problem. When using pans made from the thinner gauges, one should start the cooking process at a relatively low heat unless doing nothing much more complicated than boiling water. Articles made from thinner gauges will dent more easily than those from a heavier gauge. However, the amount of *cold rolling* in the manufacturing process partially determines an article's resistance to denting.

Aluminum is sometimes *anodized*. This electrolytic process produces a comparatively heavy oxide coating on the aluminum. Anodized articles may have color added. Very high temperatures may remove this color. Uncolored anodized articles may be used in the oven. Pans that have been anodized bake about 30 percent faster than untreated pans. Anodizing makes aluminum stain- and corrosion-resistant and gives it a harder surface. Anodized aluminum articles do not rub off on light clothing, sinks, and enamel-finished surfaces. This treatment is used for both protective and decorative purposes.[1]

4–2. GLASS

Glass for use in the kitchen is of four main types: (1) glass that will withstand oven temperatures without breaking, (2) glass that can be used for surface cookery, (3) glass that is not heat resistant and is used for accessory equipment such as mixing bowls, and (4) glass used in cabinet construction. The appearance of all glass is much the same, and care should be taken to select and use the glass for the purpose for which it was manufactured.

[1] A. G. Vraney, in a personal communication, Aluminum Goods Manufacturing Company, December, 1956.

The many possibilities for using glass in cabinet construction and kitchens are at present limited by the weight of the glass, the difficulty of obtaining it, and its cost. Glass for cabinet shelves has the advantage of making the contents of the cabinets easily visible. Drawer dividers and sliding panel fronts for cabinets are other uses. The edges of the glass are ground and polished to dull them. Glass is used for mixing bowls, refrigerator dishes, measuring cups, saucepans, cake pans, teakettles, and other articles (Fig. 4–1). Articles

Fig. 4–1. Glass utensils used for food preparation and surface cookery. (Corning Glass Works)

to be used over direct heat must be made from a specially processed glass which has a low coefficient of expansion. Some mixing bowls, refrigerator dishes, and measuring cups can be put into the oven; others will not stand oven heat without breaking.

Glass is nonporous and holds heat well, but it is not a good conductor of heat. It will break if subjected to sudden extremes of temperature or to sharp impact. It is not affected by food acids or alkalies, does not rust, and is relatively easy to care for. Glass needs no finish coating of other material. It is usually considered an inexpensive material for small kitchen utensils.

Glass can be scratched by scouring with metal dishcloths and the like. If food sticks to glass, the best procedure is to try to soak it off. If an abrasive is needed, only a very fine one should be used. Cleaning can become progressively more difficult once the glass has become scratched. Some foods such as tomatoes, lemon pie fillings, and other acid foods seem to taste better when prepared in glass. It is often stated that coffee has a better flavor when made in a glass pot.

Glass utensils are particularly well suited for use in demonstrations, as they allow the audience to see how the food is being prepared.

There is always a danger that liquid in any pan with a cover that does not fit quite tightly will completely evaporate. Covers on glass utensils do not fit tightly and therefore a bit more liquid needs to be used when cooking foods in glass than when cooking in metal pans with tight-fitting covers. It is usually recommended that a heat protector or metal grid be placed on the surface unit when glass is used over high heat on an electric range. Utensils designed to be used in the oven should not be used on surface units or burners, but utensils for top-of-the-range cookery may be used in the oven.

4–3. IRON

Iron used in household equipment is made either by casting or from sheets of metal. Dutch ovens, skillets, griddles, sinks, bathtubs, and radiators are some of the articles made from cast iron. Cast iron is heavy, hard, and somewhat brittle. Skillets may break if dropped on the floor. Iron conducts heat evenly and holds heat well because of its high thermal mass. For easy, even browning of foods and for long, slow, carefree cooking it is hard to beat. Cast iron is a porous metal. It is essential to season iron cooking utensils so that these microscopic pores are filled with a covering of fat. Foods can then be cooked without sticking. Though most cast iron cooking utensils now come preseasoned from the factory, reseasoning is sometimes necessary. To reseason scour the utensil to be treated, wash, and dry. Cover the interior with an unsalted fat. Heat in a slow oven, 250–300 F, for several hours. Remove, cool, wash, and dry. The utensil is now ready for use.

Sheet metal is used for skillets, pie and cake pans, knife blades, and panels for refrigerators, ranges, and other large equipment. It is less porous than cast metal and has greater impact resistance. It transfers heat evenly but does not hold heat as well as cast iron does. Extreme sudden changes of temperature may cause the metal to warp, and for this reason, as well as the fact that it is thinner and hence transfers heat faster, sheet iron is not as desirable as cast iron for skillets. Skillets made of

sheet metal usually have a coating of lacquer which must be removed before the skillet is used for cooking.

Both cast and sheet iron may rust if not treated or finished to prevent rusting. Utensils should be dried carefully before storing. Sheet iron used in large equipment may be Bonderized before the finish is applied. Bonderizing is a chemical treatment which makes the metal rust resistant by forming a base for the paint that prevents it from lifting or peeling. Bonderizing creates a nonmetallic phosphate coating on the metal (Fig. 4–2). This acts to keep moisture from reaching the base metal. The Bonderite[2] (Fig. 4–3) treatment may be used on steel, aluminum, zinc, and cadmium.

A somewhat newer treatment is used on steel and aluminum before porcelain enamel is applied. This treatment, known as Parker Pre-Namel,[3] simplifies the enameling of alumi-

[2] Bonderite—Registered U. S. Patent Office, Parker Rust Proof Company.
[3] Parker Pre-Namel—Registered U. S. Patent Office, Parker Rust Proof Company.

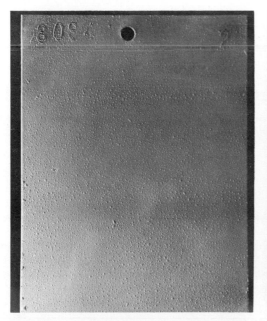 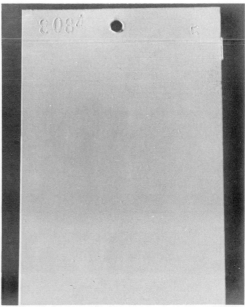

Fig. 4–2. Both panels were subjected to high humidity in 100 F temperature for 48 hours. The refrigerator finish for both panels was the same. (Parker Rust Proof Company)

A. Untreated clean steel—badly blistered B. Treated with Bonderite before painting—not blistered

Fig. 4–3. The Bonderite seal. (Parker Rust Proof Company)

num and steel. It is more economical, takes less time, and is more effective than methods used previously. Parker Pre-Namel used on steel makes it possible to eliminate the ground coat of porcelain enamel. The protective and decorative qualities of the finish coat of porcelain enamel are the same as though a ground coat were used.

For some uses iron is finished with a coating of tin or zinc, neither of which will rust.

Cast iron utensils are somewhat difficult to keep looking attractive. If cared for after each use, a skillet does not need to acquire the black crust of burned grease that is often evident on the exterior and sometimes on the interior. The outside of the skillet may be scoured. It is better not to scour the inside of the skillet because scouring removes the seasoning, but the skillet can be washed.

4–4. MAGNALITE

Magnalite is an alloy of metals of which aluminum is one. Magnalite cooking utensils are made by casting. Magnalite is a good conductor of heat, and because of its high thermal mass, it holds heat well. It is affected by alkalies but this discoloration can be removed by

use of steel wool. It is not discolored by heat, is light in weight, and is attractive in appearance.

4–5. PLASTICS

Plastics in use in the home are included within two main groups—thermosetting and thermoplastic. Several types of plastics are included in each of these main divisions. Some plastics have been misused not only by the homemaker but also by some manufacturers. It is, therefore, essential that care be given not only to the use of plastics but to wise selection.

Information about plastics has been adapted from many sources, but five sources have provided the greater part of the background material.[4]

"A plastic is any one of a large and varied group of materials which consists of, or contains as an essential ingredient, a substance of large molecular weight which, while solid in the finished state, at some stage in its manufacture has been or can be formed into various shapes by flow, usually through application of heat or pressure, singly or together."[5]

a. Thermoplastics

Thermoplastic is a type of plastic which softens when heated to temperatures normally used in forming it, without much if any chemical change, and quickly becomes more rigid upon cooling. This process of heating to soften and cooling to harden can be repeated almost indefinitely.

There are six groupings or types of thermo-

[4] Ruth Hutcheson, *How to Select and Treat Plastics,* Cooperative Extension Work in Agriculture and Home Economics, Purdue University, USDA Cooperating, No. 298–2; *Plastics in Your Home,* The Society of the Plastics Industry, Inc.; *Plastics Today: The Story of Styron in the Home,* The Dow Chemical Company, 1952; *Get Acquainted with Plastics,* U.S. Testing League. U.S. Testing Company, Inc., 1949; *When You Buy Plastics,* National Consumer-Retailer Council, Inc., 104, 1950.

[5] *Plastics Today: The Story of Styron in the Home,* The Dow Chemical Company, 1952, p. 4.

plastics with which the homemaker might be most concerned. *Acrylics* are used in articles like clock cases, salad bowls, and hair brushes. They are tasteless, odorless, nontoxic, have good resistance to cracking or breaking, and can be made colorless or in many colors. They can be made transparent, translucent, or opaque. Acrylics can be scratched by abrasive powders but are unaffected by water that is not too hot for the hand. Cleaning fluid and nail polish removers should not be used on them.

The *Cellulosics* group has four subgroups, the characteristics of which are all similar but not quite the same. Celluloid was the very first plastic in this group. Cellulosics are used for ice crushers, juicer bowls, toys, lamp shades, highchair trays, fountain pens, optical frames, telephone housings, tool handles, and flashlight cases. They are electrical insulators, light in weight, unlimited in color. They will take fairly hard knocks without breaking. They are harmed by nail polish and nail polish remover. Certain ones are also harmed by cleaning fluids. Cellulosics may be washed with warm water and mild soap, but abrasives should not be used. They are not affected by freezing temperatures but should be kept away from high heat.

Nylon is a plastic used for tumblers, kitchen funnels, brush bristles, washers, and gaskets. It can be sterilized and dry cleaned. It usually comes in a pastel or milky white color, is odorless, tasteless, and nontoxic. It can be scratched by abrasives.

Polyethylene is used in film, semirigid and rigid forms, or as a coating. Flexible mixing bowls, ice cube trays, and raincoats are made of polyethylene. It is odorless, tasteless, and nontoxic. It can stand brief contact with boiling water and may be washed in very hot but not boiling water. It will retain its flexibility even when cold. Abrasives should not be used on it. Figure 4–4 shows a step-on disposal can made of polyethylene.

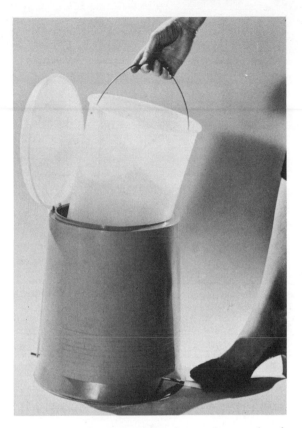

Fig. 4–4. Plastic step-on disposal can; silent, nonbreakable. (Bakelite Company)

Polystyrene is used for refrigerator dishes, utility trays, canister sets, and parts of many major appliances. It comes in many colors, is tasteless, odorless, and nontoxic. It is not affected by citrus fruit juices, but citrus fruit rinds may be harmful to it. Cleaning fluids and nail polish remover should not be used on it. Polystyrene will not withstand severe impact or bending and may be affected by a temperature as low as 150 F. Special types will have greater heat resistance.

Vinyl is available in film, sheeting, semirigid and rigid forms, and as a coating. The vinyl group is used chiefly for such articles as tile, floor coverings, raincoats, and upholstery. Vinyl products may have a slight odor when boxed, and some types will stick to lacquered surfaces. Vinyls should be washed in lukewarm water. They are very strong and tough, stain resistant, and not easily scratched. However, abrasives should not be used on them. Vinyls can be made in a wide range of colors.

b. Thermosetting Plastics

Thermosetting plastics are permanently set into shape when formed. Heat is used in this process. The thermosetting plastics do not soften or melt by heat after they have been "set." Included in this group are resins of phenol called phenolics, resins of melamine called melamine, resins of urea called urea, and casein.

The *phenolics* are electrical insulators, heat resistant, odorless, tasteless, and nontoxic. Cast phenolic is available in all colors. Other phenolic products are usually of dark colors. Phe-

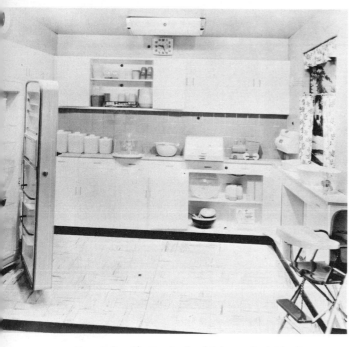

Fig. 4–5. Plastics in the kitchen—*vinyl tile* floor-covering; *polystyrene* food storage containers, refrigerator door shelves, clock case and dial, canisters, fan housing, and impeller blade (*extra-high impact*); *polyethylene* mixing bowl and strainer; *Styron* refrigerator door liner and breaker frame (*high impact*), fluorescent light diffuser, towel bar, wall tile; *Ethocel* food containers; *Saran* wrap. (The Dow Chemical Company)

nolics will take hard use and do not break or scratch easily. However, abrasives should not be used on them. Phenolics are used for radio cabinets, toaster bases, appliance handles, and light switch plates.

Melamine and *urea* are colorfast, break resistant, odorless, tasteless, and nontoxic. They are used in the manufacture of certain types of tableware, cutlery handles, and counter coverings. Products made of urea may be washed in water of temperatures up to 170 F and those of melamine up to 210 F. Melamine-laminated counter coverings will withstand temperatures as high as 300 F. Abrasives should not be used on them.

Casein is used for such articles as beads, buttons, and knitting needles. Casein articles will withstand dry cleaning but not washing. They are not flammable and do not crack easily. A wide range of colors is available.

Most of the articles shown in Figure 4–5 are made of plastic. Exceptions are the cabinets and refrigerator exterior and interior shells.

4–6. STEEL

Steel is made by refining molten pig iron. Steel is widely used in household equipment in sheet form. The gauge will vary. It is used for the walls of refrigerators, ranges, freezers, cabinets, and cutlery blades.

Steel is extremely strong and durable. It will rust if not thoroughly dried or properly treated in the manufacturing process. Bonderizing is used on steel that is to be finished with synthetic enamel. Steel is also finished with porcelain enamel, tin, and zinc. Steel is not as good a heat conductor as iron.

Steel is manufactured as *high-carbon* or *low-carbon steel*. High-carbon steel is steel which has in it 1 percent or more of carbon. Low-carbon steel has $\frac{1}{10}$ percent or less of carbon. High-carbon steel is important in the manufacture of knives, as it will take and hold a very sharp edge.

a. Stainless Steel

Stainless steel is made from recipes combining molten steel, chromium, and nickel. Manganese and silicon are also added.

Stainless steel is widely used in household equipment for wash tubs, sinks, counter tops, liners in freezers, cutlery blades, saucepans, silverware, and trim on counters and large equipment. It can be highly polished during manufacture and therefore is very attractive both for trim and for complete utensils for the kitchen. As a counter top it may have a high polish, a satin finish, or perhaps a corrugated pattern.

Stainless steel is resistant to staining; some stainless steels are almost stainproof. It needs to be thoroughly dried or it may water spot. It does not rust. If overheated, it turns dark. Sometimes it is possible to remove minor darkening by scouring, but if the overheating has been very extensive, nothing can be done about the darkening but to decide the steel is more attractive dark! It is extremely durable, not easily dented, and practically impossible to break. It can be scratched if a counter surface is used as a cutting board and this is equally hard on a knife so used. Stainless steel is not resilient and seems noisy when used as a counter top.

Because it is not a good conductor of heat, other metals may be used with it in cooking utensils to make them good conductors of heat. Stainless steel utensils that are not covered on the bottom with a good heat conductor such as copper or aluminum (Fig. 4–6) will often develop hot spots which in turn result in scorched food and pans that are difficult to clean. This can be avoided by careful use of heat. If a pan is heated slowly these hot spots do not develop.

Fig. 4–6. Cross section of an aluminum-clad stainless steel utensil. (S. W. Farber, Inc.)

Although stainless steel is usually lower in carbon content than the steel from which it is made, it is possible to buy *high-carbon stainless steel.* This not only has the characteristics of ease of upkeep and resistance to staining but it also has the ability to take and keep a sharp edge. At the present time, knives made of this high-carbon stainless steel are somewhat more expensive than comparable knives of chromium-plated, high-carbon iron or steel.

B. Materials Used for Finishes

The type of finish used on a base material is determined by the end product desired and the specifications that must be met. Finishes may be used to prevent rust and corrosion, to make an article more attractive, to make it a better heat conductor, or to make it easier to maintain.

Finishes may be divided into two groups—

mechanical and applied. Either may be used to make an article more attractive or easier to maintain. Mechanical finishes are commonly used on materials that do not rust or corrode and do not affect or are not affected by the foods or other materials with which they may come in contact. Applied finishes are used on materials that rust, corrode, or are affected by foods; they are also used to make utensils better conductors of heat.

4–7. MECHANICAL FINISHES

Mechanical finishing consists in polishing or buffing the material until it has reached the desired lustre. The two more common mechanical finishes are known as high polish and satin finish. The former is very bright and shiny and the latter has somewhat more the patina often associated with sterling silver. A third mechanical finish is known as hammered or pebbled. In this the metal is slightly dented to give it an appearance that is different from the totally smooth surface.

4–8. APPLIED FINISHES

An applied finish is one in which a second material is added over the base material, usually by the use of heat or by electroplating.

a. Chromium

Chromium-finished base metal is a very popular trim for cabinets, refrigerators, and ranges. Chromium is also used as a covering for small appliances such as coffee makers, waffle bakers, and irons. Chromium is a shiny, hard metal which requires little care except washing with soap and water and thorough drying. Fat that has splattered and burned on a chromium finish can be removed with whiting. Abrasives should not be used on a chromium finish.

A good chromium finish will have a layer of copper and one of nickel underneath it. A layer of copper is plated on to the steel base, then a layer of nickel is added, and lastly the chromium finish.

b. Copper

Copper is used as a finish on stainless steel pans to improve their heat conductivity. It usually extends beyond the angle of bend so that heat is spread up the sides of the pan more evenly (Fig. 4–7). Copper is very attractive when new but it oxidizes and darkens with exposure to air and during use. It is not difficult to polish, and there are a number of cleaners that can be used for this purpose.

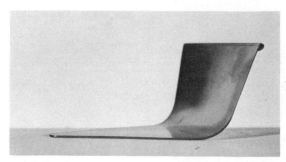

Fig. 4–7.   Cross section of a copper-clad stainless steel utensil. (Revere Copper and Brass, Inc.)

Vinegar also works well. The dark copper absorbs heat more efficiently than bright shiny metal which reflects heat. The difference between dark and shiny copper either in time or expense of fuel to the average homemaker is not appreciable. The fact, however, that there is a difference serves as a good excuse for not polishing the pans!

c. Nickel

Nickel has been used as a finish more in the past than it is at the present. It is now used widely as an alloy to add strength and heat resistance. Nichrome wire (a nickel-chromium alloy) is used as the heating element in many appliances. As stated previously, nickel is an essential ingredient in stainless steel.

Nickel looks very much like chromium when it is new but takes on a slightly yellow cast with age. It requires polishing to keep it looking new. Nickel finishes can be scratched if abrasives are used on them.

d. Porcelain Enamel

Porcelain enamel is essentially a glass material which has been made white or colored by the addition of coloring and opacifying agents. After this glass is ground very fine and mixed with a liquid, it is sprayed onto a base metal, or the metal may be dipped into the liquid porcelain enamel (Fig. 4–8). The glass is literally fused into the pores of the metal as the glass and metal are heated in ovens to approximately 1500 F.

Porcelain enamel can be made resistant to abrasion, acids, alkalies, atmospheric corrosion, heat, or combinations of these agents. It is nonporous and is easily kept clean and sanitary. Soap and water are practically the only cleaning agents needed. Should food be allowed to stick on it, a solution of soda water or a weak ammonia solution will aid in its removal. Porcelain enamel should not be scoured, as its glaze may be scratched. It is long wearing and except for chipping from sharp impact will last indefinitely. Poorer qualities are less chip-resistant. Porcelain enamel can be crazed by a sudden change of temperature such as putting ice water in a hot porcelain-enameled pan.

Porcelain enamel is used by some manufacturers as the finish on ranges, refrigerators, washers, dryers, and other appliances—both inside and out. Porcelain that is even more stain resistant is made using titanium as one of the ingredients. This *titanium porcelain* has a high degree of opacity and hence a one-coating operation may be all that is needed. Acid-resistant porcelain is highly desirable on range surfaces, the bottom surface of refrigerator interiors, refrigerator vegetable pans, table tops, and sink and drainboard surfaces.

Porcelain enamel is also used for saucepans, baking pans, tea kettles, casseroles, and other small equipment. Foods prepared in it have no color or flavor change due to the material of the pan. Porcelain enamel is not a good heat conductor, and since the base metal is often steel, which is also not a particularly good heat conductor, some care must be used to see that foods do not stick.

Porcelain enamel is not resilient and is

Fig. 4–8. The first ground coat of liquid porcelain enamel is about to be applied to this range shell. (Porcelain Enamel Institute, Inc.)

noisier when used as a table top than a more resilient covering would be.

Porcelain enamel is commonly fused onto sheet metal, but it is also used on cast iron and cast aluminum. It adds color and variety to kitchen utensils.

Porcelain enamel comes in a variety of colors as well as white. Each major manufacturer of household equipment has his own selection of colors. Some care needs to be taken to choose colors that harmonize, or results are apt to be most disillusioning. Some manufacturers are working together to produce standard colors so that various brands of appliances may be used together harmoniously.

e. Synthetic Enamel

Synthetic enamel is a plastic resin-base paint which is sprayed onto a base metal and baked at temperatures between 150 and 400 F. It is not fused to the metal in the same way that porcelain enamel is.

Synthetic enamel is used by some manufacturers for finishing the exteriors of washers, dryers, ironers, and freezers as well as on some range and refrigerator exteriors. It is lighter in weight than porcelain enamel, so the appliance finished with synthetic enamel is less heavy than one finished with porcelain.

Synthetic enamel does not chip but it can be scratched. Only an expert could consistently tell by its appearance when new, whether an appliance was finished with synthetic or porcelain enamel. Synthetic enamel is not as stain resistant as porcelain enamel. It is not used for surface-cookery pans, baking utensils, wash tubs, or oven linings.

f. Tin

Tin is used as plating and not as a base metal; hence tinned pans is a more accurate term than tin pans. Tin is a soft metal. Thus the quality of a tin-covered article depends upon the quality of the base metal, the quality of the tin, and the manner in which the article is covered. A thin layer of tin or one which has tiny bubbles in the surface is not of the best quality.

Tin is bright and shiny when new, and looks very much like aluminum. It darkens as it ages, and eventually, with use and age, it may become quite dark. Tin should not be scoured as it is fairly easy to scour off some of the tin coating, thus allowing the base metal to rust.

g. Zinc

Zinc is a hard metal. Articles finished with zinc are known as galvanized. Technically, only articles coated with zinc by electroplating should be so called. This finish protects the base metal from rusting. Zinc is applied after the article is made. It can be scoured or worn off. Zinc finishes are used chiefly for water pails, garbage cans, laundry trays, and certain other articles. Zinc is not used for cooking utensils but may be used for counter tops. Such a surface is neither resilient nor stain or acid resistant, but it is greaseproof and waterproof. It will tarnish and darken with use. It is not as attractive as many other counter-top finishes.

C. Counter and Floor Coverings

A number of materials are now in use, most of which are quite satisfactory, but there is no one completely ideal covering.

4–9. ASPHALT TILE

Asphalt tile is made of asbestos, asphaltic or resinous binders, color pigments, and plasticizers. Only small amounts of asphalt are used in most asphalt tile. Asphalt tile is available in many colors, both plain and patterned. The usual tile size is a 9-inch square approximately ½-inch thick. It is not used for counters.

Asphalt tile is neither oil nor grease resistant. There is, however, a grease-resistant tile available which has been specially processed to make it more resistant to oil and grease than regular asphalt tile. Asphalt tile does not stand up under continued high temperatures above 85–90 F, which might be reached if sun shone through glass on to the floor, or if carpeting was laid over asphalt tile in a home having a floor heating installation. Asphalt tile is a good conductor of heat. It is not considered to have much indentation resistance.

Asphalt tile should be cleaned with a mild detergent and water, rinsed, and waxed. Only a water-base wax should be used.

4–10. CERAMIC TILE

Ceramic tile is made from clay which has been specially treated and fired in kilns at a temperature of approximately 2000 F. Both glazed and unglazed tiles are available. Glazed tiles are easier to clean and are more resistant to staining.

A great variety of sizes, colors, designs, and shapes are available. Small tiles are usually mounted on paper sheets, which makes installation quicker.

The installation of ceramic tiles requires the services of an experienced ceramic tile worker. It is one of the more expensive finishes to install, but some authorities consider it one of the easiest to maintain when properly installed.[6]

Ceramic surfaces are waterproof if the tile has been properly installed. Ceramic tile is very hard and not easily scratched. It can, however, be shattered by severe impact. It is resistant to water, acids, oil, grease, and heat.

4–11. CORK TILE

Cork tile is made from cork shavings, either with or without resin binder, compressed into molds, and baked. It comes in many sizes and several thicknesses ranging from $\frac{1}{8}$ to $\frac{1}{2}$ inch.

Cork tile is not a counter covering and is not recommended for floors where the traffic is heavy. Cork may become porous and brittle if washed too often or if strong cleaners are used.

[6] Ben J. Small, *Flooring Materials,* Circular Series F4.6, Small Homes Council, University of Illinois, March, 1955.

It is not oil and grease resistant. It is very quiet when walked on.

4–12. LAMINATED PLASTICS

Laminated plastics, belonging to the thermosetting group of plastics, are sold under a variety of trade names. They consist of several layers of paper or cloth which have been impregnated with a resin and dried, a design layer impregnated with melamine resin, and a final top layer of a protective overlay sheet which has been saturated with melamine (Fig. 4–9). These layers are compressed together

Fig. 4–9. Laminated plastic. Sheet of aluminum foil is used beneath the design sheet. (The Formica Corporation)

under pressure and heat. A pressure of approximately 1200 pounds per square inch at 280 F for 60 minutes is followed by gradual cooling and lastly a release of the pressure. After this process has been completed the resulting product cannot be soaked or split apart. When lower pressures are used, the resulting product is known as low-pressure, thermoset, laminated plastic. It is used for counter coverings.

The cigarette-proof grades of these materials have a sheet of aluminum foil under the design sheet to dissipate the heat before scorching or blistering can take place.[7] However, kitchen utensils are so much larger and the resulting heat so much greater than that from a lighted cigarette that the laminates may blister.[8] They are therefore not generally recommended for use in the kitchen.

These laminated plastics are available in standard thicknesses of $\frac{1}{16}$ to $\frac{1}{4}$ inch and in sheets 3 to 4 feet wide and up to 10 feet long. They are expensive to install, as skilled workmen must be employed or the process must be done at the manufacturing plant. Recent developments have made laminate-bonded plywood available, which can be sawed, cut, and shaped to fit individual counter requirements in each home. The edges are usually finished with an edging strip. One-piece counter tops with backsplash can be made of these laminates.

Weaver[9] found that the laminated plastics were resistant to stain, heat, moisture absorption, impact, and abrasion, and had good color retention. A good grade of rigid, thermosetting plastic is more durable than the low-pressure flexible type.

4–13. LINOLEUM

Linoleum is one of the "old-timers" in the field of counter-top finishes and floor coverings. It is made from powdered cork or wood flour, linseed oil, color pigments, and resins which are bonded to a backing of felt or burlap.

Linoleum can be had in a number of different weights or gauges and patterns. Heavy gauge is approximately $\frac{1}{8}$ inch in overall thickness, standard gauge $\frac{3}{32}$ inch, and light gauge $\frac{1}{16}$ inch thick. Linoleum is resilient and quite resistant to indentation.

Battleship linoleum is more durable than other linoleums and is made especially for industrial uses. Powdered cork is added to the regular linoleum formula and the backing is usually finely woven burlap. It comes in both heavy and standard gauges in plain dark colors.

Jaspé, marbleized, and *inlaid* linoleums are made in all gauges and in all of them the pattern extends through the covering on the surface to the backing. Jaspé is a variegated pattern usually of two colors which has a striated effect. Marbleized linoleum resembles marble and is a multicolored material. In both of these, the pattern extends at random to the backing. In inlaid linoleum it extends through to the backing in a pattern. This pattern may be made by pieces cut from various colors, fitted together, and then pressed onto the backing; or the linoleum mix may be sifted through stencils onto the backing and then pressed in. *Embossed* linoleum has a raised design and is usually found in standard and light gauges. It is somewhat difficult to keep clean because of the raised design.[10]

Linoleum should be washed with a mild detergent and rinsed. The surface can be kept cleaner and brighter if it is waxed periodically, depending upon the extent of wear upon it. Either a water-base or naphtha-base wax may be used. Old wax should be removed before new wax is put on.

A special linoleum tile is sold in blocks of various sizes. It is a long-wearing covering which has been specially processed. It has no backing.

4–14. RUBBER TILE

Rubber tile is made by vulcanizing rubber and pigments under pressure. It is available in

---

[7] New York State College of Home Economics, *The Cornell Kitchen,* W. F. Humphrey Press, Inc., 1952, p. 39.

[8] Elaine K. Weaver and Velma V. Everhart, *Work Counter Surface Finishes,* Research Bulletin 764, Ohio Agricultural Experiment Station, 1955, p. 53.

[9] Elaine K. Weaver and Velma V. Everhart, *op. cit.,* p. 44.

[10] New York State College of Home Economics, *op. cit.,* p. 40.

several degrees of hardness and in thicknesses of $5/64$ inch, $3/32$ inch, and $1/8$ inch. It comes in plain colors and marbleized designs.

Rubber tile is affected adversely by oil, grease, and solvents so it is not used for kitchen counter tops. Lacquers, shellacs, varnishes, or alkaline cleaners used on it may cause it to dry out, crack, or curl. It should be installed where there will be traffic as it keeps its resiliency better if used. It is long wearing, very resilient, fire resistant, and has a high indentation resistance.

Rubber tile needs to be buffed with very fine steel wool to remove dirt and stains that do not come off with ordinary washing. An untreated dust mop should be used for daily cleaning. Only water-base waxes should be used on rubber tile.

4–15. VINYL

Vinyl is made from vinyl resins, plasticizers, and color pigments. It may have a backing of felt, cork, or degraded vinyl cemented to it, or it may have no backing. It belongs to the thermoplastic group of plastics.

It comes in a wide range of bright, clear colors and in many designs and patterns as well as plain colors. Many sizes of tiles are available in thicknesses ranging from $1/8$ to $5/64$ inch. The usual thicknesses for homes, in the vinyl with backing, are $3/32$ and $5/64$ inches. The rolls are 6 feet wide.

Vinyl is quite resistant to indentation; it is more resistant to heat than linoleum but not as much as laminated plastics. It is resistant to oil and grease. The care of vinyl is much like the care of linoleum. Either a water-base or naphtha-base wax may be used on it, and it should be waxed to protect the glossy finish.[11] Vinyl does not harden with age.

Vinyl asbestos tile has had asbestos added to the vinyl formula. It has no backing. The tile size is a 9-inch square from $1/16$ inch to $1/8$ inch in thickness. Vinyl tile is not as resistant to indentation as is the vinyl. It is resistant to oil and grease and quite resistant to moisture from concrete floors. More noise is made upon impact with the tile than with the vinyl.

4–16. WOOD

Wood used for counter tops without a covering such as vinyl, linoleum, or laminated plastic should be very resistant to wear, stains, water absorption, slivering, and warping. Beech, birch, and hard maple, all hard woods, are considered most desirable. Hard maple is the least grease absorbent. The end or edge grain of wood is best for chopping blocks because tool marks are less apparent.

Before using a new hardwood work top, it should be carefully dusted with a dry cloth and then rubbed with a soft cloth saturated with a little mineral oil until it shines. This oil should be left on overnight and the treatment repeated. After four to six hours, the excess oil should be wiped off with a soft, dry, clean cloth. Daily care should consist of wiping with a damp cloth. Ordinary soil can be removed with a damp sudsy cloth.

D. Insulation Materials

Insulation is used for many purposes: refrigerators and freezers are insulated to keep the interiors cold; ranges are insulated to keep the heat from escaping to the room; rooms are insulated to inhibit the transmission of both heat and sound; wires carrying electricity are insulated so that the electricity will not travel on unwanted pathways.

Heat always moves from a warmer to a cooler body. A perfect insulator would completely stop this transfer of heat. The ideal in-

[11] Ben J. Small, *op. cit.,* p. 5.

sulation would not burn; it would be light in weight, and would be unaffected by mold, bacteria, or insects; it would not rot and it would have the ability to remain permanently in place.

4–17. FIBERGLAS

Fiberglas is the registered trademark for a variety of products made of or with glass fibers.[12] The thermal conductivity of Fiberglas is very low. It is a good sound absorber, is moisture resistant, will not burn, and will not rot. Fiberglas has no tendency to warp, expand, or contract. Vibration does not cause the material to settle. It is clean, odorless, noncorrosive, and resilient. In addition, it is very flexible.

Fiberglas wool is fabricated in batts of nu-

[12] Owens-Corning Fiberglas Corporation.

merous sizes (Fig. 4–10). Exact shapes and sizes can be made for special insulation projects. It is used in home appliances for both thermal and sound insulation. Fiberglas cloth is used as a backing for mica. Fiberglas is also used as a base for material of laminated products which can be formed into shapes as desired.

4–18. MICA

Mica is an essential part of igneous rock and is widely used as an electrical insulator. It will not burn and, depending upon the grade, may be quite transparent. Small sheets of mica may be cemented with shellac or other insulating cement onto cloth or paper. Nichrome wire wound around mica, in the sheet form, forms the heating units of some small appliances.

 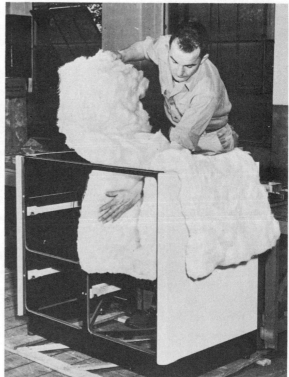

Fig. 4–10.   Fiberglas in two forms as used in refrigerators and ranges (Owens-Corning Fiberglas Corporation)

Fig. 4–11. Actual sandwich fabrication—polystyrene-foam core material being covered by the outer skin. (Courtesy Westinghouse Electric Corporation)

4–19. MINERAL WOOL

Mineral wool is made from melted rock, slag, or glass blown into fibers by steam or air blast. These fibers form a fluffy mass which can be made into different forms. In this loose fluffy form it is used to fill hard-to-reach corners and as a fill-type insulation for walls and floors and similar structures. In a granulated form it is commonly installed pneumatically, through a hose, to otherwise inaccessible spaces. In a felt form it has had a binder added and is a flexible, semirigid sheet or roll. In the board or block form it is a rigid insulation which is easily sawed or cut to fit into place.

Mineral wool has a very low thermal conductivity and is extremely light in weight. The fibers are incombustible. They even tend to smother fire. Mineral wool is resistant to changes in structure when exposed to moisture and freezing. It is also very resistant to the growth of mold or bacteria. Mineral wool insulation is practically indestructible.

4–20. POLYSTYRENE FOAM

Polystyrene foam is a man-made insulation. It repels moisture, never settles, and will not support combustion. It is light in weight. At present one use of this material is a filler between a polyester-filled Fiberglas cloth and a polystyrene sheet to form an insulation "sandwich" (Fig. 4–11) which is used in built-in refrigerators. This type of insulation and construction lowers the tooling cost, as the panels can be cut to any size and shape with an electric saw.[13] At present a free-standing refrigerator is in the planning stage.

[13] Herbert A. Ehrenfreund, a personal communication, Westinghouse Electric Corporation, November, 1956.

CHAPTER 5

Kitchen Utensils

A. Nonelectric Utensils
    5–1. Top-of-Range Utensils
        a. Saucepans
        b. Skillets
        c. Pressure Pans
    5–2. Oven Utensils
        a. Cake Pans
        b. Pie Pans
        c. Cooky Sheets
        d. Muffin Pans
        e. Casseroles and Custard Cups
        f. Roasters
B. Tools
    5–3. Measuring, Cutting, and Mixing Utensils
        a. Measuring Cups
        b. Measuring Spoons
        c. Knives
        d. Can Openers
        e. Shears
        f. Cutting Boards
        g. Bowls
        h. Blenders
        i. Beaters
        j. Rolling Pins
    5–4. Miscellaneous
        a. Spatulas
        b. Wooden Spoons
        c. Metal Spoons
        d. Graters
        e. Grinders
        f. Food Mills
        g. Strainers, Sifters, and Colanders
C. A Minimum Set of Kitchen Utensils
D. Experiments

Nonelectric utensils such as pans, and tools, such as measuring cups, beaters, and knives commonly used in kitchens are discussed in this chapter. The small electric appliances used in kitchens and eating areas are discussed in Chapter 6.

A. Nonelectric Utensils

5–1. TOP-OF-RANGE UTENSILS

a. Saucepans

A saucepan is a utensil with one handle; a saucepot has two handles on opposite sides of the pan; and a kettle is equipped with a bail. Saucepans are somewhat more commonly used at the present time than the other two. However, most of the points considered in the study of saucepans also apply to saucepots and kettles.

Although it is possible to cook satisfactorily with almost any kind of pan in any condition, it is far easier to cook well with a wisely selected pan. With the advent of thermostatically controlled surface units, it is more important than ever before to have a well-designed pan of a material that conducts heat evenly and quickly.

The saucepan should be flat on the bottom and have nearly straight sides with a rounded bend where the sides join the bottom. A rounded bend is much easier to clean than a 45-degree angle would be, and it is also far more usable when stirring puddings or similar mixtures.

A number of finishes for the top edge of the pan are quite satisfactory. It should be smooth, not sharp, and so constructed that there are no crevices where dirt and food particles can collect. The top may be cut off smooth and the edge polished slightly. This is probably the most satisfactory because cleaning is so simple. Cast utensils and some sheet metal utensils are finished in this manner. Or the edge can be bent down to the side of the pan. This is often referred to as a "beaded" edge. If it is turned down tightly enough, it does not leave much room for dirt to get up under the edge. This also serves to make the edge of the pan sturdy. If the gauge of the pan is thin, a beaded edge helps the pan to take wear.

The material should be one that conducts heat evenly and rather quickly. If it does not conduct heat well, hot spots may develop and any thickened mixture will nearly always scorch unless great care is taken to regulate the heat from the unit or burner. The material should have no effect on the food which is cooked in the pan. Some foods darken certain materials, but there is no effect on the food. The material should be easily cleaned and durable enough to withstand ordinary household use without denting. Weights of pans should be compared only between pans that have been made of the same gauge of metal.

The saucepan should be well balanced. If the handle is too heavy for the pan, it can easily be tipped over when only a very small amount of material is in the pan. To check the balance of a pan, tap the handle lightly. It will, of course, tip but if it is well balanced it will right itself. This should be done without the cover, because the cover will make the pan heavy enough to maintain balance. The pan should also be balanced when filled so that carrying it is easy.

The handle of the pan should be securely attached. A handle that turns or loosens can cause a bad accident if a pan is filled with hot food. One of the most satisfactory methods for attaching the handle is by electric spot welding. Several tiny spots are evident on both the handle and the inside of the pan where the handle has been welded, but they are almost perfectly smooth, so cleaning is no problem and the joining is quite secure. Rivets are also used and give a secure fastening. It is necessary to clean around the rivets which protrude on both the exterior and interior of the pan. The shape of rivets vary; some are more rounded than others.

Soldering is sometimes used, which means that a flux or third material has been used in the process of joining the handle to the pan. This is more satisfactory on an enameled pan than any other because the enamel covers it all. Soldering is generally thought to be less permanently secure over many years of use.

In utensils made by casting the shank of the handle is made as an integral part of the pan. To this the handle proper is attached, usually by a screw. These handles may tend to loosen with use but for a time they can be tightened by turning the screw. The threads may wear eventually and the screw then cannot be tightened. If a wood or plastic handle is put into a square shank, it cannot turn even if it does loosen. Screws are often countersunk into the handle, and this is better than if they protruded. No matter how a screw is put in, more effort is needed to keep it clean than a rivet which is smooth. Should a handle wear out, break, or be ruined by excessive heat, it is quite easily replaced if it is attached with a screw.

Handles should be made of a nonheat-conducting material. They should be designed so that the user does not have to grasp metal in the form of rivets, screws, or metal supports, since they can be hot enough to burn the hand even though these parts may be small. The material used for handles should be impervious to moisture and resistant to slipping. The design of the handle varies, and some shapes are more comfortable for one person than another.

All-metal handles are found on less expensive utensils. Some of these are hollow with an opening at one end or sometimes at both ends. These present a cleaning problem because dishwater gets inside and it is difficult to wash the interior of the handle. If a metal handle is not hollow, its edges may not be satisfactorily turned under or beaded down, and dirt collects in the crevices. Some are of a single piece of metal which has had the edges smoothed and dulled.

Some handles are ovenproof and can be put into the oven at ordinary baking temperature without harm; others cannot. One should read the directions that come with the pan.

The cover of the pan should also have a nonheat-conducting handle that is sufficiently large so that one can grasp it without fear of burning one's fingers. It should be attached so that it will not easily loosen but can be replaced if necessary. The cover should fit securely but still allow slight space for steam to escape. Either the pan or the cover should be fitted with a lip which will keep condensed steam from dripping on the outside of the pan.

b. Skillets

Skillets or frypans should be made of a material that is a good heat conductor, that holds heat relatively well, and that is fairly easy to keep looking attractive. A fairly heavy gauge of material is preferred for skillets. Cast iron skillets should be seasoned before use, either at the factory or at home.

Skillets should be flat on the bottom and finished with a smooth edge. If the edge is beaded, the beading should be such that grease and dirt do not collect under it. If either the handle or its shank has been made in one piece with the skillet, cleaning is less of a problem. A skillet that is to be used in the oven should have a handle that is not harmed by oven heat. If the handle can be removed when the skillet is to be used in the oven, the method of attaching the handle to the shank should be such that it is not easily worn down by the repeated removing and replacing. Other factors to consider in choosing a good handle for a skillet are the same as for saucepans.

It is possible to warp a skillet by misuse. Skillets should not be subjected to sudden extremes of temperature. A warped skillet will not brown foods evenly.

Skillets should be chosen with the intended use in mind. A size should be chosen that will hold the amount of food usually cooked.

c. Pressure Pans

Pressure pans have become an accepted utensil in many kitchens. The pressure canner was the forerunner of today's streamlined pressure pans.

Cooking food under pressure is fast because it is cooked at high temperatures. Care needs to be taken not to overcook foods because they do cook much more quickly than usual. Five, 10, and 15 pounds of cooking pressure in the pressure pan are common. Perhaps the most widely used is the latter. At 15 pounds of pressure the boiling temperature is about 250 F, at 10 pounds of pressure it is about 240 F, and at 5 pounds of pressure about 228 F. At high altitudes these temperatures are lower.

A pressure pan consists of a pan with a heat-resistant handle, a lid that fits tightly with a rubber gasket or a sealing ring, a safety fuse or automatic air vent, and a weight which indicates the amount of pressure within the pan.

Covers are of two main types—the flexible lid placed inside the pan (Fig. 5–1); and the domed cover placed on the exterior edge of the pan (Fig. 5–2).

Weights are classified in two groups: those that register pressure by visual means and those that register it by sound. It may in some ways be easier for the beginner to use the visual type of weight. It is necessary to learn what to listen for when using a weight which jiggles. A certain amount of jiggling per minute indicates that a specified pressure is being maintained. Some weights may be washed; others are harmed by immersing them in water. Likewise some weights can be harmed by dropping, and others are not.

The gasket or sealing ring is most important

Fig. 5.1. Pressure saucepan with flexible lid. (The Aluminum Cooking Utensil Company, Inc.)

Fig. 5–2. Pressure saucepan with domed cover. (Aluminum Goods Manufacturing Company)

if a tight seal is to be obtained (Fig. 5–3). The sealing ring and the parts of the pan and cover with which it comes in contact must be clean if a good seal is to be made. After the pressure pan has been used for some time, the gasket may lose some of its resiliency. Then it should be replaced. Gaskets will wear longer if washed, rinsed, and dried carefully after use.

The vent should always be open and free from any particles of food. It is good practice to check the vent after the cover is washed and again as it is placed on the pan of food to be cooked. The vent must be clean if the pressure pan is to operate properly.

The safety fuse or automatic air vent is made of rubber or an alloy of metals. A metal safety plug will melt when the pressure within the pan becomes too high, and a rubber safety fuse

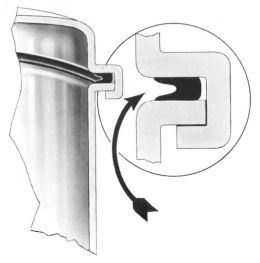

Fig. 5–3. Cross section showing domed cover, gasket, and pan. (Aluminum Goods Manufacturing Company)

will blow out when the pressure becomes excessive.

If the vent is kept clean, the recommended amount of water used in the pan, and the heat controlled, there is practically no possibility that the pressure will ever become dangerously high. A few foods are not recommended for cooking in a pressure pan. The manufacturer's directions should be followed.

Pressure pans also come equipped with thermostatic heat controls (Fig. 5–4), which eliminate much of the watching previously necessary. Once the correct cooking pressure has been reached, the heat selector is turned down, and from then on the cooking is auto-

Fig. 5–4. Heat-controlled pressure saucepan. (National Presto Industries, Inc.)

matic. However, when the cooking is complete, pressure must be released as in the nonthermostatic models.

Pressure can be released by placing the pan in cold water, by running cold water over it (but not over the automatic air vent), or by removing the pan from the heat and allowing the pressure to go down gradually. The cover should never be removed before the weight is removed, and the weight should not be removed before the pressure is down. If in doubt as to whether the pressure is down, tilt the weight slightly with a fork. If steam escapes the pressure is not yet down.

The weight should be stored in the pan and the cover placed upside down in the pan. Never store the cover on the pan in a sealed position.

5–2. OVEN UTENSILS

a. Cake Pans

Cake pans come in various sizes and materials. Loaf pans are usually rectangular; layer pans are square or round. The American Standards Association, in coöperation with the American Home Economics Association and other organizations, has set up standard sizes and depths for these pans. No recipe, however wonderful, will produce equally satisfactory products in all sizes of pans. Not only sizes for pans but recommendations as to how these sizes should be measured have been made. Measurements are made on the interior of the pan. Bottom and top measurements are often different. Recommendations have been made for loaf and layer pans. Some manufacturers now label or inscribe the exact size of the pan on the bottom of it. A boxed cake mix will yield a more satisfactory cake in the right size pan.

Aluminum baking pans are widely used. In many test kitchens they are considered the standard baking pans, and many recipes are temperature tested with them. The inside and bottom of the pan should have a satin or rather dull finish and the exterior sides a polished finish. Rounded corners rather than square or folded are desirable both for ease in removing cake and for cleaning. Cakes baked in aluminum pans do not have crusty sides. As a general rule, it is slightly easier to get an even cake in a round pan than a square one because the heat penetration is the same all around the cake. In a square or rectangular pan the heat penetration through the corners is somewhat more intense than on the sides, and the batter may be set before complete action of the leavening agents has taken place. This may result in a domed cake. (Overbeating and/or too much flour may also cause doming.) To avoid this rounded product push a little more batter into the corners than in the center, and a level cake will usually result.

Porcelain enamel cake pans are more popular in the loaf design. Cakes baked in enamel pans are more crusty on the sides.

Glass cake pans also result in crustier cakes, and cakes baked for the same time and at the same temperature as recommended for aluminum pans may be quite dark. It is recommended that oven temperature when baking cakes in glass pans be 25 F less than when baking them in aluminum pans. Glass pans do not stack easily; hence they may require more storage space than aluminum pans.

Tin darkens with use and age, and therefore its baking qualities change. A dark tinned pan will result in a much browner product than a shiny one. A shiny tinned pan produces a cake much like one baked in aluminum. A waffle-sized tin pan is supposed to give better baking results, but insofar as the authors have been able to determine it is merely a little harder to clean. Tinned pans will warp if subjected to sudden temperature changes, and a warped pan will not bake evenly.

b. Pie Pans

Pie pans have not changed much over the years. Some are available with an extra trough to catch juices that may run over from berry or fruit pies, thus making it easier to keep the

Fig. 5–5. Pie pans. 1. Anodized aluminum. 2. Heat-resistant glass. 3. Dark enamel finish. 4. Dark tinned finish. 5. New tinned finish.

oven clean. Glass and dark tin make quite satisfactory pie pans, as a browned pie crust is highly desirable. Glass is fine for baking a filled crust, since it absorbs heat readily and conducts it slowly. Care should be taken in cutting pies with extra-sharp knives because it is easy to scratch the bottom of the pans. An assortment of pie pans made of different materials is shown in Figure 5–5.

c. Cooky Sheets

Cooky sheets are made especially for baking cookies and biscuits. A cooky sheet is a flat sheet of metal which may have slightly raised edges on one, two, or three sides. It should not have all sides raised, and except for ease in removing the pan from the oven, it would be preferable not to have any sides raised. Because cooky sheets are used to bake products in a short time, they are made of lightweight materials that transmit heat readily.

d. Muffin Pans

Muffin pans commonly come in sets of 6 and 12 cups, but 8 cups are also available. A metal that does not change color or one in which the finish cannot be removed by scouring will be more satisfactory over a period of time. It is possible to buy muffin pans made from one piece of metal, which thus have no places for dirt to collect and are easy to clean. In some muffin pans the cups are made separately and inserted in a frame. This method produces a somewhat stronger muffin pan, but if care is used in storage, pans made in one piece are quite satisfactory. Muffin pans will not bake evenly if warped or bent out of shape.

e. Casseroles and Custard Cups

Casseroles are quite satisfactory when made of a material which holds heat well but is not too heavy to manipulate easily. Materials used are glass, heat-resistant china, pottery, and porcelain-enameled cast iron. They are somewhat more useful if they are attractive enough to be used for serving as well as cooking. Covers that fit increase their versatility, though for nicely browned products the cover is usually removed during the last part of the cooking time. Casseroles should not be scoured when washing as the material may be scratched. If food has stuck, it should be soaked off. The American Standards Association recommends five sizes: 10 ounces, 1, 1½, 2, and 3 quarts.

Custard cups are made of glass, heat-resistant china, or pottery. They are defined by the American Standards Association as small, deep, individual, bowl-shaped utensils especially designed for oven use. The difference between the smallest casserole and the largest cup is only 3¼ ounces. Usually custard cups do not have covers. A perfectly smooth cup is easier to clean than one which has lines or other ornamentation.

f. Roasters

Roasters should be made of fairly heavy-gauge sheet metal. If it is to be used on top of the range as a Dutch oven, very heavy-gauge sheet metal or cast metal is preferred. If it is to be used as an uncovered pan only, the broiler pan of the range may serve as the roaster. A pan about 10 by 15 by 2 inches can be used for baking large loaf cakes and larger quantities of scalloped dishes such as potatoes or corn, as well as for roasts.

Roasting is a method of cooking by dry heat; but since many cuts of meat or fowl are more tender when baked in moist heat, the pan should have a cover that fits. It is not always necessary to use the cover but it is sometimes desirable. A rack serves to keep the meat out of the fat and juices from the meat. Sometimes the rack makes it easier to remove the meat from the roaster.

The size roaster chosen should depend upon the type of food for which it is to be used. It may be desirable to have one roaster for the ordinary needs of the family and a second large one that can be used for the holiday turkey. An extra-large roaster is inconvenient for everyday use and difficult to store conveniently.

B. Tools

5–3. MEASURING, CUTTING, AND MIXING UTENSILS

a. Measuring Cups

Measuring utensils should meet American Standards Association standards. Most of the recipes in current books specify standard measures. It is rather pointless to follow a recipe with meticulous care, to follow all recommended procedures for measuring, but use cups and spoons that are not standard. Look for the words *U. S. Standard Measurement* on labels or for the capacity in ounces, since the latter can be compared with standards.

Measuring cups of transparent material have the advantage of being easier to use for liquids. Metal cups are resistant to breaking and can be used over low heat for melting small amounts of chocolate, fat, etc. Plastic cups should be made of a heat-resistant plastic, otherwise they will often be warped out of shape by hot foods measured in them or by washing in a dishwasher.

For dry ingredients the full-cup measure should be at the top of the cup so that the food can be leveled with a spatula. For liquids the cup should extend beyond the full-cup measure. The cup for measuring liquids should have a good pouring lip, so placed that it is convenient for either a right- or left-handed person to use.

Nested measuring cups are convenient for measuring fractions of a cup of dry ingredients or fat. The contents can be leveled off which makes it quite easy to get accurate measures. They usually come in 1-, ½-, ⅓, and ¼-cup sizes (Fig. 5–6).

All measuring cups should have broad enough bases so that they do not tip easily. The bend at the bottom should be rounded for ease in removing food. The handle should be an integral part of the cup or securely fastened by welding in such a manner that there are no crevices in which spilled food will collect. Glass or wood handles are better than metal ones for use with hot food. Measuring cups are easiest to clean if the top edges are merely cut off and smoothed down, rather than beaded under as some are.

Fig. 5–6. Nested stainless steel measuring cups. (Foley Manufacturing Company)

Two- and 4-cup measures are a convenience for the homemaker who prepares food in large quantities. The 4-cup measure is convenient for mixing some foods. Waffles, for example, can be mixed in a glass 4-cup measure and then poured directly onto the waffle grid.

b. Measuring Spoons

Measuring spoons should be made of a material that is sturdy—not easily bent out of shape, broken, or melted. A distorted spoon, like a misshapen cup, is not an accurate measure.

Measuring spoons usually come in sets of 1 tablespoon, 1 teaspoon, $\frac{1}{2}$ teaspoon, and $\frac{1}{4}$ teaspoon. It is sometimes wise to separate them and hang them on individual hooks, since it is then not necessary to wash four spoons when you use only one. Since measuring cups and spoons are relatively inexpensive, and often may be used in different working areas in the kitchen, it may be wise to invest in more than one set and store them at strategic points.

c. Knives

The construction of a knife determines to a great extent satisfaction in use. A poor knife is a constant annoyance, a safety hazard, and an energy user. Careful and wise use add to the life of any knife, especially a good one.

There are three major parts in the construction of a knife: the blade, the handle, and the method of attaching the blade to the handle. A well-constructed knife is likely to be made from good materials, although this is not a hard and fast rule.

Materials commonly used for blades are steel, iron, high-carbon steel, stainless steel, high-carbon stainless steel, and vanadium steel. High-carbon steel is considered to be one of the best materials for knife blades. It can be sharpened to a very fine, thin, sharp edge and will keep this sharp edge better than a low-carbon steel.

Stainless steel is desirable in that it is resistant to stains and is easy to keep looking attractive. It never darkens any foods that may be cut with it. However, it is usually lower in carbon content than high-carbon steel and therefore its ability to take and keep a sharp edge is not as good.

High-carbon stainless steels are available and have the good characteristics of both stainless and high-carbon steels.

Vanadium steel is a high-carbon steel with other elements added such as vanadium, chromium, and molybdenum. These alloy steels are tough for longer wear.

Some very inexpensive knives may be made from sheet steel or sheet iron. Although they need to be sharpened often, they can be satisfactory for certain uses. However, their use is limited because they are so easily stained and in turn may stain foods.

Much high-quality cutlery in recent years is chrome-plated, which makes it very attractive and nearly stainproof. Chrome plate can be scratched, though, and then the exposed steel may rust or tarnish. The cutting edge of a blade is not chrome-plated and usually appears dark after the knife has been in use.

Forging, beveling, and stamping are processes used to make knife blades. A forged knife blade is hammered into shape by hand or by machine and is more expensive to make than a knife made by beveling or stamping. The blade of a forged knife will taper from the handle to the point of the knife and from the back to the cutting edge. This makes a knife that is strong and firm at the handle and flexible near the point. The tapering from the back to the cutting edge makes it easier to produce a very thin cutting edge.

Beveled knives are made by cutting in half a bar of metal that is thicker at one edge than the other. They taper from the back of the knife to the cutting edge but the blade does not taper from the handle to the point. Some very high-quality beveled knives are made.

Stamped knives are made by stamping the blades from a sheet of metal. The blade is the same thickness at all points until the cutting edge is ground. Stamped knives are not as good as beveled or forged, though a stamped knife may sometimes be of a better quality than the method of making would indicate. The quality of steel used and the method of grinding determine to a great extent the quality of this type of blade.

Grinding is one of the more costly steps in manufacturing a knife. It is very difficult for the average person to evaluate the quality of a grind. In general, there are two types of grind—the "flat" grind and "hollow" or concave grind. These types are sometimes broken down still further, but the general shape of grinding falls within these two classifications.

The flat grind extends from the back to the cutting edge in a flat plane. It gives a sturdy blade and can be used for heavier duty cutting than the hollow ground blade. Hollow grinding usually starts below the back of the blade and extends to the cutting edge. A concave area on each side of the blade gradually reduces the thickness of the blade until it reaches its thinnest point at the cutting edge. A hollow ground knife blade has a thinner cutting edge which makes it easier to pare, carve, or slice.

A saw-toothed or scalloped-edge knife may be of several lengths or patterns. Grapefruit knives, steak knives, and bread knives are the ones most often finished in this manner. Scalloped knives may also be hollow ground.

The length of blade is determined by the knife's use and its comfort in manipulation. The handle and blade should be well balanced so that the knife will be comfortable to use.

The handle of a knife is of almost equal importance with the blade. If the handle is not right, the knife will be almost useless. If it is of poor construction, it will shorten the usable life of the knife.

The handle should be of a moisture- and grease-resistant material. Hardwoods are often used and are more desirable than softer woods finished with paint or varnish. Wood handles finished by smoothing and polishing are more durable than handles finished with paint or varnish. Varnish will wear off and paint will often flake or chip.

Plastic, hard rubber, metal, and plastic-impregnated wood handles are also used. The latter is growing in popularity as it is a very attractive, polished handle. It is made by impregnating hardwoods with resins and then subjecting them to intense heat and pressure. These handles are resistant to heat, stain, moisture, food, and chipping.

In plastic handles, the tang of the knife is set in the molten plastic which when cooled forms a solid piece. These handles are moisture resistant but may not be resistant to heat. However, if moisture penetrates at the point of insertion of the tang, the plastic will eventually crack apart.

The shape of the handle should fit the user's hand, be easily grasped, and held securely without strain. It is especially important that the handle of a paring knife be comfortable for the user.

The handle should be securely attached to the blade. Probably the most effective means is by use of a full tang and medium-sized rivets. The tang is the part of the blade which extends into the handle. A full tang extends the length and width of the handle. In half-tang construction it extends into at least a third of the handle and is held in place by rivets. Full-tang construction is desirable for knives which will have heavy use, such as butcher knives. Half-tang construction is usually quite satisfactory for most household knives.

A less desirable method of attaching the handles is by the collar and pin or push-tang method. The tang, which is often much less than a half tang, is inserted into the handle. A metal collar is slipped over the blade end of the handle, and a very small pin is inserted through the handle to help hold the tang in place. Often the pin is omitted and only the collar used. Neither method is very satisfactory, as the collar soon loosens and moisture and dirt get between it and the handle. Also, the tang often slips out of the handle.

Knives are designed for different purposes, and for most efficient use the proper knife should be selected. Paring knives have a short blade, usually 2½ to 3 inches. Blades may be of different shapes. Some women prefer one and some another, or several paring knives of different shapes may be desired for different uses.

The utility knife has a 6- or 7-inch blade and is used for halving oranges and grapefruit, slicing small roasts, tomatoes, cake, and nut bread. In a kitchen where only a few knives are available, this knife has numerous uses.

The butcher knife is a heavy-duty knife used for cutting meats, fowl, squash, melon, and large heads of cabbage. It has a broad, sturdy blade.

The French cook or chef's knife is used for chopping food on a board. The blade is usually 8 or 9 inches long and fairly wide at the handle end. It is set into the handle in such a way that the handle can be grasped and food chopped without the knuckles touching the board. It is highly recommended for chopping large quantities of food.

Slicers have a fairly narrow blade which is quite long—8 to 12 inches. The end is shaped in various ways, depending upon whether it is a ham slicer, roast slicer, narrow slicer, or carver. Some authorities list only the fairly straight blade knives as slicers; those that are somewhat curved and have a pointed end are called carvers.

The grapefruit knife is curved to fit the inside of half a grapefruit and may or may not have a serrated blade. It is used to loosen the grapefruit segments from the rind, to remove seed pods from green peppers, and to core tomatoes for canning.

The bread knife has a blade 8 to 10 inches long with a serrated edge. It will cut bread without crushing it and is especially desirable for slicing fresh bread.

The cleaver is a heavy-duty tool which has been described as a cross between a knife and a hatchet.[1] It is useful for cutting joints in meat and poultry and for cracking soup bones.

The kinds of knives available to the homemaker are numerous. A few well-chosen knives will be far more useful than a galaxy of poor knives not suited to the use to which they are put. Knives are used often in food preparation, even in this day of mixes and partially prepared foods. The Associated Cutlery Industries of America recommend the "Basic Six" as an absolute minimum—a paring knife, utility knife, 8-inch narrow slicer, 8-inch Cook's knife, 7- or 8-inch long-handled pot fork, and a sharpening steel.[2]

Good knives deserve good care. (1) They should be stored individually so that the blades do not come in contact with other blades and hard surfaces. Knife holders are of numerous types, but a small block of wood fitted with slots for blades is quite satisfactory. (2) A cutting board should be used in chopping and slicing operations. (3) Good knives should not be used to cut string or wire or as screw drivers or levers. (4) They should never be left standing in water or allowed to get hot.

It is not only exasperating to use a dull knife but it is also not safe. A good knife can be kept sharp for a long time by good care and intelligent use, but eventually all knives become dulled.

Steels for sharpening knives are in common use today; at least they are often sold with carving sets and sets of knives. Steels are used to perfect the cutting edge of a knife. "The conventional method is to hold the steel horizontally slightly slanted away from you in the left hand, hold the knife by the handle in the right hand, rest the edge at the heel lightly

[1] Elizabeth Beveridge, "Good Knives for the Kitchen," *Kelvinator Kitchen Reporter*, November, 1951.

[2] Lewis D. Bement, *The Cutlery Story*, The Associated Cutlery Industries of America, 1950, pp. 26, 27.

near the point of the steel at an angle of about 20 degrees, and draw the blade towards you against the edge and across the steel from heel to point. Use only light pressure. Repeat this operation on the other side of the steel with the other side of the edge. Three or four strokes on each side are enough."[3] The process perfects the cutting edge and can be done many times before a blade actually requires sharpening.

One of the oldest methods of sharpening knives was by means of an oilstone which, as the name indicates, was a stone used with a few drops of light oil. One side of the stone was coarser than the other. This side was used first and the fine or smooth side for finishing.

Hand-operated or electric sharpeners are a boon to the person who has not taken the time to learn how to sharpen a knife correctly. Disks or wheels of hard steel or aluminum oxide are so spaced that the knife must go through or over them at the right angle. However, it is still quite important to exert the right amount of pressure on the knife blade or it may be over- or undersharpened. Watching a butcher or other experienced person is one step in learning the correct procedure for sharpening knives, but practice is essential.

d. Can Openers

Manufacturers have made much progress in recent years in producing can openers that are safe, durable, and easy to use (Fig. 5–7). The Can Manufacturers Institute has issued methods and standards for testing can openers, and a can opener must pass these tests before it is allowed to be sold with the CMI seal of approval (Fig. 5–8). The testing is done under the direction of an accredited graduate engineer, and the can openers are obtained from the can manufacturer's stock by a CMI representative. Tests are made for durability, ease of cleaning the blade, corrosion of the blade, and effectiveness of the device used to attach it

[3] *Ibid.*, pp. 23, 24.

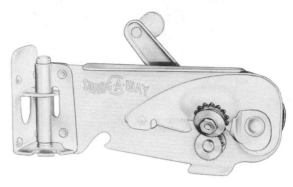

Fig. 5–7. A wall-type can opener. (Swing-A-Way Manufacturing Company)

to the wall or other surface on which it is used. It must give a clean, smooth, and complete cut.

When mounting a can opener, care should be taken to mount it in such a way that large cans as well as small may be opened.

Since the can opener blade must be clean in order to cut well, it must be washed at rather frequent intervals. Care should be taken to follow the manufacturer's directions for this. One should look for a can opener that can be washed easily.

A good wall can opener is not inexpensive, but considering the number of cans many homemakers open, it is a worth-while investment. Small portable can openers are essential

Fig. 5–8. Seal of the Can Manufacturers Institute. (Can Manufacturers Institute, Inc.)

for picnics and are suitable for vacation use at cottages but it is preferable to have a good wall can opener for the home.

A can opener that leaves a jagged edge should not be used. It should leave a turned-down edge without jagged pieces which might cut the hand. A knife should *never* be used as a can opener.

e. Shears

A pair of shears designed for kitchen use is a useful tool and may aid in maintaining knives in good condition. Kitchen shears, sometimes called poultry shears, are designed to cut up poultry and if used for this purpose eliminate the dulling of knives on bones. They are also useful for dicing marshmallows, candied fruit, opening bottles, and as small pliers. One or both blades may be finely serrated. Sometimes the blades are chrome-plated; the quality of chrome plating is of course difficult to determine, and one can usually do best by buying from a reliable dealer and established company. Handles of the shears are usually painted.

f. Cutting Boards

Cutting boards come in a variety of sizes. They should be of a hardwood which is moisture resistant. The small round size is handy if only a small amount of food preparation is done, but a larger one should be chosen if food is prepared in quantity. It is quite possible to use one side of a dough board as a cutting board and the other for rolling out doughs. It is not good practice to use the sides interchangeably, since sooner or later the cutting side gets cuts and crevices in it, which are not only a nuisance to clean but also make rolling pie or cooky dough more difficult.

Cutting boards should be washed carefully and dried. They should not be allowed to stand in the sink while other meal preparation is going on. Some people use one side of a cutting board for cutting onions only and

mark it because they think there is an intermingling of flavors if onions and other foods are chopped on the same side of the board.

g. Bowls

Mixing bowls should have slanting sides and a rounded bend at the bottom. It is much easier to mix or blend foods in a bowl with a rounded bottom than in one with a perfectly flat bottom. The size of the bowl should be chosen in relation to the amount of food that will be mixed in it. A small amount of food cannot be mixed conveniently in a large bowl, and if the bowl is too small, food will spill over the edges.

Some bowls can be used for mixing, refrigerating, and baking. It is possible to use smaller bowls as substitutes for casseroles if they are made of a heat-resistant material. For demonstration purposes glass bowls are highly useful, as the audience can see what is being mixed. They are rather heavy and tend to stay in place as foods are mixed. Foods can be stored in the refrigerator in them.

Bowls are often stored nested inside one another, but if storage space permits, it is much more convenient to store them singly.

h. Blenders

Blenders are of many varieties and at any one time there may be a number of new ones on the market, many of which make their appearance for a limited time only.

The pastry blender has been available for quite some time. It is useful not only for blending fat and flour for pastry but for mixing fat with other ingredients. The thinner the wires, the finer the blending. Wires should be of a material that will not rust and have a finish that will not wear off. They should be fastened securely to the handle which should also be made of a material, or have a finish, that will not wear off or chip.

Another popular blender is the Foley fork, (Fig. 5–9), which can be used for making pie crust, blending gravy, mashing potatoes and carrots, and for other uses. It has stainless steel blades.

Fig. 5–9. Blending fork. (Foley Manufacturing Company)

i. Beaters

There are many qualities of beaters on the market. Those of better quality will have a handle of moisture-resistant material and a finish that will not chip. The gear will be of cast metal or nylon and the blades of stainless steel. Quite thin cutting blades make a finer foam. The beater is easier to keep clean if the cutting blades do not extend to the gears, but they should not be too short or the beater will be very slow. The blades do not rest on the bottom of the bowl, but they should be as close to it as possible so that food on the bottom of the bowl will be beaten.

j. Rolling Pins

Rolling pins should be made of hardwood and have securely fastened handles. Some handles are attached to the pin in such a way that pin and handles move together. In others the pin turns while the handles are held firmly by the operator. Not all handles fit tightly, and care needs to be taken to keep them clean. Rolling pins should never be soaked in water. They should be washed, rinsed thoroughly, dried, and then air-dried before storing.

5–4. MISCELLANEOUS

a. Spatulas

Spatulas should be made of a material resistant to staining. Since a sharp edge is not essential, and sometimes not desirable, the carbon content of the steel is not important. The blade should have a flexibility appropriate to its use. If it is too flexible, the spatula is of little use for lifting foods; if it is not flexible enough, it will not slip under a cake or a piece of pie. Spatulas used for blending should be somewhat more flexible than those used for lifting.

Spatulas come in various sizes. For removing cookies from a cooky sheet and for many other uses, the long or large-size spatula is desirable. For a multitude of other uses the very small spatula is handy. There are wide spatulas and narrow ones. Some of these are known under various names, such as pancake turners or hamburger spatulas. For use as turners it is desirable to have the handle put on at an angle, which makes it easier to get the spatula under the hamburger or hotcake. Perforated spatulas are useful for foods that need to be drained as they are lifted. The type of cooking one does determines to a great extent which should be chosen.

b. Wooden Spoons

The quality of wooden spoons may differ from one spoon to another. A hardwood with a smooth finish makes a spoon more useful and easier to care for. Since the handle does not get hot this type of spoon is particularly useful in such tasks as making jelly. Another advantage of a wooden spoon is that it does not scratch or mark pans and bowls. It should not be left standing in foods, as it is easily stained and will absorb flavors. Spoons are made with either deep or shallow bowls. Since their chief forte is stirring and beating, the shallow bowls are to be preferred. For tasting and for transferring food from one place to another, a metal spoon is a somewhat better choice.

c. Metal Spoons

Metal spoons are useful for stirring and mixing when the mix is not heavy. They are also useful for tasting. For large quantities of food the long-handled spoon with a solid or slotted bowl is useful. A handle that does not conduct heat well is easier to grasp than one made of metal.

d. Graters

Graters should be chosen not only with the view of how well they will grate food but also how easily they can be cleaned. Plated ones usually show the effects of wear after a time. A grater made from too soft a metal will lose its shape with use. Some are made with punched holes which resemble the hole made by driving a nail through a piece of metal. Others are made with drilled holes which resemble the hole left in paper when using a paper punch. The punched-hole graters give a mushy product, sometimes desirable when grated food is added to cakes. Drilled holes give a product that has definite form; this is more desirable when foods are to be used for salads.

Graters are available with various sizes of holes. Some have four sizes put together in one utensil; others come in sets of three or four and are preferred by some homemakers because only the size used needs to be washed.

e. Grinders

Grinders are made of cast iron or aluminum. If cast iron is used, they should be heavily coated with tin, as a thin coating may wear off

quickly. A grinder should have a handle that is easily grasped and turned and made of wood or plastic rather than metal. The grinder should be so shaped that juices extracted run into the pan which receives the ground food rather than into the opening through which the handle is connected. In some modern kitchens it is almost impossible to find a suitable place for fastening a grinder. Sometimes breadboards inserted under the cabinet top are sturdy enough for this but often they are not. Grinders are also available with suction cups or rubber feet on the legs and with a wide base, and these do not need to be screwed in place for use. Grinders may come with an assortment of blades for various uses such as grinding meats, crackers, vegetables, and fruits. The blades should be of high-carbon steel for lasting cutting efficiency.

The grinder should be thoroughly washed and dried before it is put away. An effort should be made to keep fruit pits and bones from being put through it, as this has a dulling effect on the blades.

f. Food Mills

Food mills should be of a metal that is sturdy and not easily bent out of shape. The metal need not be as heavy as that used for grinders, because food mills are used only for such tasks as ricing potatoes and pumpkin or separating the pulp of fruits and vegetables from the skin and seeds. There should be some type of support which will hold the food mill above the counter or bowl so that food once pressed through the mill will tend to fall off the perforated or screened surface.

Food mills take up quite a bit of storage space and should be chosen according to the amount of food one might be working with at a time. They should be so constructed that all parts are easy to wash. They should be simple to take apart and easy to put back together. It's a good idea to try this before buying one, as some appear to be much more simple in the store than they are when you get them home.

g. Strainers, Sifters, and Colanders

Strainers or sieves are made of tinned wire, stainless steel, or sometimes plastic. Since the mesh of the strainers varies, they should be chosen for the purpose for which they will be used. Fine mesh is desirable for tea strainers and flour sifters. For straining vegetables, macaroni, and similar foods, a larger mesh is quite satisfactory and also somewhat easier to wash. Strainers that have two support wires crossed underneath are stronger but may be difficult to wash. Some strainers are made so that the mesh basket slips out from the supporting cross wires and ring. While this makes cleaning easier, care should be taken in storage not to jam the strainer out of shape, because then it will not be easy to take apart and put back together again. Strainers should have a mechanical means, such as a projecting part, to support them on the side of a bowl, cup, or other utensil. Handles of strainers are usually of painted wood or plastic. Although the paint may eventually chip, a wood handle is not too unsatisfactory because of the limited use most strainers get. A strainer is not a colander or food mill, and foods should not be pressed through it because this will result in the mesh pulling away from the ring support.

Because flour and water make a paste sifters present a cleaning problem. They vary as to the gauge of the mesh and number of meshes. A relatively fine mesh is desirable, and the purpose of more than one mesh is to sift the flour two or three times on its way through the sifter. However, the major reason for sifting flour more than once is to incorporate air, and if the mesh layers are close together not much is accomplished. Most such sifters are almost impossible to clean adequately.

However, sifters do not need to be washed each time they are used, unless they cannot be stored in the canister with the flour or house-

hold insects are a probem. In certain areas in the United States a flour sifter left in a cupboard would be a welcome invitation to insects. Sometimes a vegetable brush will help in the washing process, and it is also easier to wash a sifter with a removable bottom (Fig. 5–10). Sifters should be scalded and thoroughly dried before they are put away.

Sifters usually come in two sizes, a small size which holds about 2 cups and a larger one which holds 4 to 5 cups. If only a small amount of food is usually baked, the small sifter is quite satisfactory and does not take up so much storage space. It would, however, exasperate the homemaker preparing food for a large number of people.

Sifters are usually operated by a lever device or a crank. Either way the flour is not fanned over the work area as it is when the sifter must be shaken to work the flour through it.

A colander is used for draining foods and as a substitute for a food mill. The homemaker who has one may have specialized uses for it in her kitchen. Colanders should be made of a material that will not be easily bent out of shape. In selecting one notice where the holes are placed. It should be so designed that all the food can be drained. It should have handle supports or a high enough base so that it will not rest directly on the surface of the sink or another utensil.

Fig. 5–10. Five-cup aluminum sifter. (Foley Manufacturing Company)

C. A Minimum Set of Kitchen Utensils

The selection of a minimum set of utensils for the kitchen is a project that many beginning homemakers find most challenging and interesting. What constitutes such a set is open to question, because standards of living, income, habits, type of food prepared, place of abode, and many other factors enter into how "bare" this minimum can be. It is possible to cook a delicious meal over an open fire with the aid of a few sticks for cutlery and perhaps some tin cans for utensils, but most of us would not care to repeat this procedure day in and day out. Just what pieces of equipment one is willing to do without is pretty much an individual matter. To give a guide and *only* a guide to this selection, a list of the utensils needed in many homes is given below. It should be remembered that the fewer utensils one has, the fewer there are to wash after the dinner is over! Also, all the articles listed need storage space, and since this is usually limited in most kitchens, care should be taken to choose only utensils and cutlery that will be used. Some utensils have dual or multiple uses; however, one should not be carried away on this point because it is quite possible to find oneself with nothing more than a complicated gadget—too time-consuming to put together and much too much bother to clean after it is used. But within reason choices can be made for utensils in which food can be mixed, baked, and served; measured and mixed; and used for cooking, refrigerating, and serving.[4]

1 saucepan—1 quart
1 saucepan—2 quart

1 cast iron skillet—8–10 inch
1 chicken fryer or Dutch oven
1 griddle
1 glass or china casserole—1 quart
1 glass or china casserole—2 quart
1 cooling rack
1 set graduated measuring cups
1 quart glass measure
1 one-cup glass measure (liquid)
1 set graduated measuring spoons
1 small spatula
1 rotary beater
1 paring knife
1 French cook knife
1 utility knife
1 cheese slicer
1 cutting board
1 grater
1 blender
2 round baking pans—8 or 9 inch
1 loaf baking pan—10 by 15 inches
1 cooky sheet
1 muffin tin—6 cup
1 pie pan
1 set mixing bowls
1 coffee maker
1 teapot
1 set wooden spoons
1 wide spatula or pancake turner
1 can opener
1 bottle opener
1 tap opener
1 cooking fork
1 vegetable peeler
1 kitchen shears
1 rubber scraper
1 rolling pin
1 flour sifter
1 canister set
1 strainer

[4] Other lists of minimum sets of utensils can be found in *Tools for Food Preparation and Dishwashing,* Home and Garden Bulletin No. 3, USDA, November, 1951, and in *Better Buymanship, Use and Care of Kitchen Utensils,* Household Finance Corporation, No. 7, (Reprint), 1947.

D. Experiments

The experiments in this group require no special testing equipment and could well be used by beginning classes in Household Equipment.

Experiment 1. *Top-of-Range Utensils*

1. *Saucepans.* Use identical pans approximately 6 inches in diameter. Have each student or group of students prepare a vanilla pudding from a prepared mix in each pan. Use similar sources of heat. (Differences in products will be due primarily to the way in which students manipulate sources of heat.) After puddings are made, pour into custard cups. Evaluate:

a. Satisfactoriness of product.
b. Amount of stirring needed.
c. Heat setting used and amount of regulation required.
d. Scorching or sticking in the pan.

Repeat using saucepans of different (a) materials (b) sizes. Compare the results with the first experiment.

2. *Pressure pans.* Use a standard vanilla custard recipe or recipe from pressure pan instruction booklet. Pour into individual custard cups. Cover cups with aluminum foil. Place rack in pressure pan; add ½ cup water. Place cups on rack. If pressure pan with a domed cover is used, a second rack can be placed on cups and a second layer of cups placed on it. Place cover on pressure pan. Follow the manufacturer's directions for cooking custard at 15 pounds pressure for three minutes. Cool pressure pan at once. Remove custards; remove aluminum foil and chill. Evaluate:

a. Satisfactoriness of product.
b. Ease of preparation.
c. Amount of watching needed to keep pressure at right amount.

Experiment 2. *Oven Utensils*

1. *Cake pans.* Experiment 2, p. 151, Chapter 10, is suggested for studying characteristics of cake pans.

2. *Cooky sheets.* A similar type of experiment can be conducted using cooky sheets of the same size and different materials or of the same material and different sizes. Baking pans with high sides may also be used. Use a plain rolled sugar cooky or a plain butter cooky that can be put through a press. Evaluate:

a. Satisfactoriness of product.
b. Effect of size of cooky sheet on heat distribution and browning of cookies.
c. Effect of shape of cooky sheet on browning of cookies.
d. Effect of material of cooky sheet on browning of cookies.

Experiment 3. *Measuring, Cutting, and Mixing Utensils*

1. *Measuring cups.* Measure cornmeal into a U. S. Standard measuring cup. Level with a spatula. Pour cornmeal into a measuring cup that is not a U. S. Standard; a coffee cup; a dented measuring cup. Measure amount of extra meal necessary to fill the other cups or the amount by which the U. S. Standard measure exceeds the amount held by other cups.

2. *Measuring spoons.* A similar experiment can be carried out using U. S. Standard measuring spoons and other spoons commonly used for measuring by many homemakers.

3. *Knives.* Dice ½ cup celery with a paring knife. Repeat, using a French cook knife and cutting board. Compare ease and speed of accomplishing the task. Discuss relative efficiency for use of the two knives if larger amounts of food are prepared.

4. *Graters.* Grate a carrot on a grater with punched holes. Repeat, using a grater with drilled holes. Compare products. Which grater would be most satisfactory for grating carrots for a salad? For grating hard cheese? For grating orange rind for a cake? Wash the graters. Which type is easier to clean after use for grating carrots?

5. *Beaters.* Evaluate ease of use of various beaters with bowls of various shapes by whipping a measured quantity of a high-sudsing syndet in a measured amount of water. Beat for a definite time at a uniform rate of speed. Different operators will not get the same volume if they do not use the same rate of beating. However, if all the operators use uniform rates for the same time the beaters should rate in the same order for volume of suds.

6. *Sifters.* Examine sifters of different types and sift ½ cup flour with each. Compare fineness of the flour sifted in each sifter by observing the volumes after sifting. Evaluate ease of handling and washing and drying sifters.

Small Electric Appliances

The small electric appliances discussed in this chapter are those commonly used in kitchen or dining areas for food preparation. These small appliances constitute a substantial portion of the billon-dollar-a-year electric housewares industry.[1]

6–1. GENERAL CONSIDERATIONS

Some general considerations are applicable for many small electric appliances: The finish on an appliance determines to a great extent the care required. One that fingermarks easily will need much polishing to keep it looking attractive. If the appliance or parts of it will

receive much wear, the finish should be one that will not wear off easily. Finishes are described in Chapter 4.

All small appliances should carry the Underwriters Laboratories seal of approval. If the appliance has been approved, the seal should be on the appliance, or it may be on the specification sheet which describes the appliance. A reliable dealer should be able to give this information to the consumer.

Small electric appliances usually carry a one-year guarantee; a few carry a five-year guarantee. Often it is necessary to send a registration card with various data about the purchase to the company in order to have the guarantee in effect. A guarantee is nearly always void if the appliance has been tampered with in any way. If an appliance needs serv-

---

[1] Ted Weber, Jr., "What's Happened to the Electric Housewares Industry," *Electrical Merchandising*, McGraw-Hill, Publishing Company, April, 1956, p. 67.

ice, it should be returned to the company or a company-approved service center.

Storage for an appliance should be considered when selection is being made. If the storage place is too inconvenient, it may become too much trouble to use the appliance, and very little satisfaction is then had from its ownership. Particularly, heavy appliances, such as the roaster and mixer, should be stored where they do not have to be moved each time they are used. Heat-controlled pans should not be stored in the oven, since oven heat may damage plastic parts of the appliance.

Small electric appliances may be divided into heating appliances, motor appliances, and those that use both a motor and heat.

6–2. MOTOR-DRIVEN APPLIANCES

a. Food Mixers

Food mixers can save a lot of energy for the homemaker if they are properly used and stored in a convenient location. Tasks such as whipping potatoes, mixing cake batters, and making boiled frostings can be done more easily with a good food mixer. Mixers also permit easier standardization of some food preparation procedures than is possible with hand-operated beaters.

Mixers may be mounted in stands and provided with bowls or they may be portable or hand mixers. Some mixers mounted in stands may be removed from the stand (Fig. 6–1). Mounted mixer motor heads generally weigh about 3 pounds more than portable mixers. This is not particularly important if the mixer is not used as a portable mixer and can be used in the place where it is stored (Fig. 6–2).

Mixers mounted in stands are usually sold with two bowls, a large size of 3- or 4-quart capacity and a smaller one of 1- or 2-quart capacity. Some mixers have only one bowl of 4- or 5-quart capacity. The bowl to be used depends on the amount of food to be mixed. The mixer will do a better job if enough but

Fig. 6–1. Standard mixer with two bowls and removable motor head. (Hamilton Beach Company)

Fig. 6–2. Mixer with permanently attached head. (KithenAid Electric Housewares Division, The Hobart Manufacturing Company)

not too much food is in the bowl. Bowls are made of translucent and clear Pyrex and stainless steel.

Beaters are similar on many mixers. Usually there are two separate beaters much like those of a rotary hand beater. But at least one mixer has the two beaters fastened to a center shaft which is tightened in place in the mixer head with a thumbscrew. For most mixers, the beaters rotate in one place in the bowl and the bowl is also supposed to rotate. Mixers are also available with a bowl that does not rotate. Bowls are designed to rotate because of the friction generated between the beater and bowl. The batter serves to make better contact between the two. In some mixers a small plastic button is on the bottom of one beater so that good contact will be made even if the mixture is thin. The position of some beaters in the bowl can be changed while the food is being mixed, by changing the position of the turntable (and bowl) in relation to the beaters or by changing the position of the beaters. In the latter case the position of the turntable is fixed. Turntables in both types rotate.

A beater which has a planetary motion mixes food in all parts of a stationary bowl. As the beater rotates in one direction, the shaft to which it is connected rotates in another. This beater is larger and somewhat different in shape than those discussed above. Figure 6–2 shows the beater that operates with a planetary motion.

The speed control on the mixer should be easily read and convenient to use. Most speed controls also turn the motor on and off. The control should not be too easy to turn or it might be turned on accidentally. The speed with which the beaters rotate varies at the different speed settings. It is important that it remain somewhat constant at any one setting. Beaters should not slow down excessively as the mixture becomes heavier or speed up excessively as it becomes thinner.

The mixer should be well balanced. When the motor head is tilted back it should not tip the mixer. For convenience it should stay in this position and not tilt back into place so easily that it can be done unintentionally.

Most beaters are relatively easy to wash. It may be convenient, however, to have an extra set of beaters or one extra beater. If large amounts of food are prepared regularly or if the attachments are used often, a mixer with a good reputation for heavy-duty operation might be a good choice.

Most food mixers, but not all, must have a power adapter in order to use attachments other than a juice extractor. Attachments such as vegetable slicer, shredder, food chopper, and can opener usually require a power adapter. This works in a manner similar to a gear shift in a car. It makes more power available but the speed is reduced.

Manufacturers' directions should be followed for oiling and lubrication. All mixers get warm when the motor runs for a period of time but a mixer should not be used until it gets hot. Either running it for long periods of time or beating too heavy a mixture may cause the motor to overheat. If it heats excessively when used only a short time, the motor should be checked for electrical safety.

The mixer head should never be put in water. It should, however, be wiped off after use with a damp cloth. The rubber-covered

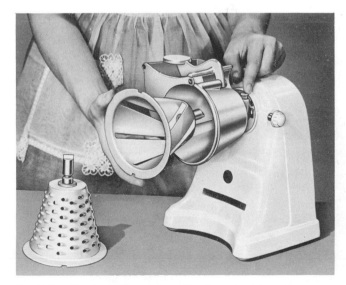

Fig. 6–3. Electric food grinder with slicer-shredder attachment. (Hamilton Beach Company)

cord should be kept clean by wiping occasionally with a damp cloth. This should be done when the cord is not connected to the source of electricity.

The electric food grinder is a motor-driven unit to which may be attached a grinder, slicer-shredder, or can opener unit. Figure 6–3 shows a food grinder with slicer and shredder attachments. The electric food grinder is sold as a separate appliance.

b. Portable Mixers

Portable mixers consist only of motor head and beaters (Fig. 6–4). The wall hanger, bracket, or stand is an accessory. Most portable mixers do not have attachments. Such mixers are light in weight—between 1½ and 3¼ pounds. They are small in size and can be put into ordinary kitchen storage drawers easily. Care should be taken not to bend the blades in drawer storage. Most of them can be operated on either alternating or direct current. They do a good mixing job for most

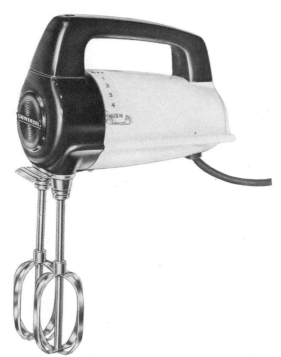

Fig. 6–4. A portable mixer. (Universal Electric Housewares, Landers, Frary & Clark)

mixing tasks. It is relatively easy to mix all the ingredients in a bowl because the beaters can be moved around. They are not recommended for mixing large amounts of food or for extra-thick mixtures.

The "on and off" switch and the speed control should be clearly labeled. Ordinarily fewer speeds are marked on these mixers than on those of standard size.

A heel rest and a storage hanger make it easier to use and store a beater. If the motor head with beaters in position can be stored near the place where the portable mixer is used most often, the mixer will be especially convenient to use. If there is no heel rest, it is difficult to put the beater down without letting the beaters rest on the counter.

A beater ejector is convenient. Smooth beater blades are easier to clean than those which are not smooth. Care should always be taken to lay the mixer down so that the beaters are near the back of the counter. This precaution will tend to eliminate the danger of a child turning a mixer on and getting a finger in the beaters.

c. Blenders

Blenders have specialized uses in food preparation. In some homes, they are used regularly.

Blenders consist of blades which cut or mix the food; a glass, metal, or plastic container for food; a cover for this container; and a base which houses motor unit, "on and off" switch, and speed control (Fig. 6–5).

Containers that are smooth inside are somewhat easier to clean. It is especially important that the top opening be sufficiently large for easy cleaning. Plastic containers may not stand the heat of a mechanical dishwasher.

The blades are usually extremely sharp and care should be taken to wash and put them away after each use. They should be kept out of the reach of children. If they are permanently attached to the container, wash by

Fig. 6–5. An electric blender. (Hamilton Beach Company)

putting water and detergent into the container and running the motor for a few seconds. It is a little difficult to remove such foods as cheese spreads, chopped dates, etc., from a container in which the blades are permanently attached.

Blenders are used to mix beverages, prepare vegetables for creamed soups, prepare mayonnaise, blend fruits and vegetables to a purée-like consistency, and to do other similar operations. Some direction booklets indicate that the final mixing for cakes and muffins should be done by hand or with an electric mixer.

The blending of liquid ingredients, shortening, and eggs can be done in the blender.

The motor and blades should be completely stopped before using a rubber scraper to push foods down into the container. The fingers should never be used to push foods down as these blades are *sharp*.

Blending is done in seconds, rarely ever in minutes. It is essential that directions be followed and blending times be clocked at least until familiarity is gained with the use of the appliance. Foods may be overblended and the motor may overheat if used too long at one time.

6–3. HEATING APPLIANCES

Heating appliances for cooking should be constructed so that feet and handles are well insulated. The handles should be so designed that pockets of hot air are not held under them. An opening between the appliance and the outer part of the handle will let the hot air rise away from the handle. The feet should be insulated so that heat from them will not mar the surface on which they rest. The feet should hold the body of the appliance far enough away from a table or counter surface so that heat radiating from the bottom of the appliance does not blister or mar the table finish. The feet should be smooth so that the appliance can be moved on a table without scratching the surface.

Heat-controlled appliances depend upon a thermostat to maintain the temperature for which the appliance is set. The accuracy of the thermostat on a small electric appliance depends primarily on the manufacturer's standards. Some appliances may have quite a wide range of actual temperatures from that set on the dial, and others will maintain temperatures within ±5 F. Once a recipe and temperature combination is found to be satisfactory, it is easy to duplicate results.

Wattage of small heating appliances is

Fig. 6–6. Dutch oven with guarded terminals. (National Presto Industries, Inc.)

generally *not* small. Before buying an appliance, it is a good procedure to check the wattage by reading the nameplate. It is quite possible that it will be so high that only one appliance can be used on a circuit at one time. Voltage requirements should also be checked on the nameplate. Most appliances do not operate satisfactorily if the voltage supplied in the home is very different from that stated on the nameplate.

The terminals on the appliance should have a guard plate so that accidental contact cannot be made with them. Figure 6–6 shows a Dutch oven with a guard plate.

Many small appliances have indicator lights to show when the appliance is heating and/or when it is ready to use. These lights are somewhat easier to see if the light is from a small bulb. If a section of the heating coil is the source of light, the "light" comes on and goes off gradually as the coil heats and cools off.

For some appliances the heat control dial and indicator light are detachable and interchangeable with other appliances manufactured by the same company. Only one heat control needs to be purchased, unless it is planned to use the appliances simultaneously. Figure 6–7 shows a group of these appliances, and Figure 6–8 illustrates the detachable control that fits each. The interior of this control

Fig. 6–7. A group of appliances using the same detachable heat control. (National Presto Industries, Inc.)

Fig. 6–8. (Above) A detachable heat control. (National Presto Industries, Inc.)

Fig. 6–9. (Below) Interior of a detachable heat control. (National Presto Industries, Inc.)

is shown in Figure 6–9. Notice the bimetallic thermostat and the tiny light bulb.

Some heating appliances can be completely immersed in water for cleaning; others can be immersed up to the indicator light or thermostatic dial control; still others must not be immersed in water at all. The thermostatic dial control, indicator lights, and heating units must not get wet. Figure 6–10 shows a frypan

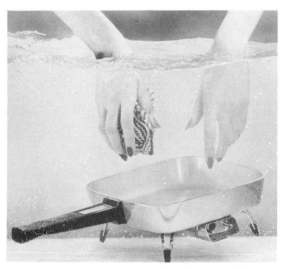

Fig. 6–10. Frypan with detachable heat control—completely immersed in water for cleaning. (National Presto Industries, Inc.)

completely immersed in water. The heating unit is sealed in, and the thermostatic dial control and indicator light have been detached. The manufacturer's directions for a particular appliance should be followed carefully. Models change from year to year; also not all the appliances by any one manufacturer will necessarily be cared for in the same manner. Cold water should not be put into or on hot griddles, saucepans, or frypans, as this may cause the metal to warp.

Appliances that are finished in chromium should be wiped with a damp, soapy cloth, then dried and polished with a dry cloth. Spatterings of fat that may have burned on can be cleaned off with whiting and water. Harsh abrasives will scratch the shiny finish. In general it may be stated that harsh abrasives should never be used. If a griddle, interior of a saucepan, frypan, or rotisserie needs scouring, it should be done only with a very fine abrasive such as a fine steel wool soap pad.

Many new heating appliances will give off a slight odor or smoke a little when first heated. This is nothing about which to be alarmed. Manufacturers' directions for first use of an appliance should be followed carefully. This first use can, in some cases, determine to a great extent the satisfaction that comes with later use.

a. Coffee Makers

Electric coffee makers are either of the percolator or vacuum-type. Either will make good coffee when used correctly. What constitutes "good" coffee varies with personal taste, and there are numerous factors which influence the flavor of coffee other than the type of coffee maker. It usually takes a few times of preparing coffee to determine the exact amount of coffee to use and the setting that is best for an individual coffee maker.

Coffee makers are made of aluminum—anodized, polished, or with a chromium finish—of copper plated with nickel and chromium, or of stainless steel. The top of the coffee maker should be large enough to put one's hand into in order to wash it with ease.

Percolators may be automatic or nonautomatic. In the nonautomatic type, the coffee is perked until the operator disconnects the percolator from the source of electricity. The percolator does not maintain a keep-warm temperature. In the automatic type (Fig. 6–11), the coffee is perked until the desired strength is attained, at which time the electricity is automatically shut off or cut down to maintain a keep-warm setting. Most present-day percolators have the keep-warm setting. In some of these, however, this setting is reached only after the percolating cycle; each time this type of coffee maker is connected, the

Fig. 6–11. An automatic percolator. (Dormeyer Corporation)

perking cycle is started. In other percolators, the keep-warm setting can be used at any time. When coffee is not served immediately, the coffee grounds should be removed from the coffee maker to keep the coffee at an optimum flavor.

Some percolators will make as few as two cups of coffee or as many as nine or ten. Others do not make less than four cups successfully. The cup marks on the coffee maker often are not accurate measures in terms of a standard measuring cup, but indicate coffee-cup measures. If the amount of water corresponding to the different markings in the percolator is determined once, it is not necessary to measure the water each time coffee is made.

The time required to brew coffee of a certain strength varies considerably with different coffee makers. However, even those that take the longest time will make a full pot of coffee in less than 20 minutes. For any one model, the strength selected, as well as the amount of coffee made, influences the length of time required.

It makes for ease in using if the coffee basket, tube, and cover can be removed at one time.

The cover on a coffee maker should not tilt forward or fall off when pouring. Even a cover which merely *acts* as if it is going to fall off is a nuisance to use! The spout should pour easily and be so constructed that it does not drip. Spouts on many coffee makers are not too easy to clean, and for that reason are often ignored by homemakers. A small brush should be used to keep the spout as clean as the other parts of the percolator. The handle should be easy to grasp, made of insulating material, and of such a design that the knuckles or fingers do not touch the coffee maker.

Only cold water should be used in percolators that start perking almost immediately upon connection to electricity. If hot water is used, the time for perking will be considerably shortened and the flavor of the coffee will be weak. In coffee makers that heat all the water before perking starts, the temperature of the water used is not so important. Such coffee makers are similar to percolators used with an exterior source of heat. However, many authorities state that the best coffee is made by using freshly drawn, cold water, regardless of the type of coffee maker used. Some percolators must be cooled before the perking process can be repeated; others will brew more coffee immediately.

It is generally recommended that the interior of a coffee maker be washed with hot water and a syndet and rinsed with clear water after each use. Periodically, the interior of all but aluminum coffee makers can be cleaned by boiling a solution of soda and water in the percolator. Aluminum baskets, tubes, and covers should not be cleaned with the soda solution. Other cleaners are also recommended by individual manufacturers. The interior of a coffee maker should not be scoured. A coffee maker should be stored with the cover off, or at least not on tightly. If this is not feasible, air the coffee maker after it has been washed and dried before putting it away.

The vacuum type of coffee maker has two

bowls—a bottom one which holds the water and houses the heating unit and controls, and a top one in which coffee and filter are placed (Fig. 6–12). When the water is heated, steam is formed and the air in the bottom of the coffee maker is forced out. As more steam is formed, pressure is exerted on the water, and the water is forced into the upper bowl. The water will remain in the upper bowl as long as the heat applied to the lower bowl is sufficient to maintain steam. When the heat is reduced, the steam in the lower bowl condenses, and a vacuum is formed. Immediately, air pressure forces the water, which is now coffee brew, back into the lower bowl. The coffee is then held at a keep-warm setting. Its strength is adjusted by changing the amount of coffee in relation to the amount of water used. The time the water is held in contact with the coffee is regulated by the manufacturer.

The upper bowl is easier to remove from the coffee maker if it has an insulated handle. The lower bowl must have a handle in order to use it as a coffee server. The cover is usually designed to fit both bowls. Coffee makers may have a signal light which indicates when the coffee is brewed.

Fig. 6–12. The vacuum coffee maker. (Sunbeam Corporation, Copyright © 1955)

Filters may be of stainless steel with very fine openings, of cloth, or a glass rod. The cloth filter must be kept clean or it may give an "off" flavor to the coffee.

One manufacturer recommends that softened water not be used with the vacuum coffee maker, since the chemicals in softened water may tend to retard the filtering process. This manufacturer also states that using too fine a grind of coffee can do the same thing.[2]

b. Cooker-Fryers

Cooker-fryers can be used for a number of different cooking operations. Foods can be steamed, stewed, and blanched as well as deep-fat fried. The cooker-fryer can also be used as a bun warmer, for making soups and pot roasts, and for popping corn.

Cooker-fryers usually come equipped with a cover and a deep-fat frying basket with a detachable handle (Fig. 6–13). The heating unit and controls are housed in the same shell as the container for the food. Cooker-fryers should be well balanced, have good insulation on the bottom, and have sturdy, securely fastened, insulated handles. A good heat-conducting material should be used for the container so that the foods will cook evenly. A thermostatic control maintains the temperature at a specified setting. The cooker-fryer should have an indicator light that shows when the fat is at the correct temperature.

There is quite a difference in the design of fry baskets, and some are much easier to clean than others. Usually this can be observed rather quickly even without using them. The handle, though detachable, should be secure when it is attached. A place to fasten the fry basket on the edge of the cooker-fryer so that fat can drain from the foods is a convenience. This fry basket also makes a convenient blanching basket. For deep-fat frying, a large surface area for the fat is somewhat more im-

[2] Directions for use of Sunbeam Coffeemaster-Model C30, Sunbeam Corporation.

Fig. 6–13. A cooker-fryer with deep-fat frying basket. (Universal Electric Housewares, Landers, Frary & Clark)

portant than a very great depth for the fat. A cooker with a fairly large diameter will enable more foods to be fried at one time.

Hot fat should be allowed to cool slightly before it is emptied into a storage container. If the cooker has a drain spout, care must be taken that it is securely fastened during the use of the cooker and completely cleaned after the fat is drained out. Crumbs from cooked food can clog the drain spout. This spout should have a valve that cannot be opened simply by turning, as this might be done accidentally while the fat is very hot. If the fat is drained out via a spout, two counter-top levels in the kitchen must be available for this. Depending upon construction of the sink and length of the spout, the sink well can sometimes be used as the lower level.

c. Frypans

Frypans can be used for frying foods, baking certain foods, toasting sandwiches, and braising foods. The thermostatic control enables an even heat to be maintained, and hence cooking is easier. The design of frypans has changed quite a lot in the few years they have been on the market. Many can be immersed in water up to a point on the handle where the dial of the thermostatic control and the connections for the cord are located (Fig. 6–14). Some frypans now on the market have a detachable heat control (Fig. 6–15). These pans can be completely immersed in water so cleaning is similar to cleaning any other pan. It is, perhaps, a little more difficult to clean the exterior of a frypan than a nonautomatic skillet because it is necessary to clean around the legs. However, because it is heat-controlled there is less scorching and burning of foods,

Fig. 6–14. Frypan with controls and terminal at end of handle. (Hamilton Beach Company)

Fig. 6–15. Frypan with detachable heat control. (National Presto Industries, Inc.)

so the interior is likely to be easier to clean.

Frypans are made of cast aluminum, pressed aluminum, and stainless steel. They are either square or round in shape and vary in depth and size. Choose a size suitable for the amount of food usually cooked. Frypans use about 1200 watts so they should be connected only to an appliance circuit.

d. Saucepans, Dutch Ovens, and Double Boilers

These pans have recently joined the heat-controlled group of electric appliances. A good electric saucepan has the same characteristics as any well-made electric appliance (Fig. 6–16). The heat control keeps the food at the

Fig. 6–16. An electric saucepan. (Sunbeam Corporation, Copyright © 1956)

desired temperature. The quantity of food used will influence the time needed for the selected temperature to be reached. Temperature settings may need to be adjusted for varying quantities of food.

e. Waffle Bakers and Griddles

Waffle bakers are one of the oldest small electric appliances. Current models are heat-controlled and usually have indicator lights.

Grids are nearly always made of cast aluminum. The size and closeness of the knobs on the grids will influence the kind of waffle that is baked. Knobs that are large and fairly close together produce a crisp waffle. If the knobs are rather small and far apart, there is more room for batter, and a softer waffle will result. Grids should not be scoured or washed. Instead, after each use brush out any crumbs with a soft brush. The baker should be left open after use until the grids have cooled. It should be closed when stored to keep the grids free from dust. Grids tend to darken with use, but this is not harmful to foods.

There should be an overflow rim around the grids to catch extra batter in case the amount needed is misjudged. This rim keeps the batter from running down the outside of the baker, which not only looks unattractive but may soil the tablecloth. If batter does get on the outside of the baker, it will be easier to remove when the appliance is cool.

The expansion hinge between the two parts of the baker should be sufficiently flexible to allow the waffles to rise as they are baked. If the baker has grids for grilling, the hinges should allow plenty of room for making grilled sandwiches without mashing them.

The thermostatic control is set according to preference for a light or dark waffle. Different types of thermostats are used. In one type the radiant heat from the baking waffle is directed toward the thermostatic control. In another the heat from the lower grid heats a strip of metal which actuates a bimetallic thermostat. In another the difference in expansion of the aluminum grid and a Pyrex rod actuates the thermostat.

The wires which carry the electricity to the top grid should be well protected from wear and guarded so that the user cannot touch them.

Waffle bakers may have interchangeable grids—one set for baking waffles and one for grilling foods. In some bakers the grids for grilling are permanently attached and the waffle grids are removable. This eases the storage problem but it adds others. The grill will need washing, whereas the waffle grids seldom, if ever, should be washed. If the grill is not cleaned well, the bottoms of the waffle grids get dirty. Waffle grids may not heat evenly in bakers with permanently attached grills. In other models, the grills are simply reversed or turned upside down. Overheating and sticking can be a problem in this type.

The grids for grilling foods should have a drip spout so that excess fat can be drained off while foods are cooking. As a rule, a container for catching this excess fat is not sold with the baker. If there are no spouts, getting the fat off the grid can be a problem. Grids should be wiped with paper toweling as soon as they are cool; then they should be washed in hot soapy water, rinsed, and dried. This is difficult to do with permanently attached grids as the heating unit and control must not be put in water. In cooking some foods, the grill will need to have a coating of fat spread over it; for other foods this is not necessary. Until familiarity with a grill is gained, it is a good procedure to follow recipes in the instruction booklet.

The space around the hinges between the two grids often gets splattered with fat. This should be wiped off after the baker is disconnected and cool.

Griddles are also available as a separate appliance (Fig. 6–17). Griddles should be made of a heavy-gauge material that is a good heat conductor. Some models have a heat control; others do not. Except for portability, a griddle without a heat control has little advantage over

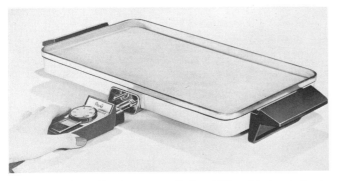

Fig. 6–17. Heat-controlled griddle. (National Presto industries, Inc.)

one used on the unit or burner of a range. If the griddle has a cover, it should be so constructed that it is easy to handle. It should not be too large to be manipulated easily with the handle or handles on it.

f. Roasters

Roasters can serve as a second oven for baking or roasting foods. Whole meals can be prepared in them, and they are also convenient for preparing large amounts of food for a crowd.

Roasters are not as heavily insulated as most range ovens, and the covers are often not insulated, which may allow them to get uncomfortably hot during baking. The handle of the cover should be of insulated material. Steam vents in the cover serve the same purpose as the oven vent in the electric range oven.

Roaster ovens use less wattage than range ovens and can be connected to an appliance outlet. However, they often take somewhat longer to preheat, so the cost of heating per unit area may not differ significantly.

Roasters are thermostatically controlled and unless the manufacturer's instructions state otherwise, the temperatures used for baking should be the same as for baking in the range oven. A light that indicates when the roaster oven is preheated is almost standard equipment. An inset pan is also standard equipment. It can be removed from the roaster and washed the same as any other large pan.

Roasters can be purchased with automatic timers, enabling the user to put the food in the roaster and go away knowing the food will be cooked at the time the user has specified. Special roaster cabinets are available. These provide for storage of the roaster at a convenient height and also provide additional storage space below. Grills and broilers are available for use with the roaster oven.

g. Toasters

The automatic toaster (Fig. 6–18) is so widely sold that many people may have for-

Fig. 6–18. An automatic toaster. (Toastmaster Products Division, McGraw Electric Company)

Fig. 6–19. A nonautomatic toaster. (Sears, Roebuck and Co.)

gotten or perhaps never have known that there is a nonautomatic toaster on the market (Fig. 6–19). It costs much, much less and is usable for many years, but the quality of the toast does depend a great deal upon the user. The heating unit is often nichrome wire wound around a mica sheet and is very similar in construction to the unit used in automatic toasters. There should be a large enough space below the heating unit so that crumbs can be cleaned out easily. The bread should flip over when the sides of the toaster are let down, and the sides should not touch the table in this process. Nonautomatic toasters are usually of relatively low wattage and can be used on house wiring which would not be adequate for higher-wattage appliances.

With the automatic toaster, it is not necessary to time the toasting and theoretically each slice of toast will be evenly browned. There are a number of factors, however, which may make it a bit improbable that each slice of toast will be evenly browned. The browning of the toast is controlled in two ways. In one method the control is set according to degree of brownness desired, i.e., the darker the toast, the greater the time. If the voltage supply is

constant and within the range for which the toaster is designed to operate, evenly browned toast will result. However, if the voltage is higher or lower than that specified on the nameplate, the time required to make toast will be changed. Also, the same setting will not produce the same degree of brownness on fresh bread and bread several days old.

The second method of controlling is by radiant heat from the toast (Fig. 6–20). As the toast browns, more heat is given off, and this activates the thermostat switch which shuts off the electricity and thereby releases the lever or spring that raises the toast from the toast well.

Some toasters have a voltage adjustment (usually on the bottom of the toaster) which makes it possible to get the desired brownness of toast. These are quite useful if the voltage supplied is consistently different from that required, but if the voltage fluctuates, they are generally not so useful.

All toasters should have a means of raising the toast from the well manually. This is necessary to remove the toast if the automatic device does not work and to remove toast for inspection as it is being browned. A fork or knife

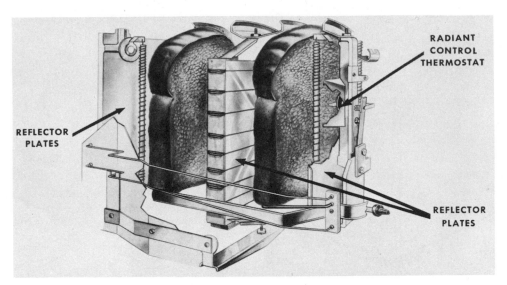

RADIANT
CONTROL
THERMOSTAT

REFLECTOR
PLATES

REFLECTOR
PLATES

Fig. 6–20.   Radiant heat toaster controls. (Sunbeam Corporation, Copyright © 1955)

should not be used to dislodge a piece of toast, since it is possible thus to injure the heating element and also to receive a bad shock if the toaster is plugged in. The latter can happen whenever the toaster is connected to the source of power, whether the switch on the toaster is on or off.

Toasters are usually insulated only at the handles and around the base of the well. The metal may well get very hot, particularly if several repeat runs of the toasting cycle are made. Toasters should be out of reach of small children, but this is generally true of most electric appliances.

There should be a crumb tray which is easy to empty and which will stay closed at other times. It should be cleaned weekly in most homes. A collection of crumbs can interfere with the making of the toast as well as with the pop-up mechanism.

Toasters are available with relatively wide slots for thick slices of bread or muffins. Some toasters are designed to raise very small slices of bread far enough out of the well so that one can take the toast out easily. Others have to be turned upside down to remove small

slices of toast. Toasters are available which make one, two, or three slices of toast at one time. One toaster has not only the oven well but an oven drawer for toasting sweet rolls and English muffins.

The wires which protect the heating unit from the toast should be small in diameter to aid in even browning of the toast. If the wires are large, light colored lines are seen on the toast.

If a light brown crunchy toast is desired, a toaster should be chosen that does not claim to be extremely speedy. The faster toast is made, the less the bread is toasted all the way through. For those who like soft toast, speed is the answer, providing of course that one starts with soft bread!

6–4. COMBINATION MOTOR AND HEATING APPLIANCES

Rotisseries are designed to broil foods on all sides without the user turning the food (Fig. 6–21). The food to be broiled is centered on a spit and secured in place by means of prongs. The spit is rotated by a motor. The rotisserie should be so designed that the area around it does not get too hot or splattered with particles of fat. If the rotisserie is completely closed, it is more like a baking unit than a broiling unit.

These appliances can get extremely hot when broiling food for an extended period, such as occurs when broiling a ham or barbecuing spareribs. The rotisserie is not insulated as is the broiler in a range oven.

A rotisserie should be connected in an appliance circuit. The heating element must not be immersed in water. The ease in cleaning a broiler depends in great part upon the ease in disassembling the various parts to be cleaned. It also follows that the various parts should be easily reassembled, without danger of incorrect assembly.

Consumers' Research Bulletin states that a rotisserie should not be used outdoors or on a patio because of the danger of electrical shock.[3] Manufacturers have not cautioned against outdoor use, but at least one recommends that the rotisserie not be left outside overnight.[4]

[3] "Rotisserie Broilers," *Consumers' Research,* Consumers' Research, Inc., February, 1956, p. 15.

[4] *Modern Cooking with Dormeyer Broil-Well with Baking Tray,* Dormeyer Corporation, p. 6.

Fig. 6–21. Rotisserie with broiler, grilling, and baking space. (Dormeyer Corporation)

Experiments

Experiment 1 can be done without any special testing equipment, but Experiments 2 and 3 require special equipment.

Experiment 1. *Use of an Appliance*

Read the instruction book carefully. Identify all the parts mentioned. Determine the wattage and voltage requirements. What type of circuit should this appliance be connected to?

Gather materials for the food preparation involved. Suggestions for foods to prepare are French toast, fried eggs, bacon in frypan; plain waffles or French toast in the waffle baker; prepared pudding mixes in saucepan; hotcakes on the griddle; refrigerator biscuits in the roaster; potato chips, biscuit doughnuts in the cooker-fryer; coffee in the coffee maker; and toast in the toaster.

Follow directions and prepare the food.

Were the instructions complete and easy to understand? If not, make suggesttions for changes. Did the appliance perform satisfactorily in the preparation of the food? Were the handles insulated adequately? Was the signal light easy to see? Did the table underneath the appliance remain cool? Was the appliance easily cleaned?

A suggested variation of this experiment is to repeat the food preparation while the appliance is still warm. What are the differences, if any, in this second run? Compare toast made in timed and radiant-heat-control toasters.

Experiment 2. *Effect of Varying Voltages on the Operation of a Heating Appliance*

Be sure appliance is cool before beginning this experiment. Determine voltage required by the appliance from nameplate data. Connect a variac, ammeter, and wattmeter in a circuit with the appliance to be tested. Set variac for the correct voltage. Preheat the appliance. If it is an appliance such as a coffee maker that should not be heated without water in it, put in a measured amount of water at a measured temperature. Check the time it takes to preheat the appliance or in the case of a coffee maker the time it takes to start perking.

Repeat at a voltage setting of 10 volts lower than nameplate requirements. What is the effect of low voltage on time required? On the current supplied to the appliance? What would it cost to preheat the appliance at your local electric rate?

Experiment 3. *Electrical Characteristics of Household Mixer Motors*

Connect a wattmeter, voltmeter, ammeter, and variac in a circuit with an electric mixer. Observe starting current and wattage, as well as steady values at different speed settings. Are current and wattage readings the same at all speed settings? Place 1⅓ to 1½ cups of flour and ⅓ cup water in the mixer bowl and mix. Observe wattage, voltage, and amperage at 30-second intervals from start until batter becomes quite stiff. If necessary, add more flour to make a very stiff batter.

How do meter readings vary as batter becomes stiffer?

Can you explain from your current and wattage readings why a mixer gets hot when a stiff batter is mixed in it?

Kitchen Planning

A kitchen which has a convenient and satisfying working area for its traditional function of food preparation and cleanup and which also is designed for important family activities ordinarily doesn't just happen. Good sources of information, careful planning and evaluation, and good use of financial resources probably were involved.

Provisions for family activities in the kitchen may include playroom for small children, space for entertaining by teen-agers or adults, dining space for the entire family, special lighting over a kitchen table because some members of the family like to read there, or anything else important to the family. Thus, good planning for family activities in the kitchen is *specialized* planning for an individual family.

Good planning of the working area to be used for meal preparation and cleanup, on the other hand, consists in applying certain general recommendations which are assumed to be valid for all families. These general recommendations are based on the premise that convenience and satisfaction in getting meals prepared and clearing away afterward are the primary objectives. Achieving them is not only desirable for the family that expects to use the kitchen, but is likely to increase the resale value of the house. Hence, the informed and effective kitchen planner may profit in two ways.

A. General Recommendations

Kitchens that are convenient and satisfying have certain general characteristics and certain special features.

1. They are safe.
2. They are well ventilated.
3. They are located to provide easy access to a back and/or front entrance and to the dining areas.
4. They have a working area reasonably free of cross traffic.
5. They have adequate plumbing facilities.
6. They have adequate wiring.
7. They are well lighted by both natural and artificial sources.
8. They are pleasing in color and pleasant to work in.
9. They are easily cleaned.
10. They utilize areas not needed for food preparation and cleanup for activities appropriate to the family.
11. They have the working area organized into reasonably compact centers.
12. They have adequate storage and counter space in each center.
13. They have convenient storage space and counters of convenient heights.
14. They have appropriate appliances in the different centers.

7–1. COMMENTS ON THE GENERAL RECOMMENDATIONS

The first ten characteristics listed above provide a general base or framework for achieving a convenient and satisfying working area. In a safe kitchen, a wall cabinet is not installed without a counter, base cabinet, or appliance below it. Proper storage is provided for knives. Sharp corners are eliminated as far as possible. Cabinet doors have good catches. In homes where small children will be in the kitchen, the appliances selected have controls not readily manipulated by small children. Cords on electric appliances are repaired or replaced when worn. Window curtains are not near a range. A step-stool and space for it are provided when some storage space is too high to be reached conveniently from the floor. Waxes that give a slippery finish are not used on the kitchen floor.

Good ventilation may be obtained by windows placed to give cross ventilation. Also, an exhaust fan removes odors and provides air circulation. The American Standards Association suggests 4 cubic feet of fresh air per minute per square foot of floor space for kitchens in institutions, restaurants, etc.[1] Applying this recommendation to a home kitchen that is 12 by 10 feet suggests that a fan with a capacity of 500 cubic feet per minute is desirable. The Cornell workers suggest that a complete change of air every three minutes is desirable in a home kitchen.[2] Assuming a ceiling height of 8 feet, the Cornell suggestion for a 12- by 10-foot kitchen would indicate a fan capacity of 330 cubic feet per minute. Kitchens can also have a room air conditioner to improve ventilation.

The location of the kitchen and the passageways into it are related to function. Since meals are prepared in the kitchen, it is reasonable that the homemaker should be able to serve them in a dining area easily reached from the kitchen. Since foods are stored in the kitchen, easy access from an outside door is desirable. Homemakers appreciate easy access to callers at both front and rear entrances. Fewer doorways are needed in a kitchen when the house plan has a hallway connecting the

---

[1] ASA 53.1, *American Standard Building Requirements. Light and Ventilation,* American Standards Association, 1946, p. 18.

[2] Glenn H. Beyer (ed.), *The Cornell Kitchen— Product Design Through Research,* Cornell University, 1952, p. 5.

kitchen with outside entrances and other parts of the house. The number of doorways in the kitchen preferably should be limited to two.

Cross traffic through the working area is avoided by locating doors so that paths between them do not cross the working area. Sometimes other considerations—for example, provision of *adequate* space for an eating area in the kitchen—make complete elimination of cross traffic impractical.

A kitchen is adequately wired when all the appliances that a homemaker may want to use at one time can be used and at correct voltage (see Chapter 2). Outlets are convenient when installed where appliances are used.

Good lighting for the kitchen is discussed in Chapter 3. Windows provide the natural lighting.

The colors to be used in the kitchen probably are best selected on the basis of the personal preferences of the person or persons who will use the room most. The following points should be considered. The ceiling and floor are usually the large areas in the kitchen, since cabinets and appliances use much of the wall space. Many conventional kitchens look "cut up" because of relatively large free-standing appliances, particularly the refrigerator, cabinets of various widths, free space between base and wall cabinets, and elaborate control panels on ranges. Hence colors used for the floor, ceiling, walls, and counters should help tie together the different appliances, cabinets, and other furnishings of the kitchen.

Individual colored appliances may blend nicely with white ones. On the other hand, in the rather compact arrangement characteristic for the kitchen working area, a colored range made by one manufacturer may or may not be pleasing with a colored refrigerator made by another manufacturer.

A kitchen that has no unnecessary sources of noise is a more pleasant place in which to work. Covering the ceiling with acoustical tiles helps reduce noise. So too does wise selection of counter and floor coverings and cabinets. (Characteristics that help minimize noise are discussed on pp. 97 and 101.)

Kitchens are easier to keep clean if some consideration is given to maintenance when selecting counter, floor, and wall coverings, and in planning storage space. Convenient and sanitary provision for disposal of garbage and waste paper is also necessary. A food waste disposer, a closed washable container with a smooth interior finish, or disposable bags are used for garbage. Containers or bags are used for waste paper.

The final point in the general framework for a well-planned kitchen, namely space for activities, may be important to the satisfaction a homemaker experiences in her kitchen, whether or not she is aware of this. For example, a homemaker may enjoy being able to see a child play in a planned space in one part of the kitchen while she is working in another part, even when she does not list this as a preference for a kitchen plan.

B. Installation of Counter, Floor, and Wall Coverings

Some characteristics of the materials used in different counter and floor coverings were discussed in Chaper 4 on materials. The paragraphs below list specific materials that are available at present and that have proved satisfactory.

Counter and floor coverings installed with few seams are likely to be easier to maintain than those with many seams.

7–2. COUNTER COVERINGS

Currently, the three counter coverings listed below have proved generally satisfactory in terms of ease of upkeep in the home, resistance to ordinary staining agents, enough resiliency to minimize noise and breakage of dishes and glassware placed on them, reasonable resistance to heat, and acceptable prices when installation costs are considered:

1. The laminated plastics such as Formica, Textolite, Micarta, and others.
2. Inlaid vinyl.
3. Inlaid linoleum. The cost of the laminated plastics at this time continues to be higher than that of vinyl or linoleum, but not as much so as when they were first introduced for home use.

The counter covering usually will be installed with a stainless steel, "nondrip" molding at the front, sides, and, if the back splash is not rounded, over the seam between the counter and the back splash. However, some companies are now supplying rounded-edge plastic tops that do not need moldings. The front and side edges are raised slightly to prevent dripping of liquids onto the floor (Fig. 7–2).

For some counter-top installations, a back splash 3 or 4 inches high or even a back splash that extends to the bottom of the wall cabinet may be desirable. However, where midway cabinets are to be installed between the base and wall cabinet, a back splash may be undesirable.

Where it is practical to do so, it is desirable to install a cutting top of hardwood, for example, edge-grained maple, on top of a base cabinet. (Edge-grained wood shows pattern

Fig. 7–1. Vinyl counter top with stainless steel edging (molding). (Sears, Roebuck and Co.)

Fig. 7–2. Raised-edge counter top with drop-in sink and surface units. (General Electric Textolite)

or grain less than flat-grained wood.) A hardwood insert, when used, is logically installed where cutting operations are done most frequently. This may be between the refrigerator and the sink or between the sink and the range. The hardwood is usually regarded as part of a continuous counter when it is adjacent to other counters.

7–3. FLOOR COVERINGS

Desirable characteristics for kitchen floor coverings include washability, resistance to soil, retention of color, and some resiliency for comfort in walking and for minimizing noise from walking. Standard-gauge, inlaid, linoleum-roll material; special linoleum tiles; floor-covering weight, inlaid, vinyl-roll material; and vinyl tiles are all satisfactory floor coverings that have been available for several years. Vinyl asbestos tiles, a newer material, have good resistance to oil and grease and hence are practical for kitchen floors.

Good installation practice is to provide an underlayer of hardboard or plywood,[3] which is nailed with a special type of nail to the wood subfloor in new installations or to the

[3] Hardboard is made by several manufacturers. It consists of woody fibers processed and pressed together to form a hard, uniformly textured surface.

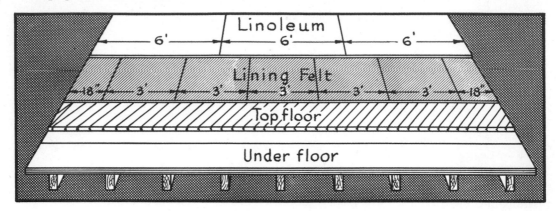

Fig. 7–3. Installation of linoleum roll material. (Armstrong Cork Company)

wood-finish flooring in existing homes. But hardboard sometimes is not used in existing houses when the top or finish flooring is firm and smooth.

For linoleum not backed with felt, a lining felt is used. This is placed between the linoleum and the underlayer or the finish flooring (Fig. 7–3).

Many vinyl asbestos tiles are most attractive. Unlike vinyl tiles and special linoleum tiles, they can be laid over concrete as well as wood. When laid over concrete a mastic underlayer is used. The Small Homes Council suggests that mastics which contain a binder (asphalt or latex) in the mix are more satisfactory than those which consist of a powdered mix (cement, gypsum, and sand) to which only water is added.[4] Vinyl asbestos tiles are currently more expensive than vinyl tiles or special linoleum tiles.

7–4. WALL COVERINGS

Kitchen walls are usually painted, but wallpaper coverings have been used for a long time, and new types of wall coverings are being developed. Desirable qualities for kitchen wall surfaces are similar to those for floor coverings, except that resiliency is not important for walls, but resistance to peeling and cracking should be considered. (Peeling and cracking are usually not a problem in properly laid floor coverings.)

Painted walls usually look better and wear longer if they are sandpapered lightly before a new coat is applied. Enamel paint is used frequently because of its hard surface. Walls covered with a gloss- or semigloss-finish oil paint are considered easier to maintain than walls covered with a flat-finish oil paint. But light reflected from flat finishes is more diffuse and hence more pleasing than light reflected from glossy finishes; hence choice of type of paint is a matter of personal preference. A reasonable compromise is to use a mixture of enamel and flat-finish oil paint.

One manufacturer of counter coverings and appliances has announced that paints made with glyptal alkyd resins which match the colors of its counter coverings and appliances will be introduced by leading paint manufacturers.

The newer type of wall coverings include enameled sheeting materials, plastic-surface sheeting materials, laminates of different types, plastic tiles, and tiles of aluminum with baked-on enamel surfaces.

[4] Ben J. Small, *Flooring Materials,* Circular Series F4.6, Small Homes Council, University of Illinois, March, 1955.

C. Kitchen Cabinets

7–5. TYPES OF KITCHEN CABINETS

Base and wall cabinets have been provided in modern kitchens for some time. Base cabinets provide storage space and counter space; wall cabinets provide storage space only. Open, quarter-round, and half-round shelves on wall and base cabinets are used for a kitchen radio or other small electric appliances, growing plants, and decorative items such as vases.

Factory-made, tall, shallow cabinets and midway cabinets are newer than base or wall cabinets. The former may be 7 feet tall. They are used for storage of canned foods and other foods that do not require refrigeration and for storage of utensils and accessory equipment that can be hung on hooks. Midway cabinets are placed at the rear of counter tops or are hung from the rear part of the bottom of wall cabinets. Logically they provide storage space for items used near them (Figs. 7–4 and 7–5).

Sometimes a counter with a drawer between base cabinets serves as a kitchen planning center where the homemaker can prepare menus and market orders and use a telephone.

7–6. CONSTRUCTION CHARACTERISTICS

a. Dimensions and Shelves

Contractor-built kitchen cabinets may be any convenient width, depth, and height. Widths of factory-made cabinets, however, are currently based on a 3-inch module. Wall and base cabinets are available in widths from 12 to 48 inches or more, though not all manufacturers make all the widths. Twelve-inch base cabinets, when supplied, are usually designed for special purposes such as tray storage or soiled-towel storage. Some manufacturers offer special assemblies of wall cabinets that

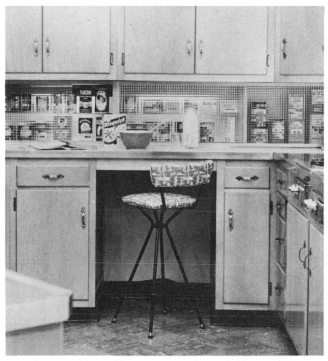

Fig. 7–4. Midway cabinets with sliding glass doors. (Mutschler Brothers Company)

total more than 48 inches in width.

Usually, single doors, hinged on the right or left, are supplied for cabinets that are up to 21 inches wide. Twenty-four-inch cabinets may have one or two doors; two are usually preferable. Cabinets 27 inches or more wide have two doors.

Wall cabinets are approximately 13 inches deep, and base cabinets are usually about 25½ inches deep when overhang of counter top is included.

Standard types of factory-made wall cabinets are 30 or 33 inches high. Shorter cabinets —15, 18, 21, or 24 inches high—are manufactured for use over the range, refrigerator, and sink.

Height of base cabinets when measured to the top of the counter is 36 to 36½ inches.

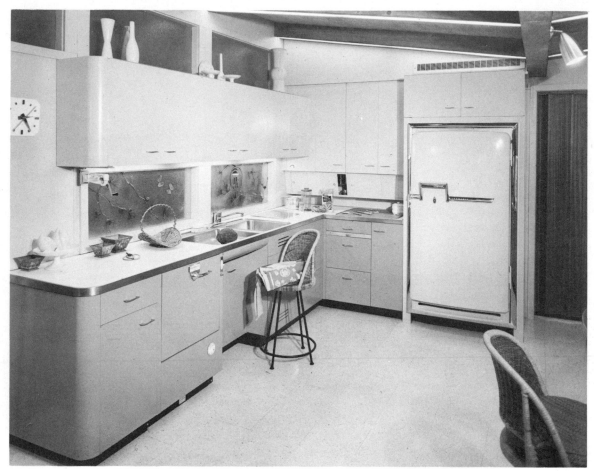

Fig. 7–5.   Metal midway cabinets suspended from bottom of wall cabinets. (American Gas Association, *American Home Magazine*)

Some manufacturers also offer low-counter base cabinets about 29 inches high for mix centers and other special uses. Toe space is provided at the bottom. Some designs introduced in 1958 have legs about 9 inches high.

Standard-height wall cabinets usually have two fixed or adjustable shelves in addition to the floor of the cabinet. Shorter wall cabinets may have one shelf or none. Standard-height base cabinets have one drawer and one fixed or adjustable shelf in addition to the floor of the cabinet; several drawers, usually three; several trays; or trays and drawers.

Wood wall and base cabinets have fixed or adjustable wood shelves. Those of steel have solid steel, or wire shelves so that stored articles will be easier to see (Fig. 7–6).

b. Corner Cabinets

Corner cabinets may be the blind type which are partly obstructed by cabinets on the adjacent wall. In such cabinets, 13 inches (wall) or 24 inches (base) of the cabinet on one wall have somewhat inconvenient storage space or none at all.

Other corner cabinets have fixed shelves that are diagonal to the walls (Fig. 7–7). Still others have rotating or swing-out shelves (Fig. 7–8).

Sometimes only a counter is used in base

Fig. 7–6. Base cabinet with pull-out tray and pull-out wire shelf. (Curtis Companies Incorporated)

Fig. 7–7. Corner base cabinet with fixed, diagonal-type shelves. (Curtis Companies Incorporated)

corners, in which case the base cabinets do not extend into a corner. Thus corner base storage is lost, but continuous counter around the corner is kept.

Also, wall cabinet assemblies are often planned to end on each of two adjacent walls with some free space at the ends of the walls near the corner, which must be adequate to permit opening cabinet doors on both walls. This type of installation avoids the cost of "turning" corners on wall cabinets.

c. Cabinet Materials and Finishes

Selection of material and finish is a matter of personal preference. Contractor-built cabinets are ordinarily constructed of wood and factory-made ones of wood or steel. Well-designed cabinets of both kinds are available in several price ranges. The doors of good-quality steel cabinets have acoustical insulation to minimize noise due to vibration when they are closed. Also, some factory-made

Fig. 7–8. Corner base cabinet with swing-out shelves. (Curtis Companies Incorporated)

steel cabinets have hardwood fronts and doors.

Finishes on wood cabinets are either clear or pigmented.[5] The usual clear finishes are

[5] Glenn H. Beyer (ed.), *op. cit.*, p. 37.

oils, varnishes, or waxes. Clear finishes are sometimes made into a stain by adding a small quantity of pigment or suitable dye. Pigmented finishes are usually enamels. Like the clear finishes, enamels used for wood cabinets are air-dried rather than baked on. Enamel finishes are considered to be easier to maintain than varnish finishes; however, the varnish finish is often preferred because of its warmer appearance. Steel cabinets usually have baked-on enamel finishes.

d. Cabinet Hardware

Hardware for kitchen cabinets includes hinges, shelf supports, drawer slides, catches and locking devices, and pulls.[6] The base metal in the better-quality metal hardware is usually brass. Platings of nickel and chromium may be used over the base metal.

Nonplated metal hardware, called "solid hardware," is considered best.

Wood and plastics are satisfactory for cabinet door pulls, push plates, and similar parts. Colored plastic pulls and push plates are decorative, but may need to be replaced if the color scheme in the kitchen is changed.

Pulls on doors are most convenient when located in the bottom third of doors of wall cabinets and the top third of doors of base cabinets. Doors need not have exposed pulls; instead they may have a grasping place on one edge for the fingers.

Hinged doors require a catch to keep them closed. Good friction catches have rubber seats. Recently developed magnetic catches are permanent and fasten securely.

Shelves may be supported in several ways. Adjustable shelves are often supported by clips, which fit into holes drilled at regular intervals in the sides of the cabinet or in metal

strips fastened to the cabinet. Knife brackets that fit into notches at the front and back of cabinets are also used for supports for adjustable shelves.

Drawer slides are used in better-quality cabinets to give smooth rolling drawers. They consist of rollers, often of nylon, treated channels, and guide strips.

e. Cabinet Features

Additional features currently available in factory-made cabinets are illustrated in Figures 7–9 through 7–12. Figure 7–9 shows a pull-out bin for storing vegetables, such as potatoes and onions, near the sink. Figure 7–10 shows a pull-out cutting board over a drawer. Figure 7–11 shows one arrangement for hanging pots and pans. Figure 7–12 shows an extension table that pulls out of a base cabinet.

A place to sit down in the kitchen is supplied by a planning desk, a recessed sink front (Fig. 7–5), a lap board that pulls out of a base cabinet, a counter that has no cabinet underneath (Fig. 7–4), or the kitchen table.

For women of average height a planning desk should be about 29 to 31 inches high.

7–7. CLEARANCE BETWEEN BASE AND WALL CABINETS

The clearance needed between base and wall cabinets depends partly on the actual height of the wall cabinet and partly on the heights of small appliances such as a blender that may be used on the counter underneath. It is recommended that the top shelf in the wall cabinet should not be higher than 72 inches from the floor. This puts a top limit of about 15 inches between counter and bottom of wall cabinet for wall cabinets that are 30 inches high and have two shelves.

NOTE: Shelves higher than 72 inches may be provided for articles used very infrequently, such as Christmas tree ornaments.

---

[6] *Ibid.*, pp. 47–48. Also, M. H. Kennedy and W. H. Scheick, *Hardware for the Home,* Circular Series F15.0, Small Homes Council, University of Illinois, October, 1946.

Fig. 7–9. Base cabinet with pull-out bin for storage of vegetables. (Geneva Modern Kitchens)

Fig. 7–11. Base cabinet with gliding pot holder. (Mutschler Brothers Company)

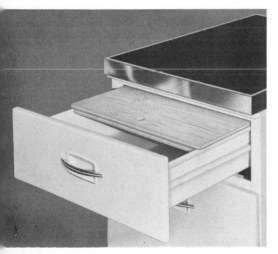

Fig. 7–10. Base cabinet with pull-out cutting board over a drawer. (Geneva Modern Kitchens)

Fig. 7–12. Extension table that pulls out of a base cabinet. (Mutschler Brothers Company)

7–8. FUNCTIONAL CRITERIA FOR KITCHEN CABINETS

The places where cabinets will be installed, as well as construction characteristics, should determine which cabinets are most desirable. Generally, base, wall, and midway cabinets will be used in conjunction with one of the three major kitchen appliances (refrigerator, range, sink) to prepare, cook, and serve foods and to clear away afterward. A homemaker needs to take fewer steps in food preparation and cleanup when small equipment and supplies are within her reach. Hence kitchen cabinets located near a major appliance should have convenient storage for articles used with that appliance.

Also, since the tops of base cabinets are usually the counters near the major appliances, enough base cabinets should be provided to meet counter requirements (see pages 110–111 and 115–116).

Four criteria are useful in deciding which cabinets should be installed in different locations: (1) ease of seeing articles that logically will be stored in the cabinet; (2) ease of grasping articles stored in the cabinet; (3) suitability for convenient storage of most frequently used articles in the top part of base cabinets and bottom part of wall cabinets. For convenient storage, similar articles, such as plates of the same size, are stacked together and unlike articles, such as plates or bowls of different size, are separated. (4) The last criterion is suitability for storage of less frequently used articles in the bottom part of base cabinets and the top part of wall cabinets. Examples of less frequently used articles are large roasters and extra or "company" dishes.

Less bending is required with pull-out or roll-out drawers in base cabinets than with shelves. Heavy utensils are best stored on roll-out drawers or on shelves.

CHAPTER 8

Kitchen Planning (*Continued*)

A. Kitchen Units and Work Centers

The concept of work centers in the kitchen derives in part from the readily recognized major activities carried out in the kitchen: preparation of foods, cooking, placing of foods on serving dishes, and dishwashing.

Functional kitchen planning involves organization of *centers* which contain the counter space, utensils, accessories, and a major appliance or appliances needed to carry out these activities conveniently. In addition, functional kitchen planning is concerned with assembling the separate centers to form a convenient and complete *kitchen unit* or working area.

Types of kitchen units are considered first, partly because the complete kitchen working area is a more familiar concept than work centers.

8–1. TYPES OF KITCHEN UNITS

Which type of kitchen unit is used may depend on the preference of the planner, but the types that can be used are often limited partly by door and window openings in the space assigned for the kitchen.

The types most emphasized in conventional kitchen planning are the U, the broken U, and the L. Other types are the one-wall, the corridor, and the island (Figs. 8–1 and 8–2).

The U-shaped kitchen has one major appliance on each of three adjacent walls with continuous (uninterrupted) counter between appliances. Usually, the sink is at the base of the U and the sides are ordinarily not of equal length. The U is considered the most step-

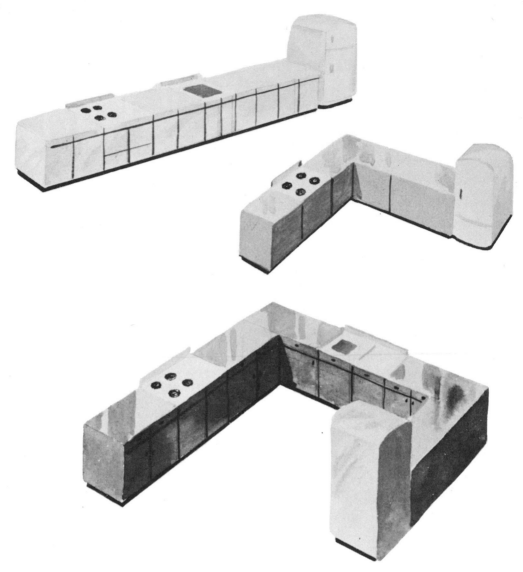

Fig. 8–1. One-wall, L, and U assemblies. ("Live Better Electrically")

saving type provided only one person works in the kitchen. The Purdue workers, for example, report that when a dinner and a breakfast were prepared, served, and cleared away, less travel was required in the U-shaped kitchen than in the L- or corridor-shaped ones.[1]

Other advantages of the U-shape are that the work centers can be assembled in normal sequence, distances between appliances are relatively short, a large continuous window area is possible, and counter space is gained by turning two corners.[2]

The broken U usually has some architectural part, such as a door or passageway, in one side that interrupts the continuous arrangement of work centers. This break in the

[1] *Easier Homemaking,* Purdue University Station Bulletin 529, 1948, p. 41.

[2] *Handbook of Kitchen Design—A Report of an Investigation in Space Use,* Technical Series C5.32R, Small Homes Council, University of Illinois, 1950, p. 42.

Fig. 8–2. Kitchen with surface units in an island. (Mutschler Brothers Company)

continuous arrangement may necessitate extra counters to meet recommendations for counter space near each appliance, because the same counter will not be in two centers. Also, the door or passageway may encourage cross traffic and thus hamper the person working in the kitchen. On the other hand, the model kitchen designed for the American Heart Association to show how a woman with a heart condition can do her work best is a broken U.[3] The break in this is not a passageway in the assembly line but a cleaning closet and a wall storage cabinet (Fig. 8–3).

The L-shaped kitchen has two major appliances on one wall and the third on an adjacent wall, all three connected by continuous counter. Probably the chief advantage of the L-shape is that it may make space in the room available for an eating area, child's

play area, or other family activity. Also, the L is usually considered a more convenient arrangement than the U when more than one person works in the kitchen at a time.

The corridor or two-wall kitchen arrangement has two major appliances on one wall and the third on an opposite wall. This arrangement ordinarily would be planned when doors or other architectural features on opposite walls prevent a U or L arrangement or when considerations of cost of corner cabinets outweigh the convenience of continuous counter.

The one-wall arrangement, as the name implies, has all three major appliances on one wall. If this type meets recommended counter and cabinet spaces, it is long and therefore likely to involve excessive walking. If it does not meet recommendations on counter and cabinet, it can be short. Short one-wall units are used in small apartments where space is at a premium. Sometimes one-wall units are used because they can be purchased in a single

[3] *The Heart of the Home,* picture edition, American Heart Association, p. 14. Also, Lillian M. Gilbreth, Orpha Mae Thomas, Eleanor Clymer, *Management in the Home,* Dodd, Mead and Company, 1954, pp. 82–84.

1. **SHELVES**
   (Open from both sides)

2. **GARBAGE DISPOSAL AND PARING CENTER**

3. **DOUBLE SINK**

4. **WASHING MACHINE**

5. **REVOLVING SHELVES**

6. **WORK CHAIR**

7. **MIX CENTER**
   (Baking and mixing)

8. **REFRIGERATOR**
   (Handle of door is next to mix counter)

9. **STORAGE FOR CLEANING TOOLS**

10. **GROCERY STORAGE**
    (Week's supply for family of four)

11. **STORAGE FOR COOKING UTENSILS**

12. **RANGE AND OVEN**

13. **WORK COUNTER**
    (Wheeled table underneath)

14, 15. **STORAGE FOR COMPANY DINNERWARE**

16. **STORAGE SHELF**

17. **DINETTE BENCH TOY AND HOBBY STORAGE**

18. **DINETTE TABLE**

19, 20. **DINETTE CHAIRS**

21. **RECORD PLAYER RECORD STORAGE**

22. **PLANNING CENTER AND BOOK SHELVES**

23. **ROCKER**

Floor plan of the work simplification kitchen and dinette

Because you usually serve from the stove and return dishes to the sink, these two areas have been placed conveniently near the entrance to the dinette.

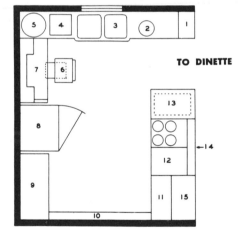
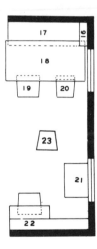

Fig. 8–3.   Broken U kitchen with planned family activity centers. (Reproduced by permission from the booklet "The Heart of the Home," published by the American Heart Association and its affiliates)

package. (See factory-made kitchen centers, section 8–5).

A complete island plan would have each work center isolated. Some kitchens in older houses are like this because of openings in all four walls. Also, some of the very newest kitchens shown by equipment manufacturers at conventions are planned to have at least one island, for example, the range center. The island in these new kitchens is not necessarily against a wall but may stand free in the room. To be most satisfactory, each isolated center must be planned with adequate counter and storage space near the major appliance.

8–2. CLEARANCES, EATING AREA, AND DISTANCES BETWEEN APPLIANCES

Maud Wilson recommends a minimum clearance of 4 feet between fronts of two pieces of equipment likely to be used by two workers at the same time.[4] From this recommendation, one derives 8 feet as the minimum width of

a U-shaped kitchen that has base cabinets 2 feet deep on each side of the U.

The space needed for an eating area in the kitchen depends on the number of people who will eat there and on the size of the table. Most present-day kitchen tables are rectangular. A 30- by 40-inch table is convenient for four people. Additional space must be allowed for chairs and for getting in and out of them.

a. Distances Between Appliances

Distances between any two major appliances should be such that the amount of walking between them is reasonably small, while at the same time counter and cabinets between appliances are adequate.

On the basis of an analysis of kitchen plans which meet its requirements on storage and counter space, the Small Homes Council recommends these limits on distances between center fronts of free-standing appliances and a specific figure for the sum of the distances[5]: 4 to 6 feet between sink and range; 4 to 7 feet between sink and refrigerator; 4 to 9 feet be-

[4] Maud Wilson, *Considerations in Planning Kitchen Cabinets,* Agricultural Experiment Station Bulletin 445, Oregon State College, November, 1947, p. 60.

[5] *Handbook of Kitchen Design—A Report of an Investigation in Space Use, op. cit.,* p. 15.

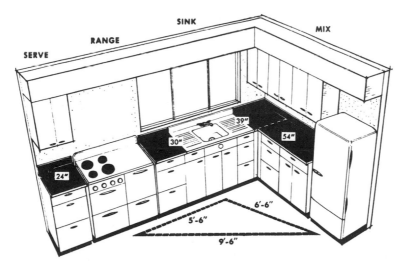

Fig. 8–4. L-kitchen with satisfactory work triangle. (Reprinted by permission of the University of Illinois Small Homes Council from its copyrighted publication, *Handbook of Kitchen Design—A Report of an Investigation in Space Use*)

tween range and refrigerator. Thus the sum of the three distances should not exceed 22 feet.

The distances between center fronts of major appliances form a "work triangle" (Fig. 8–4). A good work triangle is so oriented with respect to door openings that traffic does not cross it.

The distances between appliances shown in Figure 8–4 may be verified approximately by making the following assumptions: the range is 42 inches wide; the sink bowl is 30 inches and each drainboard 15 inches wide; the refrigerator is 30 inches wide; clearance between edge of 54-inch cabinet and refrigerator is 6.56 inches; and the distance between a plane through the right-hand edge of the sink bowl and the plane of the surface of the refrigerator door is 4.36 inches.

The Small Homes Council recommendations on distances between appliances were developed for free-standing appliances. But the general principles of reasonably small walking distances between appliances, adequate counter and cabinet space near appliances, and limited cross traffic through the working area probably are sound for kitchens with built-in appliances and a working space that is not a triangle.

8–3. WORK CENTERS

Usually at least three work centers are planned: a mix or refrigerator center, a sink or dishwashing center, and a cooking and serving center. When four are planned, the cooking or range center is distinct from the serve center. Sometimes five centers are planned, in which case the refrigerator may be part of a distinct center instead of part of the mix center.

Irrespective of the number of separate centers planned, storage at point of first use is accepted as a basic principle. That is, any article regularly used first in a particular center is stored in that center if possible. Organization within centers is planned so that work normally will proceed from right to left, since for right-handed persons this method of working usually involves smoother and fewer motions. Also, the centers are planned to be part of a total kitchen unit in which the work of food preparation and cleanup may proceed with minimum retracing of steps.

a. Mix Center

In a four-center plan, the refrigerator is the major appliance in the mix center (Fig. 8–4). Storage space is provided for commercial mixes, sugar, flour, shortening, spices, and other foods used in mixing operations; utensils such as bowls, baking pans, casseroles; and accessory equipment such as sifter, mixer, beater, grinders, rolling pin, measuring cups and spoons, mixing spoons, and refrigerator dishes. A minimum of 15 inches of counter, 24 to 27 inches deep, is recommended at the opening side of the refrigerator.[6] Also, if this counter is part of a continuous 3-foot counter recommended for mixing, it should be between 31 and 34 inches high for women of average height.

b. Sink Center

The sink center of course contains the sink and, if one is provided, the dishwasher. Provision is made here for food waste and waste paper disposal. Storage space is provided for dishwashing supplies; cooking ware requiring addition of water for use, such as teakettles, double boilers, and coffee makers; vegetables and fruits that do not require refrigeration but do need washing or peeling, such as potatoes and oranges; foods for which water is needed at the start of preparation, such as canned soups, dried beans, and so on; measuring cups (for water); and cutlery and accessories for cutting, peeling, and straining.

Dinnerware is stored in the sink center, the

[6] Maud Wilson, *op. cit.*, pp. 26, 28.

serve center, the dining area, or in all three areas. Storage of dinnerware in the sink center contradicts the principle of storage at place of first use, but nevertheless has some practical advantages—for example, putting away the clean dishes requires less walking. Also, when the sink center is close to the serve center, dishes in which food is served will be close to the serve center.

A minimum of 36 inches of counter to the right of the sink bowl for soiled dishes and 30 to 32 inches to the left of the sink bowl for air-drying of rinsed dishes is recommended when dishes are washed by hand.[7] A counter height of 38 inches is recommended by Wilson as desirable, because this places the base of standard sink bowls at a reasonable level.

Fifteen inches or more of the 36-inch counter to the right of the sink may do double duty as the 15 inches or more recommended at the left of the refrigerator, assuming the kitchen is planned with refrigerator at the right and range at the left of the sink. In fact, except for correct counter heights, the 36-inch counter to the right of the sink can fulfill three recommendations, the third being 3 feet of continuous counter for mixing operations. And this triple use of counter between sink and refrigerator is common because practical considerations of space tend to dictate compromises—and optimum counter heights usually lose in the compromise.

c. Range Center

The range is of course the major appliance in the range center, which also has storage space for skillets, saucepans, and lids; stirring spoons, ladles, turners, etc.; seasonings and shortening used directly at the range; and foods used with boiling water, for example, macaroni, noodles, etc.

[7] The 32-inch recommendation is from Maud Wilson, *op. cit.;* the 30-inch recommendation is from *Handbook of Kitchen Design—A Report of an Investigation in Space Use, op. cit.*

Counter space of 21 to 24 inches adjacent or near the range is suggested for setting out dinner plates and serving bowls. Again, from the type of operations carried out in this center, the proper height of counter top is 31 to 34 inches.

d. Serve Center

Unlike the other centers, the serve center has no major appliance. Storage is provided here for trays, small electrical appliances such as toasters and waffle bakers, some cutlery, and sometimes linens such as placemats. Counter space provided in this center should be 21 to 24 inches as suggested above.

Since the serve center is the end of the assembly line, it is a good location for a cart or table on wheels. Furthermore, if the cart is "garaged" under the counter, it is less likely to get articles heaped on it.

e. New Trends

Separate oven and surface cooking appliances may be placed in different parts of the kitchen. In some mass-produced houses this seems to be done simply to emphasize that the kitchen has built-ins, and counter and storage are not provided near the oven. One logical separation is to have the refrigerator and oven in the mix center, and the surface cooking equipment in the "cooking" or "range" center. On the other hand, separate oven and surface cooking equipment *can* be in one center. One of the most "advanced" kitchen arrangements the senior author has seen has a "push-button cooking center" that consists of a built-in conventional oven, built-in electronic oven, and built-in surface units housed in a framework that has counter space.

8–4. THE CORNELL WORK CENTERS

A Cornell University group of workers from several areas (home economics, social psychology, architecture, and engineering) has developed a set of work centers[8] designed for complete assembly to form an "optimum" kitchen; or one or more centers may be used with existing equipment and cabinets to form a "composite" kitchen.

The mix, range, and serve centers have C frames to which are attached base and upper cabinets and a lighting valance (Fig. 8–5).

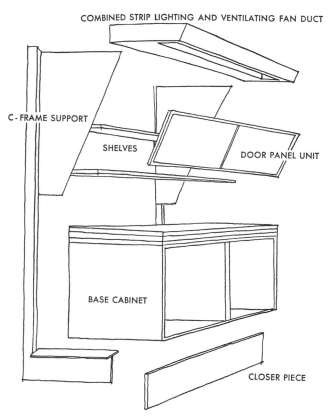

COMBINED STRIP LIGHTING AND VENTILATING FAN DUCT

C-FRAME SUPPORT

SHELVES

DOOR PANEL UNIT

BASE CABINET

CLOSER PIECE

Fig. 8–5. Exploded view of structural components of a Cornell kitchen center. (*The Cornell Kitchen—Product Design Through Research*, Cornell University, Ithaca, New York, 1952)

The valance over the range center has a ventilating fan and duct system. The C-frame support also carries the electric wiring. The height of the counter tops is adjustable over an interval of 6 inches.

[8] Glenn H. Beyer (ed.), *The Cornell Kitchen— Product Design Through Research,* Cornell University, 1952, pp. 58–64.

The upper cabinets of the mix, range, and serve centers have half-shelves to provide accessible storage. The base cabinets have pull-out trays and drawers in place of fixed shelves. The mix center has built-in flour and sugar bins in the upper cabinet and a bread and cake box with vertical and horizontal partitions in the base cabinet.

The range center has four electric surface units and controls set into the counter top. (The oven is in the refrigerator center.) The inner compartments of the base cabinet for this center are interchangeable with those in the base cabinets of the mix and serve centers.

The serve center provides storage for dishes, glasses, silverware, table linen, small electric appliances such as a toaster, and miscellaneous items such as lunch boxes that might properly be stored in this center.

The refrigerator center has a C-frame support and superstructure for the refrigerator, oven, shelves, and trays (Fig. 8–6). The built-in refrigerator and the adjacent built-in oven are mounted at waist level. The wiring for oven and refrigerator is built into the back panels of the work center.

The back of the sink-center top has a continuous line of storage bins for fruits and vegetables, soaps and synthetic detergents, canned and packaged foods, paper towels, and accessories (Fig. 8–7). (These storage bins replace conventional wall cabinets over the sink.) The sink bowl or bowls are drawn or formed in the one-piece counter top. Water supply piping and drain piping are built into the sink and closed with unions so they can be attached to the home piping system. Below the counter top are a swing-out compartment with receptacles for waste paper, garbage, and tin cans and three fixed compartments. One is an open space with a footrest for use when the worker is seated. Another provides space for a dishwasher or for sliding trays. The last (right-hand) space provides storage for drying towels and for dishpans.

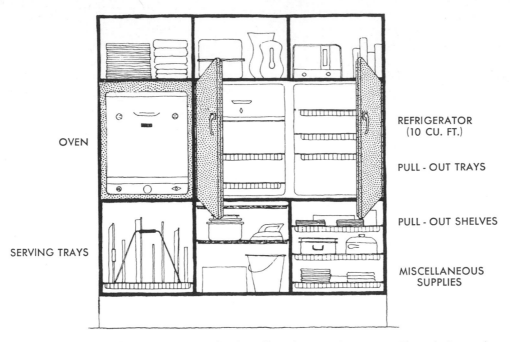

OVEN

REFRIGERATOR
(10 CU. FT.)

PULL - OUT TRAYS

PULL - OUT SHELVES

SERVING TRAYS

MISCELLANEOUS
SUPPLIES

Fig. 8–6. Cornell refrigerator center. (*The Cornell Kitchen—Product Design Through Research,* Cornell University, Ithaca, New York, 1952)

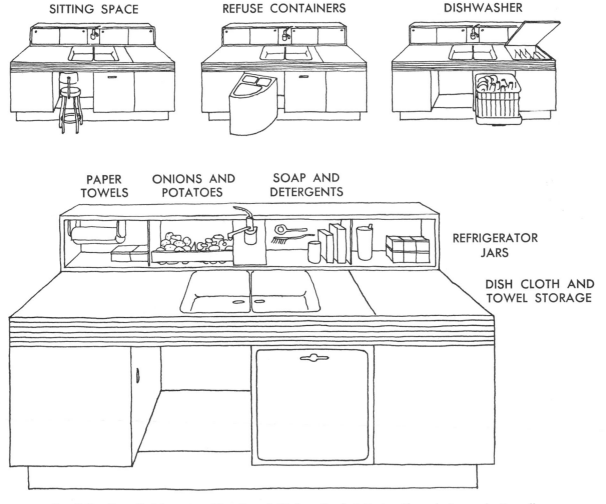

SITTING SPACE

REFUSE CONTAINERS

DISHWASHER

PAPER
TOWELS

ONIONS AND
POTATOES

SOAP AND
DETERGENTS

REFRIGERATOR
JARS

DISH CLOTH AND
TOWEL STORAGE

Fig. 8–7. Cornell sink center. (*The Cornell Kitchen—Product Design Through Research,* Cornell University, Ithaca, New York, 1952)

8–5. FACTORY-MADE KITCHEN CENTERS

Some manufacturers offer several appliances assembled in a single unit or package. These factory-made packages are available in compact units with little counter space as well as in deluxe units which offer a wide variety of features.

A type used in small apartments includes an apartment-size range, sink, and under-counter refrigerator, assembled to have a total frontage that may be as short as 6 feet. The counter space in these smaller models may consist of the top of the under-counter refrigerator and a short drainboard at the right-hand side of the sink. The model shown in Figure 8–8 does not include an oven.

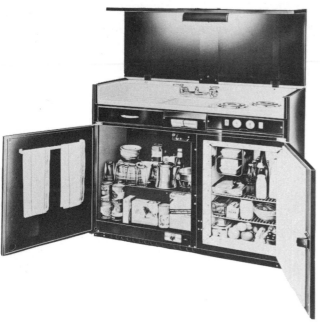

Fig. 8–8.   Factory-made kitchen center. (Dwyer Products Corporation)

Deluxe kitchen "centers" may omit the refrigerator but include such appliances as a washer-dryer, dishwasher, and food waste disposer. These deluxe models are used in some higher-priced, mass-produced houses and sometimes in custom-made houses. Also, in some instances, they may be a practical solution when it is necessary to remodel a badly arranged kitchen.

The deluxe model illustrated in Figure 8–9 is 9 feet long and has a one-piece top with sink bowl and four surface units. Shallow cabinets are provided above the counter top. The under-counter appliances include a washer-dryer, food waste disposer, electric dishwasher, and oven. The center has internal plumbing connections so that single hot and cold water supply lines serve for the entire center. Drain piping is the same as that required for a double-bowl sink. The center has internal wiring so that one cable carries the power supply to all appliances. A circuit-breaker panel is provided, with individual circuit breakers for each appliance. An appliance plug-in panel is located at the left end of the counter back splash. Base cabinets can be added at either end of the center. This permits the homemaker to increase counter and storage space.

a. Automatic Appliance Center

One manufacturer offers an automatic appliance center for simultaneous use of five small electric appliances (Fig. 8–10). This "center" is equipped with two outlets, three pull-out extension cords, automatic timer, and a circuit-breaker panel with five "mini circuit breakers."

The appliance center itself must be connected to a three-wire, 230-volt supply. But the wiring within it is such that each of the two outlets and the three extension cords is part of a separate 115-volt circuit. The center can be installed in a wall, as shown in Figure 8–10, or on a counter. This unit, plus appropriate small electric appliances, counter, and cabinet could well be the kitchen "cooking center."

Fig. 8–9. Factory-made, deluxe kitchen center. (General Electric Company)

B. Small Homes Council Scoring Sheet [9]

This scoring sheet applies to "small" kitchens with free-standing appliances and factory-made cabinets. It is divided into two parts. The first part assigns points, on a scale of 100, for storage cabinets, counters, and distances between appliances. A total base cabinet *frontage* of 11 feet zero inches to 13 feet 6 inches is assigned 25 points. Fewer points are assigned for more or less base cabinet frontage. A total wall cabinet *frontage* of 8 feet 6 inches to 14 feet zero inches is likewise assigned 25 points, and a greater or smaller wall cabinet frontage is assigned fewer points.

Points are next assigned for length of counter at different locations and total counter. Maximum credit is assigned, for example, for 15 inches or more of counter adjacent to the refrigerator; 36 inches or more to the right of

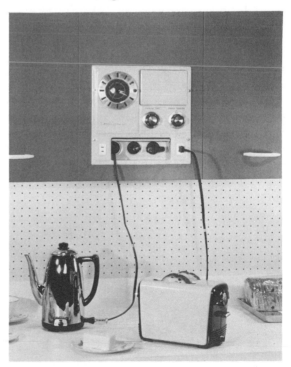

Fig. 8–10. Automatic appliance center. (Courtesy Westinghouse Electric Corporation)

[9] *Handbook of Kitchen Design—A Report of an Investigation in Space Use, op. cit.,* pp. 72–73. Also, *Kitchen Planning Standards,* Circular Series C5.32, Small Homes Council, University of Illinois, October, 1949.

the sink, assuming that the refrigerator is at the right and the range at the left of the sink and dishwashing is done by hand; and so on. Maximum credit, 10 points, is assigned for 8 feet 6 inches or more of total counter.

Points are next assigned for distances between center fronts of appliances and total length of the work triangle in accordance with the recommendations quoted in section 8–2.

The second part of the scoring sheet subtracts points for undesirable features in the kitchen. For example, 10 points are subtracted if there are less than 42 inches of wall cabinets within 6 feet of the center front of the sink. Ten points are subtracted if the total window area is not more than 10 percent of the total floor area of the kitchen. Ten points are subtracted if cabinets extend into a corner alongside the end of the range or the refrigerator. Five points are subtracted if traffic through the kitchen crosses the work triangle, and so on.

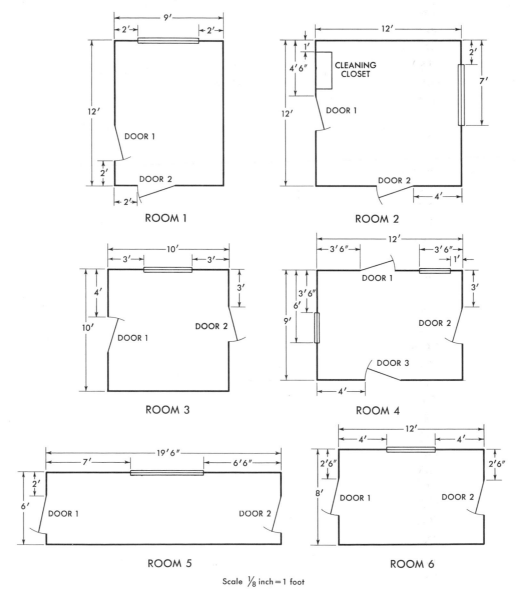

Scale ⅛ inch = 1 foot

Fig. 8–11.   Room plans.

C. Kitchen Planning Exercises

1. Verify the approximate correctness of the three sides of the work triangle shown in Figure 8–4.

2. Prepare kitchen plans to scale for the rooms sketched (Fig. 8–11). In drawing your plans use a height to top of base-cabinet counter of 36 inches. Allow 14 to 15 inches between base and wall cabinets. Use 30-inch-high wall cabinets over counters. Assume that window sills are 3 feet 6 inches from the floor and the windows themselves are 3 feet high. Assume that passageways leading to dining areas and halls are 3 feet wide and cleaning closets are 3 feet wide, 16 inches deep, and 7 feet high. Mark which door you select for the one leading to the dining area. Evaluate your plans in terms of length of sides of work triangle, counter recommendations for different centers, and base- and wall-cabinet frontages. Do not count frontage of wall cabinet over the range or over the refrigerator. Do not count frontage of any other wall cabinet whose base is more than 52 inches from the floor.

3. Modify rooms slightly and draw plans for the new rooms. For example, in room 1 decrease the 9-foot dimension to 8 feet; in room 5 increase the 6-foot dimension to 8 feet; in room 6 move a door or doors a foot or two. Also in any room select a different door for the dining area from the one used previously. Do not decrease the ratio of window area to floor area.

4. Draw a sketch to scale of your mother's kitchen, your own kitchen, or that of an understanding friend. Take an inventory of stored foods, exclusive of those in the refrigerator and freezer, utensils, accessories, small appliances, dishes, and linen stored in the kitchen. Change the original plan, on paper, to provide more convenient storage for the articles in the inventory. Indicate where they will be stored in the new plan.

   The locations of the range and the refrigerator can often be changed at moderate cost, but it may be quite expensive to move a sink or dishwasher more than 4 inches or so, due to the fact that the drains on these appliances are vented through an outside stack.

   Be prepared for unusual "finds." One student of the senior author who carried out this project at home during a Thanksgiving recess uncovered canned baby foods purchased for a brother who was then 18 years old!

CHAPTER 9

Sinks, Food Waste Disposers, and Dishwashers

The kitchen sink is one appliance always associated with kitchens and quite generally kitchens do have sinks. The food waste disposer is sometimes described as the appliance that "really changes life in the kitchen." About 6.6 percent of the wired homes in the United States had food waste disposers in 1956.[1]

An automatic dishwasher is often near the top of the list of major appliances that homemakers say they would like to have. Those operated by electricity are the usual type in the United States. About 4.6 percent of the wired homes had electric dishwashers in 1956.[1]

A. Sinks

Only people who sell sinks usually get rhapsodical about them. On the other hand, homemakers who work at a discolored sink, mounted in a counter that is cracked and peeled, are not likely to be pleased with the sink center.

Actually, good selection of a sink is important for several reasons: (1) Of all the major appliances in the home, the kitchen sink is likely to be the least frequently replaced. (2) Work at the sink is less fatiguing when its *depth* is such that the homemaker can have good posture when working there. (3) Work in the kitchen is less fatiguing when the *width* of a sink installed in a counter is appropriate for the available kitchen work area. A sink that is too wide may make the work triangle (Fig. 8–4) too large. Good selection is based partly on knowledge of types, materials, and dimensions of the sinks on the market.

9–1. TYPES OF SINKS

Counter sinks are sinks that are installed in a counter. They are sold separately or as part of plastic sink tops. The sinks may consist of single or double bowls with one or two drainboards or without a drainboard. If the sink has drainboards, bowls and drainboards are made in one piece.

Counter sinks should have an integral ledge at the rear for faucets.[2] Also, for sinks not part of a sink top, a rim should be installed that completely covers the joints between the bowls or drainboards, and the counter in which the sink is installed. Sink tops have such a rim as part of the assembly.

In modern installations, the space under a counter sink is covered with a recessed or non-recessed sink front that has two doors. This sink front is built or purchased to match the fronts of the base cabinets in the kitchen.

Cabinet sinks are bowls, with or without drainboards, that are mounted in specially made cabinets.

A *combination sink and tray* is one bowl and one laundry tray, and generally a sliding top part that may be moved so as to cover either the sink or the tray. In most models the sink is at least 8 inches deep and the tray at least 13 inches deep. Counter types and cabinet types are available. The laundry tray may be at the right or left of the sink. If dishwashing is done by hand, and if soiled dishes are placed at the right of the sink and the clean dishes at the left, the laundry tray should be at the left.[3]

A *sink-dishwasher* or *dishwasher-sink* consists of a sink and under-counter dishwasher assembled in one cabinet under a single top.

[1] *Electrical Merchandising,* Statistical and Marketing Issue, McGraw-Hill Publishing Company, January, 1957.

[2] J. T. Lendrum, *Plumbing,* Circular Series G5.0., Small Homes Council, University of Illinois, October, 1950.

[3] Merna M. Monroe, *Ideas to Consider When You Buy a Kitchen Sink,* Maine Agricultural Experiment Station Bulletin 494, October, 1951.

Some manufacturers call this appliance an electric sink dishwasher.

Except for very small sinks, the bowls of counter sinks, sink tops, and cabinet sinks usually are installed so that the front of the bowl is about 3 inches from the front of the counter. As pointed out by Monroe, a narrower distance, such as 1 or 1½ inches, would be more comfortable for many women.

9–2. DIMENSIONS

Except for special shallow models and sinks with laundry trays, most of the newer sinks have bowls 7 or 7½ inches deep. Because sink bowls are set into 36-inch high counters, women of average height are likely to prefer the 7-inch over the 7½ inch depth.

Single-bowl counter sinks are available with bowls from 12 to 32 inches wide and from 12 to 20 inches front to back. Usable interior dimensions are less than quoted sizes. Double-bowl counter sinks are available from 32 to 42 inches wide and from 16 to 20 inches front to back.

Plastic sink tops may be purchased in various widths and with sink bowls having the dimensions listed above.

The width of cabinet sinks is quoted in width of cabinet; cabinet sinks are available in 42- to 72-inch widths. Again the dimensions of the bowls are as quoted above.

Current models of sink-dishwashers are 48 inches wide.

Counter sinks of very small size, for example, 12 inches by 12 inches, are used both as extra sinks and in kitchenettes. The widest cabinet sinks, 66 inches or 72 inches, often have double bowls, double drainboards, base cabinet drawers, and cupboards.

The best size of counter sink depends partly on the dishwashing habits of the person who will use the sink most. The best size of cabinet sink depends on dishwashing habits, utility of cabinet storage space, special features provided

in the cabinet, and other factors suc[h] able space in the kitchen and fi[r] sources.

Whether a two-bowl or a one-b[owl] more desirable also depends on the[ ] a two-bowl sink, dishes can be was[hed in one] bowl and rinsed in the other. Als[o] drainer is used in the rinsing bowl, available for emptying "forgotter[ ] limitation of the two-bowl arrange[ment is that] only a rather small drainer will fit [in one of] the bowls, unless the double-bowl s[ink is a] large model.

A single-bowl sink 30 to 32 inches wide is likely to accommodate all the soiled dishes one would want to put into it at one time. If a faucet dishwasher is used, a single bowl serves for washing and rinsing; otherwise an extra rinsing pan must be provided, unless one uses a small dishpan and drainer in the single bowl.

Monroe summarizes the matter in this statement:[4] "You can hunt for a sink which allows you to continue with your present methods of washing and rinsing dishes, or you can change your methods to fit the facilities of the sink." A point that might be added is that you need to have in mind the sizes of dishpans and drainers currently on the market when you hunt for a sink.

If an automatic dishwasher is used, the kitchen sink logically can be smaller than otherwise.

9–3. MATERIALS AND CARE

The materials used for sink bowls are white or colored enameled cast iron, white or colored enameled steel, 18–8 stainless steel, and Monel metal. White enameled cast iron and white enameled steel are most usual. Monel metal is very satisfactory but is more expensive than either cast iron or enameled steel.

The finish material used on enameled sink bowls is not the same for all sinks. Some manu-

[4] *Ibid.*, p. 10.

facturers fuse two or three coats of porcelain to cast iron or steel and others apply a "vitrified enamel." When porcelain enamel is used, the final coat should be acid resistant. Vitreous ware has an acid-resistant glaze finish so a finish coat of vitrified enamel *is* acid resistant.

Correct care of a sink depends upon the materials used. Porcelain enamel and vitrified enamel will acquire scratches, chipping, and discoloration over time, if care is not taken. Probably the most practical method for maintaining the appearance of a sink for many years is to use plastic mats on the floors of the bowls and over the divider of a two-bowl sink. This minimizes scratching of the surface.

Because the finish is *acid resistant* and not *acidproof,* acidic foods should not stand in the sink for several hours; furthermore, the sink should be washed with a nonabrasive cleaner whenever acidic foods have been in the sink.

Chlorine bleaches are effective in making enameled sinks look brighter.

9–4. FITTINGS

Combination faucets with a swing spout are more convenient than single faucets and are customary for present-day installations. Preferably, this is installed in the rear ledge of the sink. Usually the combination faucet is chrome-plated brass and the body of a separate rinser spray is a plastic material.

Nonsplash metal aerators are provided with some faucets; rubber aerators that fit over the spout may be purchased in hardware stores. Both types of aerator need to be replaced occasionally.

A pull-out spray, useful for rinsing dishes and for cleaning fruits and vegetables, may be installed in the combination faucet. It may also be installed to the left or right of the combination faucet.

A new type of combination faucet has a single lever for controlling temperature of water and rate of water flow (Fig. 9–1).

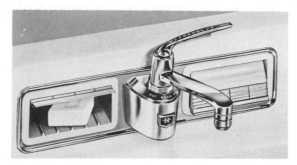

Fig. 9–1. Single-lever, swing-spout faucet. (Hotpoint Company)

Sink strainers are either a flat type without stopper or a basket type with stopper. (The basket type sometimes is called the crumb-cup type.) Better-quality strainers are made of chrome-plated brass or stainless steel.

Additional fittings needed with sinks are drains, traps, and valves. It is well to be aware of the fittings needed because costs of counter sinks and sink tops are usually quoted without fittings. Costs quoted for cabinet sinks may or may not include fittings.

9–5. FEATURES

Some of the features available on current sink models are illustrated in Figures 9–2 through 9–5. A corner installation, which appeals to many women, is shown in Figure 9–2. This may be inconvenient, however, if two people usually work near the sink at the same time.

The deluxe cabinet sinks shown in Figure 9–3 have a number of special features, as noted in the caption for the illustration. The models illustrated are 42 to 66 inches wide.

The stainless steel two- and three-bowl sinks shown in Figures 9–4 and 9–5 are rather new types. Note that the shallow "sit-down" bowl is used for cleaning vegetables, fruits, shellfish, etc. Sitting down when washing dishes by hand is somewhat less convenient, because the forearms should slant downward rather than upward when washing dishes.

Fig. 9–2. Corner installation of sink with sink front that matches cabinet fronts. (Geneva Modern Kitchens)

B. Food Waste Disposers

The food waste disposer handles a sanitary need in the kitchen and eliminates the task of carrying certain types of waste to an outside garbage can. Suburbanites who do not have garbage collection service appreciate food waste disposers even more than city people, provided the cesspool or septic tank, if used, has an adequate capacity.[5] Rural homemakers also appreciate disposers.

Current models of food waste disposers handle vegetable parings, fruit rinds, fruit pits, fibrous material such as corn husks, carrot tops and celery, eggshells, seafood shells, fats and greases, coffee grounds, bones up to chop-bone size, and other food wastes. Instead of storing these food wastes in a container for later removal from the kitchen, they are put down the drain as they occur in food preparation and after each meal. Food waste disposers are *not* designed to handle paper, tin cans, glass bottles, crockery, cloth tea bags, string, wires from milk-bottle tops, aluminum foil, or large bones.

[5] Size of septic tanks is discussed in section 9–8, pp. 126–127.

9–6. CONSTRUCTION: TYPES AND PRINCIPAL PARTS

A disposer is a motor-driven shredding device in which food wastes are cut into small particles. All models are designed to operate with cold water running through them. Besides flushing waste through the disposer into the drain line, the cold water solidifies fats and greases, so that they can be shredded and washed down the drain. Unsolidified fats would coat the inner walls and shredding mechanism of the disposer.

The top of the disposer is mounted in the sink, replacing the flange in the sink opening and the strainer. The motor is located in the metal housing in the lower half of the disposer. The shredding action takes place above a water seal that protects the motor. The drain outlet from the disposer is located just above the water seal (Figs. 9–6, 9–7, and 9–8).

a. Types

The types of disposers currently available are the continuous-feed type and the twistop or top-control type.

The continuous-feed type can be used in two ways. One is to scrape or feed waste into the disposer as it operates. The other is to add waste before the disposer is turned on. The twistop type must be loaded before it is used because the starting switch is in the top control part of the disposer. Waste is fed in and the top control is rotated into position to start operation.

When the twistop disposer is not in use, its top serves as a sink stopper as well as a strainer. Since the top of the continuous-feed type does not serve as a stopper, a separate sink stopper or plastic disk is used with it.

b. Dimensions and Capacities

Waste disposers are roughly cylindrical in shape and have overall dimensions from approximately 7½ inches wide by 11 inches long to 9½ inches wide by 17 inches long. The specifications for some models include a volume capacity or liquid-plus-waste capacity. For the longer models this capacity is about 2 quarts.

c. Shredding Mechanism

Two types of shredding mechanism are used in disposers. Both of them have a hard, corrosion-resistant, stationary cylinder called the

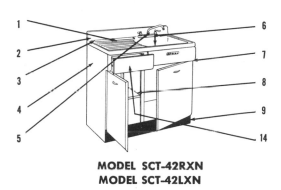

MODEL SCT-42RXN
MODEL SCT-42LXN

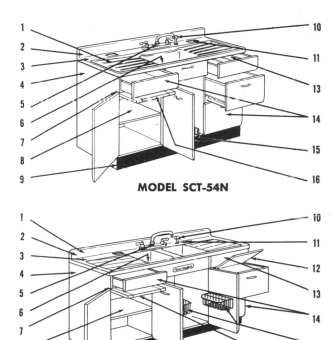

MODEL SCT-54N

MODEL SCT-54XN

MODEL SCT-66N

Fig. 9–3. Deluxe cabinet sinks. (Kelvinator Division, American Motors Corporation)

1. One-piece sink top covered with three coats of *porcelain enamel.* Final coat is acid resistant
2. Four-inch high back splash
3. Utility ledge for small articles
4. Steel frame processed for rust protection and with two coats of *baked-on* enamel
5. Mixing faucet
6. Strainer cup and stopper
7. Recessed front
8. Fixed steel shelves
9. Recessed toe space
10. Rinsing spray
11. Formed soap dishes
12. Bread and cake drawer (Accessory)
13. Cutlery drawer with dividers and linoleum-lined bottom
14. Storage drawers
15. Plated wire racks for storage of cleaning materials
16. Slide-out maple cutting board

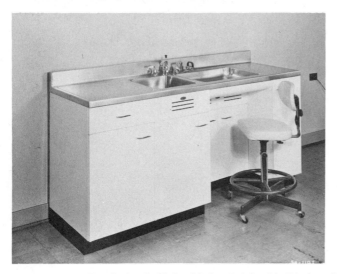

Fig. 9–4.   (Left) Double-bowl sink with "sit-down" shallow bowl. (Elkay Manufacturing Company)
Fig. 9–5.   (Right) Three-bowl, "sit-down," peninsula-type sink. (Elkay Manufacturing Company)

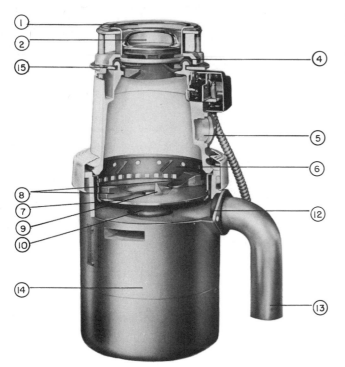

Fig. 9–6.   Cutaway drawing of a twistop-control waste disposer. (General Electric Company)
1. Stainless steel sink flange.   2. Twistop control.
4. Cushioned mounting.   5. Dishwasher drain connection.   6. Metal shredder made of jet-plane stainless steel alloy.   7. Impeller plate.   8. Impellers.
9. "Activator" for flipping bulky food waste.   10. Water seal.   12. Rubber cushion for drain line.
13. Drain outlet.   14. One-third-horsepower motor.
15. Key-hole mounting.

shredder, and both have slots on the interior of the shredder to strain the waste. The two different shredding mechanisms are illustrated in Figures 9–6 and 9–8. The model shown in Figure 9–6 has fixed knife blades or shredding knives mounted on the interior of the shredder and an impeller plate keyed directly to the motor shaft. Two impellers (pushing parts) are located at the ends of a diameter of the impeller plate. When the motor is turned on, the motor shaft and attached impeller plate rotate and the impellers push or whirl the food waste against the shredding knives. The shredded waste falls below the impeller plate and the cold water carries it down the drain outlet. (Other models that use this mechanism have drain holes in the impeller plate for the waste. There are still other models on the market that have impelling surfaces on the underside of the plate to aid in pushing the waste into the drain.)

The model illustrated in Figure 9–8 uses rotating knife blades instead of rotating impellers.

d. Electrical Characteristics of the Motor

The motor of current disposer models is usually a ⅓ horsepower capacitor type de-

Fig. 9–7. Front view of continuous feed disposer with rotating blades. (Waste King Corporation)

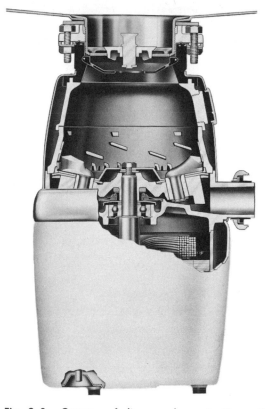

Fig. 9–8. Cutaway of disposer shown in Figure 9–7. (Waste King Corporation)

signed for use with 110- to 120-volt, 60-cycle alternating current. The motor is sometimes described as water-cooled, and it is—but the manufacturers may have tongue in cheek when they put this description into the specifications.

Most models have a thermal overload protective device built in. If provided, the reset device that starts the motor again, after the cause of a stoppage has been corrected, is commonly a button that is pushed by the user. At least one deluxe model, however, has an automatic reset mechanism.

9–7. CONTROLS

Besides the disposer reset mechanism, an "on-off" switch is provided, which may be installed in a wall or may be part of the twistop. One deluxe model features an automatic reversing switch. Each time the twistop is turned to the "on" position, the direction of the motor is reversed. The advantage of this feature is that both sides of the knife blades can be used regularly.

A flow interlock control is a very desirable accessory for a disposer. This is a combination water valve and electric switch. The water valve is in the cold water supply, and when cold water flows through it at a correct rate a plunger is lifted, which causes the electric switch to close. The flow interlock switch is series-connected with the disposer "on-off" switch. Installation of this switch in the circuit thus insures that the disposer will operate only when cold water is flowing at a correct rate. (The correct rate is a rate above a minimum value. See section 9–9, p. 127.)

The disposer in the patients' kitchen of the Minnesota University Hospitals' new Rehabilitation Center has a single switch for motor *and* water.

9–8. INSTALLATION

Local electrical and plumbing codes should be followed when installing a disposer. For the electrical part, manufacturers recommend an individual-equipment circuit fused with a 15-ampere fuse for a disposer, or an individual equipment circuit·fused with a 20-ampere fuse for a disposer and electric dishwasher.

Manufacturers' specific recommendations on plumbing vary according to whether the disposer is to be used with a one-bowl sink, one bowl of a two-bowl sink, or a combination sink and dishwasher. In all cases, if the local plumbing code permits, any grease trap in the kitchen sink waste line should be removed before installing the disposer.

In general, a P trap or a double trap is used on the outlet side of the disposer if the outlet drain goes into a wall, and an S trap if it goes into the floor. (Fig. 9–9). (A special trap is sometimes required by a community or a state.) A trap with special fittings that lengthen the S is often suggested to serve for the disposer and the drain of the second bowl of a two-bowl sink.

Separate drains and traps may be used for the disposer and the dishwasher. A less expensive installation is to have the dishwasher drain through the disposer; current models of disposers have a drain connection for a dishwasher (Figs. 9–6, 9–7, and 9–8). If this type of installation is used, an air-gap assembly or antisiphon assembly should be included in the drain line between dishwasher and disposer to prevent possible back siphonage of waste water into the dishwasher. The disposer *must be empty* when the dishwasher is in operation; otherwise waste in the disposer may interfere with rapid flow of water from the dishwasher.

Besides the plumbing installation at the sink, some consideration must be given to the ultimate disposal of the waste. Some cities do not permit connection of food waste disposers to the city sewerage system. A prospective purchaser of a disposer should of course check on this before purchase. A septic tank can be used if its capacity is adequate.

Recommendations on size of septic tank can often be obtained from the State Health Department or from the State Extension Serv-

Fig. 9–9. Representative plumbing installations for a food waste disposer. (General Electric Company)

ice. A 500- or 600-gallon tank is often suggested for new homes. Actually, the size needed depends on the number of persons in the household and on factors associated with some of the water-bearing equipment, such as number of bathtubs, showers, and toilets and provision for disposal of backwash water and brine effluent from mechanical water softeners, as well as disposal of liquid waste from food waste disposers.

Several manufacturers of food waste disposers note in their literature that the appliance may be installed in houses that use cesspools. *But,* installation of a food waste disposer will cause a cesspool to fill faster than would otherwise be the case.

9–9. USE

For a single load in the disposer, drop or scrape waste into the hopper, turn on the cold water, and turn on the switch. A grinding sound indicates that waste is being shredded. When the grinding sound ceases, wait a few seconds, turn off the switch, and turn off the cold water.

For continuous feed, turn on the cold water, turn on the switch, and drop or scrape waste into the hopper. Scrape waste directly into the unit while it is operating. When the waste is ground, turn off the switch and turn off the cold water.

The rate at which cold water should flow varies for different models; 2 gallons per minute or approximately 1 quart in eight seconds is typical, but some models use more. If a flow interlock is part of the installation, the disposer will not start until water is flowing at the lowest required rate.

Do not stuff or pack waste tightly into the hopper. In addition, if the manufacturer's booklet so specifies, cut fibrous waste such as carrot tops into short lengths. A full load of waste may be disposed of in five to thirty seconds; harder materials take longer. If convenient to do so, mix soft waste with hard.

Under normal use conditions, disposers require no regular attention. *No* drain-cleaning chemicals should ever be used, because the corrosive action of drain cleaners might damage the interior of the disposer. To clean the appliance, fill the sink with cold water and, with the cold water running, operate the disposer until the sink is empty.

An obstruction may cause a disposer to jam or stall. *Know* the recommendation of the manufacturer for correct procedure in case the disposer jams. In general, if the disposer jams due to an obstruction such as a fork or a paring knife, reach first for the cold water faucet and next for the switch. *Then* reach into the disposer for the fork or knife. In other words, protect your hands first by having the disposer positively off before you retrieve the fork or knife.

C. Dishwashers

Faucet dishwashers and electric dishwashers are available. Electric dishwashers are major appliances used to wash cooking utensils and a complete service of glasses, dishes, and silver for six or more persons at one time. Faucet dishwashers, on the other hand, are fixtures or small appliances used in the sink to wash dishes, utensils, and other items individually.

9–10. INSTALLATION AND USE OF FAUCET DISHWASHERS

In 1957 different models of faucet dishwashers cost $8.00 to $50.00. The lower-priced models are either connected to the sink spout each time the device is to be used or installed permanently in the sink ledge in place of a rinser-spray. The more expensive models usually are part of a swing-spout, mixer-faucet assembly sold as a complete unit, with instructions for installation by the homeowner. (Some homeowners will want to obtain skilled help in making the installation.)

One type of combination spout-and-faucet dishwasher is illustrated in Figure 9–10. To

Fig. 9–10. Combination spout and faucet dishwasher. (Adrian Division, Hoover Ball and Bearing Company)

use it the black plastic cover at the top is taken off; then a teaspoon of liquid, synthetic detergent (syndet) is added to the metal cylinder, the cylinder is filled with cold water, and the cover is replaced.[6] The hot and cold water

[6] Mild syndets are used with faucet dishwashers (see p. 247). Sudless dishwashing compounds, especially formulated for electric dishwashers, are recommended by manufacturers for electric dishwashers.

faucets are turned on until the water that comes through the spout is at the temperature to be used for dishwashing.

The plastic brush handle is grasped and the *diverter* control knob under the spout pulled out, causing the water to flow through the dishwasher instead of the spout. Pressing the white button on the handle causes sudsy water to flow.

A right-handed person holds the article to be washed in the left hand and washes the article with the dishwasher held in the right hand. When the washing and rinsing are done, the diverter button is pushed in and the faucets turned off.

A nylon brush is provided for glassware, china, and silver, and a brass wire brush for pots and pans.

The faucet dishwasher has some definite advantages over conventional hand dishwashing. Clean water is used for each article, and it can be at a higher temperature than that in a dishpan. If the faucet dishwasher is permanently installed, it is available and convenient to use for a few or many articles. When a food waste disposer and faucet dishwasher are both installed in a sink, rinse-scraping, washing, and rinsing of dishes can be a single, continuous operation.

9–11. TYPES AND CONSTRUCTION CHARACTERISTICS OF ELECTRIC DISHWASHERS

Electric dishwashers operate rather simply. Hot water containing a dishwashing compound cascades at high velocity over the stationary dishes and other items. After the wash part of the cycle, the water and the soil from the dishes drain or are pumped out of the appliance and the dishes are rinsed with clear water. Most present-day models also have a heating element to dry the washed load. This drying part of the cycle can be used, too, for warming dishes on which food is to be served.

The dishwasher can be used for all tableware that can withstand high temperature. Fine china, hand-painted dishes, wooden articles, and some plastic tableware should not be either washed or warmed in electric dishwashers.

a. Types and Dimensions

Cabinet dishwashers and low and counter-height mobile dishwashers as well as sink-dishwashers are available. Some of the models are the top-loading type; others are front loading.

Under-counter models are usually installed under a continuous counter top that covers one or more base cabinets as well as the dishwasher. Free-standing models, as the name implies, are complete units with individual top. Usually they are installed near the sink as one unit in the base cabinet assembly of the sink center.

Mobile dishwashers are stored in any convenient location and moved to a hot water faucet for use. Generally they are used near a

sink because hot water is available at the sink and the sink bowl serves as the sump for draining the dishwasher. Sink-dishwashers, as indicated earlier, are combination units with a single counter top for sink and dishwasher.

An under-counter, top-loading model is illustrated in Figure 9–11, a mobile, top-loading model in Figure 9–12, and an under-counter, front-opening model in Figure 9–13. In front-loading models, the lower rack is usually rolled onto the dropped door for loading and then rolled back into the tank for the

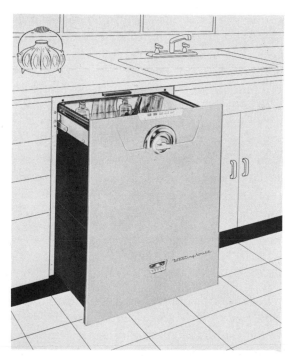

Fig. 9–11. Top-opening, under-counter electric dishwasher. (Courtesy Westinghouse Electric Corporation)

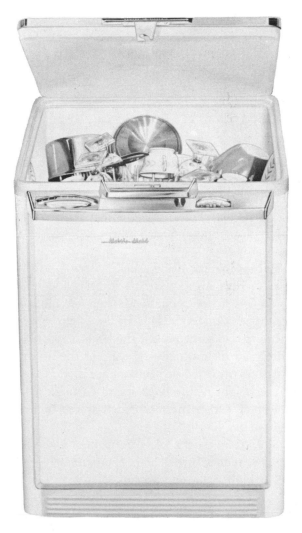

Fig. 9–12. Mobile dishwasher with top-opening lid. (General Electric Company)

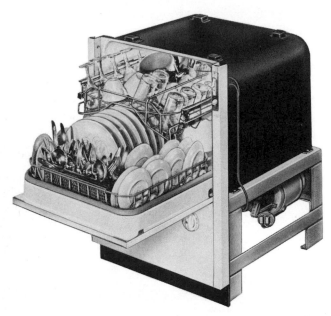

Fig. 9–13. Front-opening, under-counter dishwasher. (KitchenAid Home Dishwasher Division, The Hobart Manufacturing Company)

dishwashing cycle. Experimental work at the State College of Washington indicates no decided advantage of one type over the other. "However, the front-opening required fewer body motions for loading and unloading, while the top-opening required fewer arm motions for loading."[7]

Except for sink-dishwashers, currently available models are 24 or 30 inches wide and about 24 inches deep. Under-counter models are approximately 34½ inches high. Free-standing and some mobile models are approximately 36 inches high, exclusive of the height of casters provided on some mobile models and of the height of the back splash on models so equipped. Other mobile models are 33 inches high.

Sink-dishwashers of current manufacture are 48 inches wide and approximately 36 inches high, exclusive of back splash.

[7] Anna L. Wood, Shirley Ribelin, and Fay Lange, *Location and Counter Area Requirements of a Mechanical Dishwasher,* Washington Agricultural Experiment Stations, Bulletin No. 526, June, 1951.

b. Construction Characteristics

Gravity-drain and pump-drain units are available in dishwashers. Apart from the drain provision, the different models made by any one manufacturer usually have similar interior construction features and operating components. Models made by different manufacturers differ in the mechanisms used for recirculating water at high velocity. The construction characteristics of one under-counter model are described below.

Under-counter models are sold without counter top and side panels. The one shown in Figure 9–13 is 24 inches wide. The tank is supported in a steel frame and its interior finish is porcelain enamel. The center part of the tank bottom is depressed to form a sump. This sump is filled with approximately 2⅓ gallons of water, before the wash part of the cycle and before each of the two rinses. After the wash and after each rinse, the water drains through the sump.

The racks for dishes, utensils, silverware, etc., are coated with a plastic material for protection during loading and unloading. The racks glide in and out separately. In addition, the upper rack may be raised or lowered to accommodate a combination load of tableware, utensils, tall stemware, and large bowls.

The standard finish for the front panel is white baked-on enamel. Colored enamel, satin-finish stainless steel, and antique copper are available for the model shown. Some manufacturers provide a porcelain finish on the front panel.

9–12. OPERATING COMPONENTS OF ELECTRIC DISHWASHERS

The principal operating components of a dishwasher which are of interest to the user are the wash mechanism, strainer system, provision for draining, provision for electric drying, and the timer.

a. Wash Mechanisms

The high velocity of the recirculated water is obtained in different models by a revolving wash arm, a revolving spray tube, or an impeller. A revolving wash arm located just above the sump is used in the dishwasher shown in Figure 9–13. After the sump has filled with the correct amount of water, a centrifugal pump integral with the motor starts, forcing water through six jet openings in the arm (Fig. 9–14). The openings at the end of the arm are set at such an angle that as the water leaves them the arm is caused to revolve at approximately 60 revolutions per minute. The other four openings are set so that the fan-shaped jets of water from them overlap to form a spinning wall of water. Forty-five gallons of water are recirculated per minute.

A revolving water spray tube mounted near the top of the tank is shown in Figures 9–15 and 9–16. As for the wash arm, when the sump is filled, a pump motor starts and water is pumped to the spray tube. The water swirling through the tube causes it to rotate at approximately 500 revolutions per minute, and a rotating spray of water issues from the holes in it. As the spray of water strikes the cup containing the dishwashing compound, some of the compound is picked up. The wash water with dishwashing compound is recirculated by the pump during the entire wash period.

An impeller with two sets of blades, centered in the bottom of the tank, is shown in Figure 9–17. During the wash and rinse periods, the motor and impeller rotate at 1725 revolutions per minute. One set of impeller blades is designed specifically to pick up water from the bottom of the tank and force it to cascade up, around, and over the items being washed. The other set of blades is designed for forced air circulation during the drying period.

b. Strainer System

A strainer is provided in dishwashers to prevent recirculation of food particles in the wash and rinse waters. For the dishwasher shown in Figure 9–17 this is a screen mounted around the bottom of the impeller. Other types of strainers are used by other manufacturers.

c. Drain Provision

Forced draining by a separate drain pump and gravity draining are provided on different models. One might think that a valve that opened and closed at correct times during the cycle would be the simplest possible provision for draining. And, in fact, a valve is generally used. One manufacturer, however, provides an even simpler mechanical arrangement—a special, slotted drain ring mounted permanently around the lower portion of the impeller. When the impeller is rotating, this ring and the impeller itself throw water back into the tank, and no water drains out of the dishwasher. When the impeller stops rotating, the water is not thrown back, but drains out. Thus draining is accomplished without a valve.

d. Heating Element

The dishwashers shown in Figures 9–15 and 9–17 have a ring-shaped, metal-sheathed heating element in the sump. This element is on during the wash, rinse, and dry periods for these dishwashers.

During the wash and rinse periods, the heat given off by the heating element helps maintain a high temperature of the water and the articles being washed. During the dry period, it dries the articles. In some models, the impeller acts as a fan for forced circulation of the heated air; in others, vents at the bottom and top of the door permit natural circulation of the hot air. Still others have a separately powered blower and heating element mounted

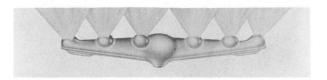

Fig. 9–14. Fan-shaped jets of water from revolving wash arm. (KitchenAid Home Dishwasher Division, The Hobart Manufacturing Company)

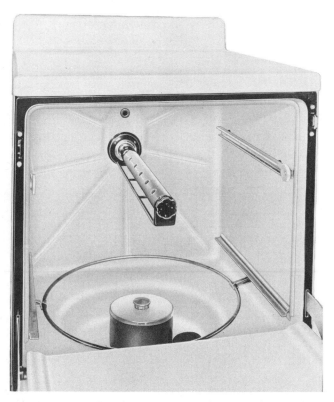

Fig. 9–15. Revolving water spray tube. (Frigidaire Division, General Motors Corporation)

Fig. 9–16. Water spray from tube shown in Figure 9–15. (Frigidaire Division, General Motors Corporation)

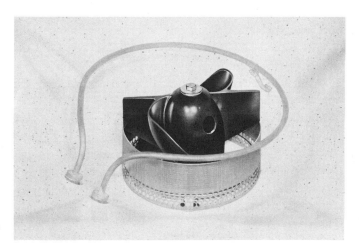

Fig. 9–17. Impeller, strainer, and Calrod unit. (Hotpoint Company)

outside the tank. The blower forces hot air into the tank only during the drying period.

e. Timer Mechanism

An automatic electric timer mechanism is now commonly supplied to control the wash, rinse, and dry parts of the cycle. For some models, the user turns the timer dial to "on" to start the dishwashing cycle; for others a start switch is depressed. If a separate start switch is provided in addition to the timer dial, the user operates the dial manually *only* to stop operation during the cycle—in order to add a forgotten article, for example—or to turn the dial to the dry setting when dinnerware is to be heated in the dishwasher.

9–13. TIME FOR COMPLETE CYCLE AND AMOUNT OF WATER USED

Different models vary, of course, in the time required for the complete cycle, cycling characteristics, and amount of water used per cycle. Specific information on a particular model is given in the user's booklet and on specification sheets. Characteristics of dishwashers of three manufacturers are listed below.

The dishwasher shown in Figure 9–13 has one 5-minute wash and two 1-minute rinses. Filling, washing, draining, and rinsing are complete after 11½ minutes. The drying time is 23½ minutes. The time for the complete cycle thus is 35 minutes. A total of 7 gallons of hot water is used.

The dishwasher shown in Figure 9–15 has a preflush to drain cool water from the pipe and flush residue off the dishes, a regular wash, two rinses, and a dry period. The time for filling, washing, draining, and rinsing is approximately 21 minutes. The drying time is 24 minutes. The time for the total cycle is about 55 minutes. The water consumption for the complete cycle may vary a little, according to the amount of water used in the preflush. The user's booklet states that the cycle requires less than 10 gallons of water.

The dishwasher shown in Figure 9–17 has an overhead spray, two 5-minute washes, two 1-minute rinses, and a 30-minute dry period. Total time for the cycle is actually about 50 minutes.

9–14. INSTALLATION, USE, AND CARE OF ELECTRIC DISHWASHERS

Safe, convenient, and effective use of a dishwasher requires appropriate water supply, proper drainage, correct electric circuit connections, convenient placement of the appliance, and use of the dishwasher according to the manufacturer's recommendations. For satisfactory operation, the hot water system in the house must deliver water to the dishwasher at a temperature of about 140 F to 150 F. The water pressure should not be less than 10 to 20 pounds per square inch. (The minimum water pressure required varies for different models.) Furthermore, the water should preferably be soft or at least not very hard, and should not contain an appreciable amount of iron (see Chapter 18, p. 246).

a. Installation

Planning pays. A permanent type of installation in older houses can cost almost half as much as the dishwasher. In houses where plumbing was planned for future installation of an electric dishwasher, and in new houses, the installation costs may be as little as one-eighth the cost of the dishwasher.

The Washington State study cited earlier reported that one location of the dishwasher was not entirely better than another, but locating the dishwasher to the left of the sink had some advantage in reducing arm motions and steps.[8] However, the Cornell sink center shown in Figure 8–7 has the dishwasher at the right of the sink.

[8] *Ibid.,* p. 13.

Local plumbing and electrical codes must of course be followed. Some manufacturers provide air-gap assemblies as accessories for areas in which local plumbing codes require an air gap in the inlet hot water line, in the drain line, or in both lines. When no local code is imposed, the recommendations of the manufacturer should be followed. Usually a separate turn-off valve is suggested for the hot water line to the dishwasher. The correct type of drain from the dishwasher depends partly on the drainage system of the dishwasher itself.

The National Electrical Code requires a 15-ampere, individual-equipment circuit for the dishwasher, a 20-ampere branch circuit for the dishwasher and a limited number of small appliances, or, as stated in the section on food waste disposers, a 20-ampere circuit for a dishwasher and a food waste disposer.

Dishwashers are now provided with a new type of three-pronged plug designed for installation in a three-wire, grounded, 115-volt circuit (see p. 7). Two of the prongs carry current and the third, which is U-shaped or round, is designed to make contact with the ground wiring *before* the two current-carrying prongs make contact with the current supply wires. Only the newest houses are likely to have special three-wire, 115-volt circuits for the kitchen, but special adapters are available for receptacles or outlets of conventional two-wire, 115-volt circuits. The receptacle itself must be grounded.

b. Use and Care

Specific recommendations as given in the user's booklet should be followed. A few general recommendations are summarized below.

1. Hard, burned-on, and excess food usually should be removed from pots and pans before placing them in the dishwasher. One manufacturer's booklet, however, suggests that if pans are washed in the dishwasher first, burned-on food will be softened so that subsequent washing by hand will be easy.

2. Empty liquid from glasses, cups, and miscellaneous containers. Scrape or rinse dishes free of waste such as bones, large scraps of meat, starchy foods, and cigarette or cigar ashes. (If one thinks a moment it seems unlikely that re-circulation of cigarette ashes in the wash water could contribute to the cleanliness of the load.)

3. Load the dishwasher so the articles to be washed get the best exposure to the washing mechanism. Method of loading is so important that it is usually spelled out in detail in the booklet.

4. Use the dishwashing compounds recommended by the manufacturer. Some manufacturers indicate explicitly that unless the recommended dishwashing compounds are used, the dishwashing results will not be satisfactory. However, several compounds are usually recommended, and since water varies in different areas, it is worth while trying several to determine which is best for the local water supply. If the water is very hard, some dried articles will show water-spotting. (At least one manufacturer has a device that automatically adds a wetting agent to the last rinse as an aid for avoiding water spotting.)

5. Wait several minutes after the end of the cycle before trying to remove dishes from the appliance. They are hot! If you are in a hurry, open the door at the end of the cycle and the load will cool faster.

6. Some users store the washed dishes in the dishwasher between uses of the appliance. Small families, on the other hand, find it convenient and more economical to scrape and store soiled dishes in the dishwasher as they accumulate and operate the dishwasher only once a day. If this procedure is followed, prerinsing of soiled dishes is likely to be helpful.

7. Clean the strainer with a brush and sudsy water as necessary. Also clean the container for the dishwashing compound as necessary. Occasionally wipe the interior of the tank to remove any film that may have collected. Maintenance of the exterior surfaces depends on the finish provided. Follow instructions in the manufacturer's manual.

D. Experiment and Field Study

Experiment 1. *Height of Working Surface and Depth of Sink Bowl for Convenient Dishwashing.*[9]

A. Work surface height that permits you to stand approximately straight with arms slanting somewhat naturally from the chest
1. Fill a pan that is approximately 6 inches deep two-thirds full of water. (The hydrators of some refrigerators are 6 inches deep.)
2. Place pan on a working surface approximately 27 inches high with the front of the pan about 2½ inches from the front of the working surface. Wash two or three dishes with a dishmop.
3. Carry out step 2 on a working surface 28 inches high.[10]
4. Carry out step 2 on a working surface 29 inches high.
5. Carry out step 2 on a working surface 30 inches high and/or one 31 inches high.
6. Which height permits you to stand approximately straight with arms slanting somewhat naturally from your chest?

B. Depth of pan or bowl for your dishwashing habits
1. Use the work-surface height you found most convenient in Part A and a pan 6 inches deep. Fill the pan two-thirds full with warm or hot water. (*Warm* water is used with a cold hydrator.) Add a sudsing-type syndet. Place several dishes and a few odd pieces such as cream pitchers in the pan. Wash the dishes and the odd pieces.
2. Can you wash dishes conveniently in a pan that is only 6 inches deep without sloshing water or suds on the floor?
3. What depth of pan would you estimate as most desirable for your dishwashing habits?

Field Study of Electric and Faucet Dishwashers

A. Electric dishwasher
   If practical to do so, observe a homemaker use her dishwasher and chat with her about the appliance.
1. How frequently (times per day) does she use it?
2. What preliminary work—scraping and/or rinsing, for example—does she do before placing dishes in the dishwasher?
3. Does she wash all her soiled dishes, glasses, pots and pans, including broiler pan, in it?

---

[9] This experiment is modified from Monroe's study, *op. cit.*
[10] Some typewriter stands are about 27¼ inches high. A 28-inch high surface can therefore be obtained with a typewriter stand and a ¾-inch board. Some tables, some pull-out lapboards, and many old and new desks are 29 inches high. Some modern kitchen carts are 30 inches high and some are 31 inches high.

4. Which articles, if any, does she regularly do by hand? Why does she do them by hand?
5. Is the water supply soft or hard?
6. Does she know at what temperature water is delivered to the dishwasher?
7. Is she on the whole pleased that she owns a dishwasher?
8. Summarize briefly your personal observations on how the dishwasher is used.

B. Faucet dishwasher

If practical, observe a homemaker use her faucet dishwasher. Chat with her about it and get the answers to Questions 1 through 7 above. In addition, summarize briefly your personal observations on how the faucet dishwasher is used.

CHAPTER 10

Gas Ranges

A. Construction, Use, and Care

10–1. TYPES

The gas range is available in many different types, each of which may be varied within its group by special features. All should carry the seal of approval of the American Gas Association. The standard type may vary in width from 36 to 42 inches; it has an oven and broiler heated by the same burner, and four surface burners; it may or may not have some of the special features found on the more deluxe ranges.

The apartment-size range varies from 19 to 26 inches in width. It also has an oven and broiler heated by the same burner, and four surface burners (Fig. 10–1). Its chief advantage is that it requires less space and is less expensive than standard-size ranges; in fact, if it is purchased without any special features it may be quite inexpensive.

The 30-inch range may not be exactly 30 inches in width. The oven width is not 30 inches, but this range usually has an extra-large oven (Fig. 10–2). Some models of this size are equipped with many special features while others are stripped down.

Most deluxe models are "CP" ranges. These letters within a circular seal signify that the range has met not only the American Gas Association standards but also other standards of convenience, performance, and economy (Figs. 10–3 and 10–4). A *Gold Star* label was introduced in 1959. Gas ranges with this label meet AGA standards, certain basic specifications and two out of five optional specifications.

Fig. 10–1. Apartment range. (The Tappan Stove Company)

Fig. 10–2. Deluxe 30-inch range with rotisserie. (The Tappan Stove Company)

Fig. 10–3. The CP seal. (Gas Appliance Manufacturers Association, Inc.)

Fig. 10–4. Forty-inch CP range. (Geo. D. Roper Corporaton)

a. Domestic Gas Ranges

The American Gas Association defines a domestic gas range as a self-contained, gas-burning appliance designed for domestic cooking purposes and having a top section and an oven section. It may have a broiling section.[1] Some gas ranges designed for cooking also have a section used for space heating or for use with another fuel. This chapter considers only ranges designed solely for cooking. Because many ranges do have a broiling section this will be considered in detail, as well as ovens and surface burners.

b. Built-In Domestic Cooking Units

The latest additions to consumers' choices are built-in surface burners and oven (Figs. 10-5, 10-6). These provide different possibilities in kitchen arrangements. Built-in gas cooking appliances for the home are known as *units*. The top or surface unit may include burners, griddle, and deep-well cooker or any combination of the three. The oven unit is designed for installation in a wall cabinet, a partition, or on a counter. It may be a separate oven, it may have a broiler below, or it may have a broiler in the oven itself. The broiler unit may be a separate broiler, it may be combined with a rotisserie, or it may be a rotisserie unit. The American Gas Association defines any combination of oven, broiler, or rotisserie as a unit.

10–2. CONSTRUCTION

Desirable features of construction and standards of performance for gas ranges presented in this chapter have been adapted in part from material of the American Gas Association's *Approval Requirements for Domestic Gas Ranges.*[2]

[1] *Approval Requirements for Domestic Gas Ranges,* American Gas Association, Inc., vol. I, 1957, p. 73.
[2] *Ibid.,* vols. I, II.

Fig. 10–5.   Built-in surface burner unit. (Geo. D. Roper Corporation)

Fig. 10–6.   Built-in oven unit. (Geo. D. Roper Corporation)

a. Frame and Exterior

The frame of the range is made of steel or iron, welded, riveted, or held together by screws. While the frame is very important to the life of the range, it is difficult for the homemaker to check it when buying a range. Here she must depend upon a reliable manufacturer and dealer and upon the requirements set up by the American Gas Association. The presence of the American Gas Association seal is assurance for the homemaker that the range will give safe and efficient performance and that it is of substantial and durable construction (Fig. 10–7).

Fig. 10–7. American Gas Association seal of approval. (American Gas Association, Inc.)

Panels of sheet steel or sheet iron attached to the frame give the range the shape commonly attributed to a conventional range. If these panels have been Bonderized or otherwise given a rust-resistant treatment before the application of enamel coatings, they will be rust resistant. If synthetic enamel is used to coat the panels, they will be resistant to chipping and somewhat lighter in weight than if porcelain enamel is used. However, synthetic enamel will scratch more easily, is less stain resistant, and is undesirable for oven linings and the top surface of the range. By studying specification sheets the prospective buyer can determine the kind of finish used on the range.

Range exteriors come in many colors and finishes. Enamel is still the most popular finish and can be found in almost any color of the rainbow, although each manufacturer generally limits color choice to a few colors. Metallic finishes are also popular. They do not tarnish but sometimes require a little more care than porcelain enamel. Some metallic finishes may look a little water-spotted when wiped with a damp cloth and will need to be wiped with a dry cloth to polish. The latter step is not so necessary with enamel finishes. Some thought should be given to color choice, since a kitchen could become a confusing array of colors that neither blend, match, nor complement each other.

For comfort and economy a range should be insulated. According to American Gas Association standards the insulation must be enclosed and protected from objectionable exposure to air and flue gases and applied so as to produce and maintain uniformity of insulation. The material used for insulation is usually rock wool or Fiberglas.

b. Main Functional Parts

Surface burners may be arranged in a number of ways. In the cluster arrangement four burners are grouped at one end of the range top, leaving work space on the opposite end, or are located in the center, leaving a smaller work space at each end. The divided arrangement has two burners on either end and work space in the center. Burners may also be placed along the rear of the work surface, leaving counter space at the front. Another arrangement is a staggered one with two burners at the back of the work surface and two at the front. Choice of burner arrangement is determined largely by individual preference. If several large utensils are used at one time, a divided or staggered arrangement might be preferred, as it allows room for utensils to extend beyond the burners without touching one another. The cluster arrangement gives a larger work space. It is somewhat easier for a tall woman to work at a range with burners at the back than for a short woman for whom it is difficult to reach as far.

On the apartment-size range it may be somewhat difficult to make sure that handles of utensils do not extend beyond the work surface and thereby constitute a safety hazard. It is also a little more difficult to use extra-large utensils on the apartment-size range because the burners are sometimes quite close together.

Surface burners are of three main sizes. Specifications for the minimum gas input for regular, giant, and simmer burners have been set up by the American Gas Association. The gas input rating is measured in British thermal units (Btu's) per hour. The regular surface burner has a minimum input of not less than 9000 Btu's per hour, the giant burner 12,000 Btu's, and the simmer burner 1200 Btu's. Several manufacturers have added either additional settings or different-size burners to their line of ranges. A keep-warm setting which is lower than the simmer heat is now widely used on deluxe ranges. CP ranges must have at least one giant burner.

Burners are usually equipped with a burner bowl or aeration plate which surrounds the burner head. The bowl is made of porcelain-enameled steel, aluminum, or stainless steel.

It serves to control the amount of secondary air around the burner, reflect heat, and catch spillovers. If it is very shallow, it is not efficient for the latter purpose. It is highly desirable that a burner tray also be a part of the standard equipment on a range. If the range does not have aeration plates or burner bowls, it must have a burner tray, and this should be large enough to catch a major spillover. Burner trays should be rust resistant and have no edges that are hard to clean or sharp since they might cut the user.

Burners should be so constructed that they can be easily removed for cleaning purposes. At the same time it must be impossible to put them back in the wrong place, and they should fit into the right place easily.

When the gas valve is turned on, gas from the manifold flows into the mixer tube. At the same time air enters the mixing tube through the primary air inlet. Thus gas and air are mixed first in the mixing tube. When the mixture reaches the ports in the head of the burner, the gas is ignited, either manually or by a pilot light (Fig. 10–8). Air surrounding the burner head also mixes with the gas and, when the total air-gas mixture is correct, a pretty blue flame with a deeper blue inner cone results. If there is too much air in the air-gas

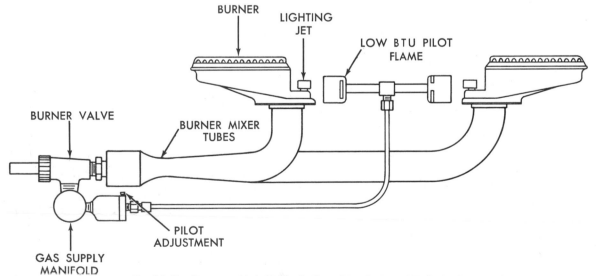

Fig. 10–8. Burners with individual pilots. (Lincoln Brass Works Inc.)

mixture, the flame will tend to dance and not "sit" on the burner. If there is too little air, the flame will be yellow and carbon will be deposited on utensils used on the burner. The air adjustment on most ranges is relatively easy to make but requires patience. It is necessary to put the burner bowl and grate into position in order to check the burner flame properly. However, if the amount of gas coming into the burner needs adjustment a service man should be called.

Grates for gas range burners are made from cast iron or stainless steel. Cast iron grates are usually covered with porcelain enamel which makes them more attractive, easier to keep clean, and rust resistant. Cast iron will break if dropped at just the right angle, but otherwise will last indefinitely. Stainless steel grates will not break but they do change appearance with use. When new they are bright and shiny, but heat causes them to darken, and this darkening cannot be removed. They do not rust. American Gas Association standards require that grates must be so designed that they cannot be firmly placed in any but the proper position or if placed improperly that combustion shall not be impaired. The grate arms must support a utensil as small as $2\frac{1}{4}$ inches in diameter placed centrally over the burner. Grates must also be designed so that they do not rock or shift laterally more than $\frac{1}{8}$ inch.

Ovens vary in size. A standard size averages approximately 20 inches wide, 16 inches deep, and 16 inches high. Ovens are usually finished in porcelain enamel, though chromium-finished ovens are also popular. The porcelain enamel may be white, though it is commonly gray or blue or gray or blue speckled with white. Darker enamels show soil less, but all ovens need to be cleaned quite often if they are given a reasonable amount of use. Vapors and greases from food deposit on the oven linings and they are easier to clean if cleaned often. To meet American Gas Association requirements, oven linings must have a rust-resistant finish.

The oven bottom should be easily removed and also easily replaced. The shelves in ovens should be nontipping when pulled part way out and should be so designed that they cannot be pulled all the way out accidentally. Oven shelves or racks are designed to be pulled part of the way out and then catch with a stop-lock. They should remain level at this point. The shelf should also have a back rail which indicates to the user that the back of the shelf has been reached and prevents foods from being pushed off the back. Oven racks should be made of rust-resistant material.

Shelf supports are easier to clean if they are somewhat rounded and not too close together. Several rack positions are convenient. However, it is highly unlikely that a user will adjust racks in too many different positions, and too many rack supports make the oven difficult to keep clean.

A glass window in the oven door is a convenience, especially for people who just have to peek. Standard oven temperatures and baking times can be thrown distinctly awry by opening the oven door too much during baking. The glass in the window should be especially well installed so that vapors cannot collect between the layers of glass.

The vent or flue outlet is the opening provided for the escape of the products of combustion, excess air, and vapors from cooking foods. The vent has an opening in the oven and on the back splash. Modern ranges are usually vented on the front of the back splash. This allows the range to be placed flush against the wall without the wall becoming discolored. It is important that the vent openings in conventional ranges never be closed if the oven burner is to operate as it should and foods are to bake properly. Many new kitchens have hoods with fans to remove the vented vapors.

In retained-heat ovens the vent closes when the heat is turned off. These ovens also have extra-heavy insulation so that heat does not escape from them as readily as from ovens not designed for use of retained heat. The amount of time the heat is on and the temperature at which the thermostat is set are determined by the type and amount of food to be cooked. Manufacturers' directions should be followed.

Broilers are becoming more and more important as popular methods of food preparation change. Broiling is cooking by direct heat, with food placed beneath the flame. The temperature is adjusted by the height of the flame and the distance food is placed from it.

Broilers are described as low or waist high. Low broilers are placed beneath the oven and are heated by the same burner that heats the oven. They must have at least a 3½-inch height for adjusting the broiler pan from the bottom of the flame and three shelf positions.

The waist-high broiler is usually located adjacent to and at the same height as the oven. It requires less bending or stooping. It has a much greater distance for possible adjustments of broiler pan from the flame.

Waist-high broilers may also be located in the oven, in which case they must be so designed that it is impossible to use the oven burner and the broiler burner at the same time. Waist-high broilers do make possible more flexible pan arrangements than can be obtained with the low broiler and are somewhat more convenient to use.

The broiler pan is usually made of enameled steel or sheet aluminum. Preferably it is 1½ to 3 inches deep and fitted with a grid. The deeper pans allow fat and juices from the food to drip away from the intense heat of the flame. These pans may also serve as roasting pans.

The grid should have enough slits or openings in it to allow the fats and juices to drip through easily but not so much open space that too much heat can reach the drippings in the broiler pan. A grid that is similar in construction to oven racks is more difficult to clean than those that have wider strips of metal and openings placed farther apart. Broiler grids are usually of cast aluminum, stainless steel, chromium-plated steel, or enameled steel.

Some broiler pans are grooved and the grooves are slanted to a well at one end in which the drippings collect. The well may be so located that it is not directly under the flame.

To change the temperature of broiling foods during cooking it is usually necessary to remove the broiling pan from the oven or broiler, remove the rack, replace it at the desired height, and then replace the broiling pan. However, a few ranges now have convenient mechanical grid positioners. By moving a lever to the left or right, the height of the pan is changed without removing it from the oven or broiler. This eliminates handling a very hot pan and at the same time makes it easy to change the speed with which the food is cooked.

The rotisserie is a rotating device which enables foods to be broiled on all sides without the user having to change the position of the foods (Fig. 10–2). It is popular for broiling fowl, kabobs, barbecued ribs, and other foods.

c. Controls

Gas, air, and/or electricity supplied to a gas range are regulated by manual, semiautomatic, or automatic controls. The burners are controlled by turning valve handles, by mechanical timers, or by special thermostatic devices. The most common device used for controlling surface burners is the valve handle which turns to shut the burner off or turn it on. These valve handles may have different settings indicated either by a click sound, by feel, or both. Such valve handles must be clearly marked so that the "off" position cannot be mistaken.

A pilot is a device to light a burner automatically, eliminating the regular need for matches. When it is used all burners must be provided with means for automatic ignition. Pilots supply a very small amount of heat. All constantly burning pilots, except those which are a direct part of an automatic pilot, should have a gas input rating of not more than 300 Btu's per hour. The pilot flame is blue with a yellow tip. It has no air-mixing throat as does a regular burner. The adjustment of a pilot may be by means of a small screw near the manifold which can be turned to regulate the rate at which gas enters the pilot tip and consequently the height of the flame.

A small tube called a flash tube connects the pilot with the burner head. The flash tube is contiguous to the burner at a point where there is a special port called a lighter port. When the gas-air mixture flows through the mixing tube and into the burner head, it reaches the lighter port first and goes through the flash tube to the pilot. The mixture is immediately lighted by the pilot, and because of the large proportion of air in the flash tube, the flame flashes back to the burner head

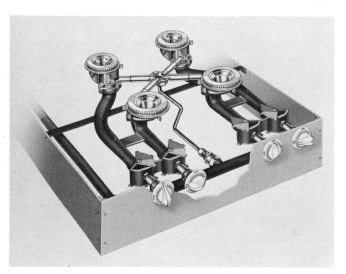

Fig. 10–9. Cluster burner arrangement—one pilot serves four burners. (The W. J. Schoenberger Company)

where the gas-air mixture in the ports is ignited. According to American Gas Association standards this should take place within four seconds after the gas is available at the burner ports. Flash tubes are usually made of a lightweight metal and are often separate from both the burner head and the pilot. Flash tubes that are permanently connected to the burner head do not get out of alignment as easily as those that are separate. Burners with individual pilots do not have flash tubes.

A range may have a separate pilot for the oven burner, broiler burner, and each surface burner (Fig. 10–8); for each two surface burners; or one pilot for all four surface burners (Fig. 10–9). Single-point ignition is also used on some ranges. Here one pilot is always lighted. When a burner is turned on, the main pilot ignites a secondary or auxiliary pilot for that burner, which in turn ignites the burner.

Electric ignition is provided on some models. When a burner is turned on, an electric connection is made which heats a small coil red hot. This opens a gas valve to a pilot, the pilot flame lights, and then the gas in the burner head is ignited.

When the oven burner is provided with a constantly burning pilot, the burner must be under the control of an automatic pilot. One make of automatic pilot is electromagnetically controlled. When the constantly burning pilot is extinguished for any reason, the electromagnet is deënergized and the gas valve is closed. Gas from the burner, and in some cases from the constantly burning pilot, is shut off. Manufacturers' instructions vary slightly about the procedure to use in getting the automatic pilot functioning again. It is necessary to reheat the thermocouple junction located adjacent to the constantly burning pilot. One method is as follows: (1) relight the constantly burning pilot and (2) after 30 to 60 seconds depress a valve button—usually a red button. This operates a keeper disk which will then allow gas to flow, and thus the automatic pilot will operate. As long as the pilot flame is lighted, the temperature will be high enough to keep the magnet energized, and the valve will remain open. Always read the specific instructions that come with a range.

The oven thermostat is usually an hydraulic type and may be described as having four main parts: the bulb, the capillary tube, the diaphragm or bellows, and the dial. The bulb is located in the oven and the capillary tube leads from it to the diaphragm. The dial is outside the range and its setting determines the tension of the diaphragm. As the oven is heated, the liquid in the bulb expands and pressure is exerted against the diaphragm. This in turn gradually closes a valve which controls the flow of gas to the burner (Fig. 10–10). The amount of pressure that must be exerted to close this valve depends upon the setting of the dial. If the dial is set for 400 F more pressure must be exerted than if it is set for 300 F. As the flame in the burner is cut down, the heat in the oven is reduced. As the oven cools, the pressure against the diaphragm is reduced and the gas valve is allowed to open again.

Some gas always flows to the burner after it is lighted, even when the main valve is closed by the thermostat. This gas, flowing through a small by-pass valve, gives a flame on the burner which is called a bead flame. As a rule this bead flame is about the size of a match head.

Occasionally a thermostat may not be calibrated exactly. However, the oven should be checked several times before assuming that the calibration is not exact. (Suggestions for foods to use in checking oven temperatures are given at the end of the chapter on electric ranges, pp. 172 and 173.) If the thermostat does need recalibration it should be done by a qualified service representative.

Oven burners have long had thermostatic controls, but the device has only recently been used with surface burners to control the tem-

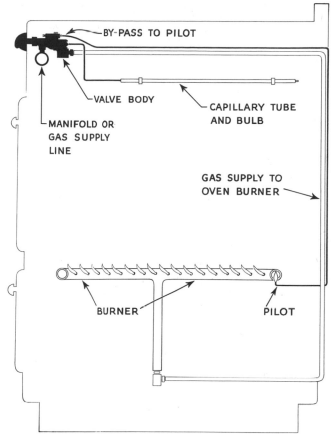

Fig. 10–10. Oven burner, pilot, and thermostat. (Robertshaw-Fulton Controls Company)

perature of the saucepan or skillet in which food is cooked (Fig. 10–11). After the temperature on the heat control is set, the flame goes on full, is lowered, or is turned off—as the sensing element reacts to the temperature of the pan.[3] The sensing element is a spring-backed unit. For successful operation the pan used must be flat on the bottom.

Thermostatic burner controls vary. In one type, after the desired temperature has been reached the gas may turn completely off and be reignited by a pilot light when the pan cools. Another type has two heat-flow capacities, the one used being determined auto-

[3] Home Economics Department, *Encyclopedia of Top-Burner Cooking with Controlled Heat,* Robertshaw-Fulton Controls Company, 1955, p. 2.

Fig. 10–11. Thermostatically controlled surface burner. (Robertshaw-Fulton Controls Company)

matically by the heat setting. This burner has a by-pass flame so that there is always a burner flame once the dial is turned on. A third one is a throttling type which controls the flow of gas according to the temperature selected.[4]

Successful use of thermostatically controlled burners requires appropriate saucepans. They should be of material that is a good heat conductor, be flat on the bottom, be of a size to cover the cooking area, should not tip, and should have a tight-fitting cover. As in using the oven thermostat, the dial must be set at the correct temperature for the food to be cooked. Large utensils with large quantities of food take longer to cook than smaller utensils with smaller quantities of food, but both can be done successfully. With only a few exceptions the utensil should not be preheated.

The automatic timer is a clock device which will turn the flame on to heat the oven at a predetermined time and turn it off when the cooking time has elapsed. Models differ in details of operation, but all are operated in conjunction with an electric clock. The first step in using an automatic timer is to make sure the electric clock is running and is at the correct

[4] *Ibid.,* p. 4.

time of day. Then the time to stop cooking and hours to cook or the time to start cooking and hours to cook are set. The oven control is set at the desired temperature. On some ranges there is a switch to set for automatic operation. When the cooking period is completed, this switch may turn back to manual control automatically, or it may have to be turned to manual before the oven can be used manually.

10–3. USE AND CARE

Regardless of how well chosen a range may be it will not give its best service unless it is used wisely. One of the first steps in good use is to *read the instruction book carefully and completely.* Almost all range manufacturers now issue an instruction book with each new range. Some are much better written and more informative than others, but each is worth reading.

If the range is correctly installed, it will be level. If it is not level, it is impossible to bake nice even cakes.

Burners, grates, drip trays, and burner bowls should be kept clean by frequent washing. If spilled food is allowed to burn on these surfaces, it is much more difficult to remove. Any food spilled on enamel surfaces should be wiped with a dry cloth if the enamel is hot, provided the enamel is not too hot, and when the surface has cooled thoroughly cleaned with a damp cloth. Burners, except those with aluminum heads, may be cleaned by boiling in soda water, rinsing thoroughly, and drying in the oven.

The correct way to use a gas burner is to put the utensil on the burner, *then* turn the burner on. When the cooking period has ended, turn off the burner, *then* remove the utensil. As the gas flame is hot instantly there is no need to allow a burner flame to stay lighted while the pan is off the range—it is more economical and safer to turn the burner off when no utensil is on it.

Do not waste fuel. Water, unless under pressure, will not heat above 212 F. Use the burner on full to bring water to boiling temperature quickly, but turn it down to simmer to hold it there. If this practice is followed water evaporates less quickly, foods are less likely to stick, and there is less vapor in the air to deposit on kitchen surfaces and add to house cleaning problems.

For economical use and for speed do not heat more water than is needed. If a pint is needed to make a gelatin salad there is no reason to heat a quart.

Oven doors should fit properly so that heat does not escape. One way of checking this is to observe the casing around the oven door after baking a few products. If this is slightly discolored by vapors from foods baking in the oven, the door does not fit as tightly as it should. Ordinarily this can be easily adjusted by a service man. Doors will not fit properly if the range is not level. Although oven doors are made to hold quite a lot of weight, they are not made for chairs or for use as a step-stool.

Cake pans should be filled about two-thirds full. If there is too much batter it will run over the edges of the pan during baking. If there is too little the cake will be thin, poor in texture, and not brown on top if baked a standard length of time at a recommended temperature.

Pans of food should be so placed in the oven that there is good heat circulation around each. This in effect means that pans should not be placed directly above one another, touching one another, or touching the sides of the oven. This caution is more important in baking pies, cakes, or cookies than in oven meals, but all baked foods will be better if this rule is followed.

Don't peek when baking foods. If standard recipes are baked in recommended pans placed in thermostatically controlled ovens for the required length of time, it is not necessary to keep looking at the food. Every time the oven door is opened cool air is allowed to enter and this in itself will change the amount of time required for baking. Excessive peeking means that the fuel bill will be higher than necessary.

The automatic timer can be set to go on and off during any time not to exceed 12 hours. However, the choice of foods to be placed in the oven helps to determine how far ahead the timer should be set. Some foods reach spoiling temperature relatively quickly. Depending upon the temperature in the house, and the kind of pilot in the oven, the user will need to decide which foods to use for this type of meal. As a rule one should be cautious about foods which contain milk, fish, fowl, and other foods which are known to spoil rather easily.

A large sheet of aluminum foil should not be used in the oven, as it will interfere with the circulation of heat. If used directly on the oven bottom it may become overheated and adhere to the oven bottom, making cleaning almost impossible. If it "must" be used when baking a juicy pie, cut a sheet just large enough to catch the drip from the pie and put it on the rack just below the pie. It seems a bit impractical for manufacturers to spend great amounts of time, money, and effort in designing an oven in which the heat circulation will always produce evenly browned cakes and then for the homemaker to ruin all this by a few cents' worth of aluminum foil improperly placed in an oven.

It is not necessary to preheat the broiler grid and pan when broiling foods, as the basic idea of broiling is to cook foods by direct heat from the flame rather than on a hot grid. Furthermore, the grid will be easier to clean if foods are placed on a cool grid. When broiling a few hamburgers, if you turn them so that they will be in the same position on the grid as before it will be much easier to wash the grid. After foods are broiled remove the pan and grid from the broiler compartment, let them cool slightly, sprinkle with detergent, and cover with a dampened cloth or paper towel. When the meal is over the grid can be cleaned easily.

Do not store the broiler pan and grid in a broiler compartment that is directly below the oven. Heat from the oven flame is hard on the material of an empty broiler grid and pan.

10–4. SPECIAL FEATURES

There are many special features on gas ranges, some in the gadget class and others widely accepted. It is up to the consumer to evaluate these special features according to her own needs and desires. Pull-out towel racks, hooks for hanging stirring spoons and pans, salt and pepper shakers, condiment sets, platform lights, clocks, minute minders, and convenience outlets are a few of the many special features available.

Minute minders or time reminders will measure time up to several hours. When the time set has elapsed, a bell or buzzer will sound. Some minute minders ring indefinitely until turned off. This has the advantage of making sure that the user will hear it sooner or later. Others only ring once. Another type will measure two lengths of time intervals, one up to one hour and the other up to 10 or 15 minutes. In appearance the minute minder that measures time for several hours looks much like an automatic timer but should not be confused with it. Minute minders only signal when a specified amount of time has elapsed; they do not control the flow of gas.

The automatic remote-control roast meter is a device which measures the inside temperature of the roast, turns the oven off, and sounds a buzzer when the meat is done. A metal probe is inserted into the center of the roast in the same fashion as a meat thermometer is placed in a roast. The metal probe is connected by wire to a plug which fits into an opening in the oven wall and is connected to the automatic roast control on the front of the range. The roast control dial is set for the degree of doneness desired.[5]

Electric convenience outlets are provided on many gas ranges. The wiring within the range is for a 15-ampere circuit and care should be taken not to overload it. One outlet may be controlled by the automatic timer. Wiring to the range depends upon the house circuit to which the range is connected. The overload protection is not located in the range, but at the fuse panel in the house.

Platform lights are found on the back splash of the range. They should be located so that light shines into pans or utensils used on the work surface but not in the user's eyes. If the light is to shine effectively upon the work surface, it needs to be several inches above that surface. A number of platform lights have as their chief contribution attractiveness and glamour rather than usefulness. If the bulb is covered by a glass or plastic diffusing cover it is easier to keep the bulb clean. Most any platform light makes a good night light if one is needed in the kitchen.

A gas range should hardly be chosen for the type of electric clock on it. However, if it is to serve as a kitchen clock it should have numbers which are large enough to be seen a few feet away. The face of the clock should be covered so that it is easy to clean. Neither the clock nor any other special features should be located so that heat from the oven vent will cause them to soil and darken.

B. Liquefied Petroleum Gases

British thermal unit ratings at which various performance tests should be conducted vary with the type of gas. The American Gas Association lists a heating value of 3175 Btu's per cubic foot for butane gas, 2500 Btu's for

[5] The Tappan Stove Company.

propane gas, 525 and 1400 Btu's per cubic foot for butane-air mixtures, 1075 Btu's for natural gas, 525 Btu's for manufactured gas, and 800 Btu's for mixed gas.

Because the British thermal unit content of liquefied petroleum gases is different from that of natural or manufactured gases, some adjustments in burners need to be made when changing from one type of gas to the other. Although these adjustments may be relatively simple, it is highly recommended by authorities in the field that they be made by service representatives familiar with the appliance.[6]

The American Gas Association recommends that ranges made for use with liquefied petroleum gas be so designed that they can be

[6] Arthur C. Kreutzer, in a personal communication, Liquefied Petroleum Gas Association, Inc., May, 1956.

converted for use with natural gas by the substitution of different burners and orifices. Ranges made with double coaxial orifices use the same burner for all types of gases; they should be shipped by the manufacturer ready for use with LP gas.

Each range must be permanently marked as to the type or types of gas for which it is to be used.

If a user moves often, it might be well to buy a range designed for use with all types of gases, such as one made with the double coaxial orifices.

The National Fire Protection Association issues a pamphlet entitled *Recommended Good Practice Rules for Liquefied Petroleum Gas Piping and Appliance Installations in Buildings,* and these standards are followed by most states.

C. American Gas Association Standards

The standards set up by the American Gas Association are subject to the approval of the American Standards Association. They are reviewed and revised periodically every two or three years. These standards represent the basic requirements for safe operation, substantial and durable construction, and acceptable performance. Since many of the construction and performance requirements are too involved for the average person to evaluate, the blue star seal of approval is placed on each gas range that meets the minimum requirements of the association (Fig. 10–7). It is an im-

portant seal and no gas range should be purchased that does not carry this seal of approval.

The standards for domestic gas ranges are written in two volumes. Volume II, which has been added recently, is a completely separate set of standards for built-in domestic units, though they are much the same as those for other domestic gas ranges. Separate performance requirements are given in both volumes for those ranges using liquefied petroleum and for those using liquefied petroleum gas-air mixtures.

D. Experiments

Experiments 1–6 require no special instruments or equipment and could well be done by beginning classes in household equipment. Experiments 7 and 8, for ranges using natural gas, are designed for more advanced students and some special equipment is required. For these students, the American Gas Association's *Standards for Domestic Gas Ranges,* Volumes I and II, would be a valuable detailed reference.

Experiments have been adapted in part from tests used by the American Gas

Association, with modifications to fit college conditions of time, laboratory space, techniques of students, and ranges and testing equipment available.

Experiment 1. *The Prospective Purchaser Examines a Range*

1. Is the nameplate easily found? What information does it give? How would this be useful to you—the homemaker user?
2. Does it carry the AGA seal? The Gold Star seal?
3. What is the overall height of the range to top of backsplash? The counter height? How wide is it? How deep is it? Will it fit flush to the wall?
4. Where are the vent openings located—inside and outside the range?
5. How many burners does it have? What size are they? How are they controlled?
6. What material is used in the burners? Will they require any special care in cleaning to keep them attractive?
7. Are the burners easy to remove and replace?
8. Are the aeration bowls designed to catch a reasonable amount of spillovers? Would the size of the aeration bowls be convenient for you to handle when washing?
9. Is there a burner tray? Is it well made? Can it be easily removed from the range?
10. Where are the control valves located? Are they well marked? Easy to reach? Removable for cleaning underneath? Are they the lock type?
11. Does the oven door fit tightly? At how many positions will the door stay open? Will it stay just ajar? (This makes it easy to cool the oven.)
12. Does the oven burner light automatically? Is it easy to light manually? Can you see the burner flame easily through an observation hole or by means of door to the oven burner compartment?
13. Does the oven burner have a constantly burning pilot?
14. Does the flow of gas to the oven and broiler stop if the pilot is extinguished accidentally?
15. How large is the oven—depth, width, and height? Will it hold the Thanksgiving turkey?
16. How many rack positions are there? Would the rack supports be easy to clean?
17. Are the racks rustproof? Nontipping? Do they have a backrail?
18. Where is the thermostat bulb located? Is it in such a position that it is protected from being accidentally hit when putting pans of food in the oven?
19. Does the oven have a light? How is it controlled?
20. What material is used for the oven and broiler linings?
21. How many broilers are there? Are they conveniently located?
22. How many positions are available for the broiler pan?
23. How is the height of the broiler pan changed?
24. Would the broiler grid be easy to clean? What material is used for the broiler pan? The grid?

25. What special features are on the range?
26. Does the range have toe space?
27. What is the finish of the range? Is it acid resistant? Are there many places for dirt to collect? (Around raised letters of the brand name, crevices, extra decoration and trim?)
28. Are the directions for use and care in the users' booklet clear?
29. What does the guarantee or warranty promise the buyer?

Experiment 2. *Uniformity of Oven Heat Distribution by Evenness of Browning of Plain White Cakes*

Either a good plain white cake mix or a standard white cake recipe may be used.

Adjust rack to approximate center of oven. Turn on oven to temperature recommended by recipe or cake mix.

Prepare pans for baking. Use aluminum pans 8 or 9 inches in diameter. All pans should be alike.

Prepare cake mix or cake recipe, following directions carefully so that all cakes will be made by the same procedure.

Divide batter equally into two pans (for a box cake mix).

Stagger pans on the center rack. Pans should not touch each other or the sides of the oven. If using more than one oven, all pans should be placed in the same relative position in each range. Place at least two pans in each oven.

Bake for the required length of time. Be accurate in measuring the time.

Judge for evenness of browning, doneness, texture, and amount and type of crust.

This experiment may be varied to study effects of materials of pans, or diameter and depth of pans. For the former use pans as nearly the same size as possible but made of different materials. For the latter use pans of the same material but of different diameters and depths. For both experiments use ranges that have given comparable baking results in the first part of this experiment.

Experiment 3. *Uniformity of Broiler Heat Distribution by Brownness of Toast*

Follow directions for Experiment 3, Chapter 11, on electric ranges with the following changes.

Place broiler pan between 2 and 5 inches from burner ports, close broiler door, and permit bread to toast for 8 minutes (or less)—not more than 10 minutes.

Does the uniform broiling area meet the AGA requirements of 35 percent? The CP requirement of 1 square foot or 80 percent of the grill area, whichever is greater?

Experiments 4, 5, 6. *Convenience of Use for Different Types of Cookery*

It is suggested that students follow Experiments 4, 5, and 6, Chapter 11, on electric ranges.

Experiment 7. *Thermal Efficiency of a Gas Range*

Determine gas pressure with gauge or manometer. If necessary, adjust pressure regulator to obtain 7 inches pressure. Follow directions in Experiment 8, Chapter 11 on Electric Range, for additional, relevant instructions.

Record gas meter reading when utensil is put over heat. Turn burner on full. Heat water to 200 F. Turn off burner and record gas meter reading.

Compute thermal efficiency using the following formula.

$$\text{Thermal efficiency} = \frac{(W + W_v) \times (O_2 - O_1)}{\text{Btu/cu. ft.} \times Q \times CF \times K}$$

Where: W = weight of water in pounds.
W_v = water equivalent of utensil [weight of utensil in pounds $\times$ 0.22 (0.22 is specific heat for aluminum)].
O_1 = initial temperature of water in degrees Fahrenheit.
O_2 = final temperature of water in degrees Fahrenheit.
Q = gas consumption as shown by meter in cubic feet.
CF = Correction factor to reduce observed gas volume to 30 inches of mercury pressure at 60 F.
K = 1.0 and 0.875 for open and solid top ranges, respectively.

Experiment 8. *Broiler Performance*

Adjust gas pressure to 7 inches water column.

Turn broiler flame on full. Close both oven and broiler doors. Let broiler heat for 15 minutes.

Read gas meter at the end of that time.

Make six lean ground beef patties that weigh about ⅓ pound each and are approximately 4 inches in diameter.

Place the meat patties on the broiler grid. Place one meat patty under the pilot or as close to it as possible.

Place broiler pan in broiler compartment so that the top of the meat patties will be 2 inches from the burner ports.

Broil patties for five minutes on each side.

Turn off flame and read gas meter.

Check gas consumption, doneness of patties, and effectiveness of burner and pilot adjustments. Neither the burner nor pilot flames should go out nor should the automatic pilot shut off the main gas supply while patties are broiling. Check meter hands for speed of rotation to see if the burner flame is cut down during the cooking process.

Conventional Electric Ranges

A prospective purchaser is confronted with a rather enormous array of features on modern electric ranges of the conventional type. Special features such as a motor-operated spit in the oven permit special types of food preparation. An individual must decide for herself which features are likely to be useful for her food preparation habits. Two points should be considered for electric ranges that are currently available: (1) a large number of features does not do away with the need for planning menus and thinking creatively about the foods to be prepared; (2) an electric range is ordinarily purchased to be used for many years. One should therefore purchase a range that is constructed for durability as well as satisfactory cooking performance. Thus, general considerations for conventional electric and gas ranges are similar.

In addition to a wide choice of features on conventional ranges, prospective purchasers who have the financial resources have a choice between a conventional electric range and an electronic range, which is discussed in the next chapter.

The material in this chapter covers basic construction, electrical components, controls, use, and care of conventional ranges. Types of features currently available are noted. The inspection experiment at the end of the chapter is planned as a guide to prospective purchasers, as well as a laboratory experiment.

A. Construction, Use, and Features

The essential characteristic of conventional electric ranges is basically rather simple. Heat generated when electric current flows through surface or oven resistance elements is used to cook foods.

Conventional electric ranges are either free-standing or "built-in." For built-in ranges, a framework containing the surface units is installed in a counter top of a base cabinet and another framework containing the oven is mounted either in a wall or in a special oven cabinet. Free-standing and built-in ranges have the same basic operating parts: switches, flat surface units designed for direct contact with cooking utensils, and top and bottom oven units that heat food by heating the air and lining of the oven, and radiation.

11–1. CONSTRUCTION

The depth of free-standing ranges, exclusive of handles, is approximately 25 inches (Figs. 11–1 and 11–2). The overall height-base to top of back splash (portion above the top cooking surface)—varies from approximately 39 to 49 inches for different models. The height to the top of the cooking surface is usually 36 inches.

Width is the usual variable noted by a prospective purchaser. Apartment-size models are approximately 20 to 21 inches wide; an increasingly popular range is 30 inches wide; standard-size ranges are usually 36 inches wide; deluxe ranges are 39 to 42 inches wide or wider. The exact dimensions for any particular model are given on the manufacturer's specification sheet.

The underlying structure or framework usually is a one-piece welded unit. The back exterior panel is often synthetic enamel on steel. The cooking surface and the oven lining are usually porcelain on steel. The side panels are synthetic enamel or porcelain on steel. Often the oven lining is made in one piece to make cleaning easier.

The sides, top, and bottom of the oven have insulating material between the oven lining and the frame. The oven door also includes insulating material. This insulation decreases heat loss from the inside of the oven. Ovens are often vented through a surface unit.

Storage compartments and/or drawers are frequently provided. These are usually used for storage of utensils.

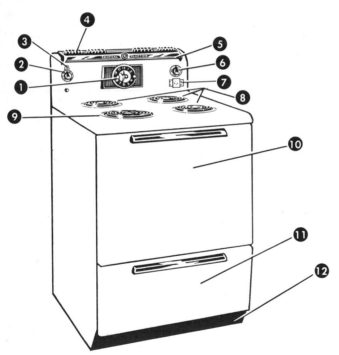

Fig. 11–1.   Names of parts for a 30-inch range. (General Electric Company)
1. Combination oven and minute timer. This assembly includes a minute minder and automatic (timed) control for oven and appliance outlet.   2. Oven thermostat control.   3. Oven cycling light.   4. Push-button surface unit switches.   5. Full-width fluorescent lamp. 6. Oven selector switch marked for broil, bake, time bake, and off.   7. Appliance outlets and fuse.   8. Tubular-type, 6-inch surface units.   9. Eight-inch surface unit.   10. Oven door.   11. Storage drawer door.   12. Toe cove.

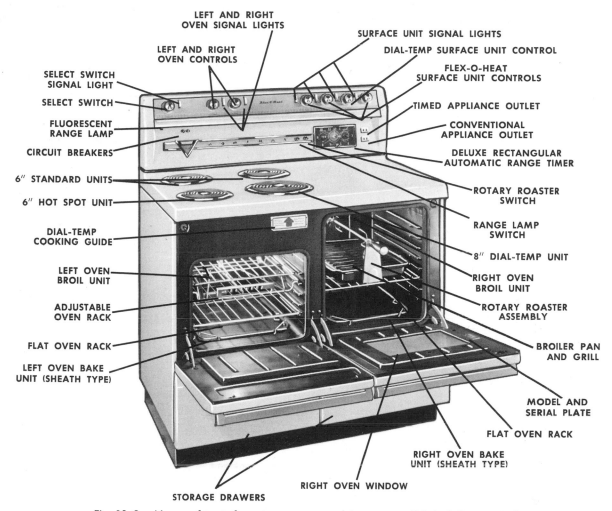

LEFT AND RIGHT
OVEN SIGNAL LIGHTS

SURFACE UNIT SIGNAL LIGHTS

LEFT AND RIGHT
OVEN CONTROLS

DIAL-TEMP SURFACE UNIT CONTROL

FLEX-O-HEAT
SURFACE UNIT CONTROLS

SELECT SWITCH
SIGNAL LIGHT

SELECT SWITCH

TIMED APPLIANCE OUTLET

FLUORESCENT
RANGE LAMP

CONVENTIONAL
APPLIANCE OUTLET

CIRCUIT BREAKERS

DELUXE RECTANGULAR
AUTOMATIC RANGE TIMER

6" STANDARD UNITS

6" HOT SPOT UNIT

ROTARY ROASTER
SWITCH

RANGE LAMP
SWITCH

DIAL-TEMP
COOKING GUIDE

8" DIAL-TEMP UNIT

LEFT OVEN
BROIL UNIT

RIGHT OVEN
BROIL UNIT

ADJUSTABLE
OVEN RACK

ROTARY ROASTER
ASSEMBLY

FLAT OVEN RACK

BROILER PAN
AND GRILL

LEFT OVEN BAKE
UNIT (SHEATH TYPE)

MODEL AND
SERIAL PLATE

FLAT OVEN RACK

RIGHT OVEN BAKE
UNIT (SHEATH TYPE)

STORAGE DRAWERS

RIGHT OVEN WINDOW

Fig. 11–2. Names of parts for a two-oven, very deluxe range. (Admiral Corporation)

a. Ovens

The size of the oven varies for different ranges. Most ranges have one oven, but some deluxe models have two, usually of unequal size. Oven volume is not easily estimated by the eye. The following dimensions are taken from specification sheets for the complete line of one manufacturer: oven of apartment-size range—16 inches wide, 15 inches high, 20¼ inches deep; oven of 30-inch range—16 inches wide, 18 inches high, 20¾ inches deep; oven of standard range—same as that of 30-inch range; ovens of deluxe range—larger oven,

same as that of 30-inch range and smaller oven, 16 inches wide, 10½ inches high, 20¾ inches deep. This manufacturer thus uses the same oven size for three of the four ranges described, namely, for the 30-inch range, the standard range, and the larger one in the two-oven range.

Other oven sizes are used by other manufacturers. For example, a few 30-inch ranges have ovens 24 inches wide. One deluxe 40-inch range has a single oven 30 inches wide.

Two racks and four or more pairs of rack supports or glides are usually provided for each oven. But various methods are used to provide more than four oven rack positions. Some ovens have more than four pairs of rack supports. Some have an offset, reversible rack, which can be at either of two heights in the oven, according to the way the user places it on the rack supports. Some · manufacturers provide a rack that may be raised or lowered by a lever.

Racks should be made of corrosion-resistant material and should have a rear rail and a stop-lock feature so they cannot accidentally be pulled all the way out of the oven.

Oven doors are attached to the framework so they will remain flat in the fully open position. A stop may also be provided so the door will remain ajar—open about 3 inches—for broiling. For some models, the door may be counterbalanced to remain open at several or even all positions between ajar and fully open. Door handles are attached by screws, in case replacement of the handle is necessary.

11–2. ELECTRICAL COMPONENTS

Electric ranges are usually rated to operate on a three-wire, 115/230- to 120/240-volt supply. The three-wire supply permits two-wire, 115–120-volt circuits and two-wire, 230–240-volt circuits within the range.

The plug of the range cord has three prongs and the cord has three wires. To make the discussion below specific, assume voltage supply for the range is 115/230 volts. When the range is connected, one prong of the plug of the range cord is at plus 115 volts, another is at zero volts, and the third is at minus 115 volts. The three wires in the range cord connect the prongs with terminals on a terminal block inside the range.

The framework of the range is grounded, usually to the neutral or zero-volt conductor of the supply circuit.

The resistance elements of oven units are part of a two-wire, 230-volt circuit; that is,

the resistance element of an oven unit is connected across the plus 115-volt and the minus 115-volt terminals of the terminal block. Top oven units sometimes have two resistance elements and bottom units generally have one. Both open-coil and tubular or metal-sheathed types are used (Fig. 11–3).

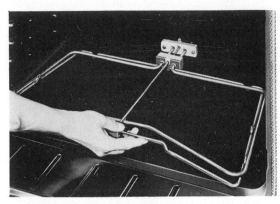

Fig. 11–3. Tubular oven unit used at bottom of oven. (Courtesy Westinghouse Electric Corporation)

The bottom oven unit is usually rated at some value between 2000 and 3000 watts. Maximum wattage of the top oven unit is now between 2000 and 4000 watts, this maximum wattage being used for broiling. During preheat and bake, on the other hand, only one resistance element of the top unit is used for many models. Total wattage of top and bottom units during preheat and bake is thus likely to be approximately 4000 to 5000 watts.

In a few models a receptacle for a unit is provided near the center of the oven so that a user can place the top or upper unit either at the top of the oven or approximately in the center of the oven. In this case the upper unit is covered with a plate. When the upper unit is placed in the center of the oven, the bottom half of the oven functions as a "half-size" oven.

The resistance elements of surface units that are thermostatically or time controlled may be part of a two-wire, 230-volt circuit. On the other hand, the resistance elements of surface units not thermostatically or time controlled are usually part of a *three-wire,* 115/230-volt circuit; that is, the elements are connected to all three terminals on the terminal block (Fig. 11–4).

Four surface units are usual: three or two 6-inch units and one or two 8-inch units. The "6-inch" and "8-inch" figures are nominal diameters. The units are also described as "regular" and "giant" units, respectively. Surface-unit assemblies most commonly consist of one or two tubular elements connected to a small terminal block, a support for the element or elements, a metal ring, and a reflector pan. If one tubular element is used, it contains two or three coils insulated from each other; if two are used, each contains one coil (Fig. 11–5). A few manufacturers use two open-coil resist-ances mounted in a grooved disk of insulating material in place of tubular elements.

The electrical connections between the resistance elements in each surface unit and the three-wire supply at the main terminal block of the range are determined by the position of the surface-unit selector switch.

Six-inch units used by different manufacturers have wattages between 1000 and 1650; a rated value of approximately 1200 watts is common. Eight-inch units usually have rated wattages between 1900 and 2200. Rated wattages are given for the highest heat setting. Wattages for successively lower settings decrease by a factor of two, approximately, for units with five or three heat settings, provided the two elements of the unit have the same re-

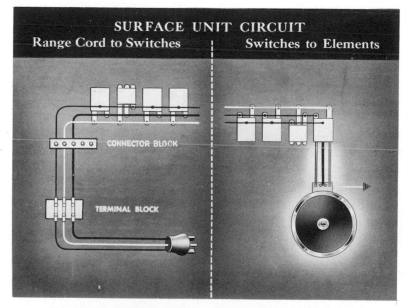

Fig. 11–4.   (Frigidaire Division, General Motors Corporation)

Fig. 11–5.   Cutaway view of tubular elements of a surface unit. (Hotpoint Company)

sistance (see section 11–3). For example, the wattage for the next to highest setting for a unit with five heat settings is approximately half that for the highest setting; that for the middle setting is approximately half that for the next to the highest setting; and so on. Thus the wattage at the lowest setting of a unit with five heat settings is approximately one-sixteenth of the wattage at the highest setting, if the two elements of the unit have the same resistance.

A "super speed" unit which may not have an extra-high *rated* wattage is provided on some models. For example, a super-speed 6-inch unit may be *rated* at 1650 watts. But a much higher wattage may be used initially for a very short time.

Electrical accessories such as the range light and an electric minute minder are part of a two-wire, 115-volt circuit; that is, the electrical accessory is connected across the grounded

terminal and the plus or the minus 115-volt terminal. The appliance outlet circuit is a 115-volt circuit fused with an accessible plug-type fuse or circuit breaker.

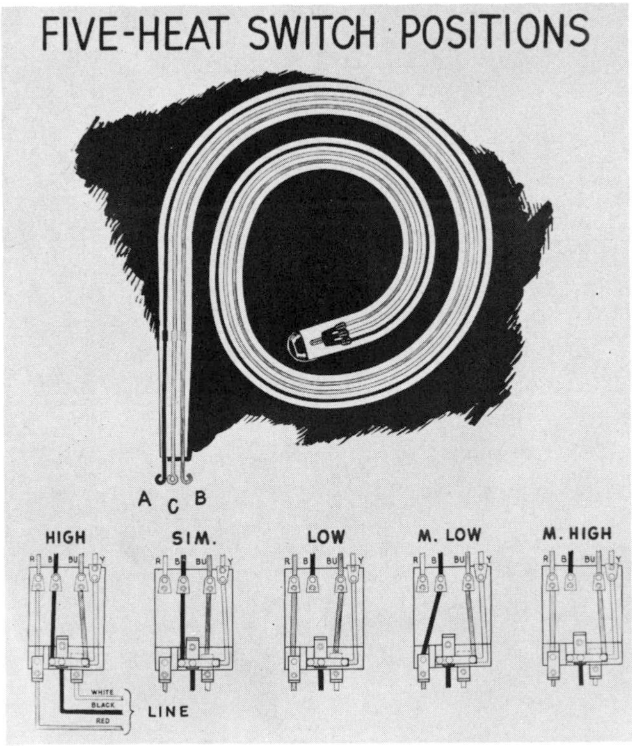

11–3. CONTROLS

Controls are provided for surface units and for oven units.

a. Surface Unit Controls

Figures 11–6 and 11–7 show the electric circuit for a switch used with a five-heat surface unit not thermostatically or time controlled. In both illustrations the switch is connected to a three-wire, 115/230-volt supply. For the highest heat setting, A, of Figure 11–7, the resistance elements R_1 and R_2 are connected *in parallel* across 230 volts; for the next highest setting, B, the resistance element R_1 is connected across 230 volts; for the middle setting, C, R_1 and R_2 are *series-connected* across 230 volts; for the next to lowest setting, D, R_2 is connected across 115 volts, and for the lowest setting, E, R_1 and R_2 are series-connected across 115 volts.

When resistance elements are connected in parallel, the total or effective resistance of the combination is less than the resistance of either element. In a series connection, the total or effective resistance of the combination is equal to the sum of the separate resistances. Thus the largest current flows through the surface unit at the highest heat setting because the parallel connection is equivalent to a relatively low resistance, and this is across 230 volts. The smallest current flows through the unit at the lowest setting because the series connection is equivalent to a relatively large resistance, and this is across 115 volts.

Additional flexibility of heat settings of surface units is obtained with either a time-control device or a thermostatic control. The switch of a time-controlled unit is turned to different settings just as an ordinary switch is

FIVE-HEAT SWITCH POSITIONS

Fig. 11–6. Parts of a surface unit switch for five heat positions. M. High is the next-to-highest setting. (Frigidaire Division, General Motors Corporation)

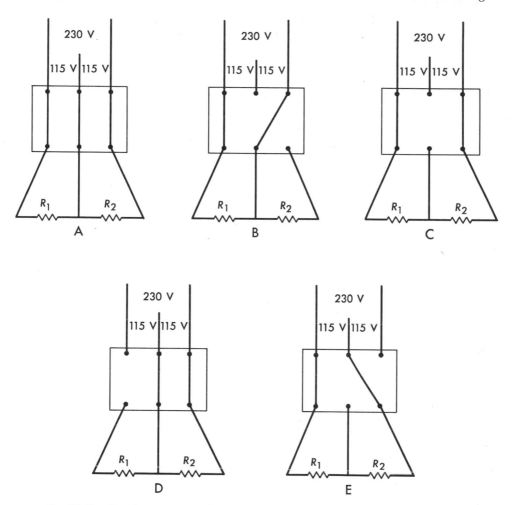

Fig. 11–7. Electric connections for a switch that controls a five-heat surface unit.

turned. However, its position controls "on" and "off" cycling of the unit. At the highest setting, the unit is on all the time; that is, electric current is supplied to the unit continuously. At lower settings, electric current is supplied intermittently, and relative lengths of on and off times vary according to the setting.

Current deluxe ranges may have one or several thermostatically controlled surface units, each of which has a separate thermostatic control.

Because controlled units have not been used widely as long as conventional units, their advantages and limitations are not as well defined. Controlled units in general do not completely eliminate the need for stirring of products. Rather, the controlled units are likely to require less "watching" of the product, and a longer cooking time. Also, at the present time, controlled units seem to have no special advantage for products like noodles. On the other hand, except for portability, controlled units with suitable utensils have advantages similar to those of some small electric heating appliances that are thermostatically controlled.

The hydraulic type of mechanism used for controlling a surface unit is basically similar to that used for controlling oven units, but differs in some aspects. A "sensing element" with a movable shield is mounted in the center of the controlled unit on the cooking surface of the range (Figs. 11–8, 11–9, and 11–10). A capillary tubing filled with a heat-sensitive liquid connects this sensing element with a diaphragm below the cooking surface of the range. A heat-sensitive liquid expands appreciably when heated and contracts appreciably when cooled.

For the unit illustrated in Figure 11–10, the diaphragm moves so as to open and close the electric circuit of the surface unit in accordance with changes in temperature of the sensing element. An alternate type of operation used by other manufacturers is to have the diaphragm move to change connections to the resistance elements of the surface unit, thus changing the wattage input to the surface unit.[1]

The sensing unit is mounted in a spring-controlled shield. This spring construction provides the close contact needed between pan and sensing element.

Details of construction and operation vary for different models. The selector switch is usually marked in numbers or temperatures, but some manufacturers mark it for cooking "zones," such as fry, boil, and low, *and* for high, medium, and low settings within each zone.

The user places the utensil with food in it on the surface unit and turns the selector switch to a particular temperature, number, or cooking zone. This switch is set only once, for example, boil-low for fresh or frozen vegetables or fry-medium for poultry and fish. The unit supplies heat to bring the food to the temperature corresponding to the setting of the switch and maintains this temperature automatically. Recommended settings for different foods are given in the user's booklet for

the range. Different settings may be given for uncovered versus covered pans because the sensing element responds to the temperature of the bottom surface of the pan rather than that of the food in the pan.

Recommended settings are established by cooking different foods in a utensil provided with a thermometer or other temperature-measuring device. Aluminum utensils are usually used for these tests, and current range booklets usually recommend that aluminum or aluminum-clad utensils be used with thermostatically controlled surface units. Well-balanced pans with flat bottom surfaces are recommended. Glass utensils can be used only for foods cooked in water.

b. Oven Controls

Although other types of thermostats, such as bimetallic ones, can be and have been used for range ovens, the hydraulic thermostat has come to be rather universally used in the United States for range ovens. This has an hydraulic component and a switch component. The hydraulic component is a narrow metal tube which is closed by a small bulb at one end and by a diaphragm at the other and is filled with a liquid which is sensitive to temperature changes. The bulb of the thermostat is mounted in the oven, often at the center of one side or the center of the back. The diaphragm is located in the switch component.

The action of the thermostat is as follows. As the oven heats, the liquid in the bulb expands and exerts pressure on the diaphragm. When the temperature of the bulb reaches the dial value set by the user, the diaphragm causes the switch to open, thereby breaking the circuit to the oven.

Figure 11–11 shows electrical connections for an oven thermostat. The timer switch shown there is an accessory, needed only if the oven has an automatic timer for timed control of the oven. To trace the circuit of Figure 11–11, assume that both the timer switch and the

---

[1] Information is not yet available, either from published reports of experimental work or from observations by users, to indicate the superiority of one type of thermostatic operation over the other.

Fig. 11–8. Monotube-type, thermostatically controlled surface unit. (Frigidaire Division, General Motors Corporation)

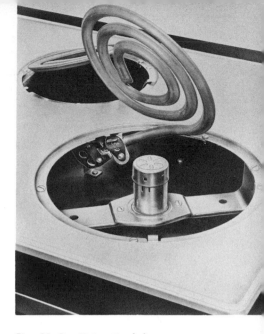

Fig. 11–9. Unit raised from surface of range to show housing for "sensing element." (Frigidaire Division, General Motors Corporation)

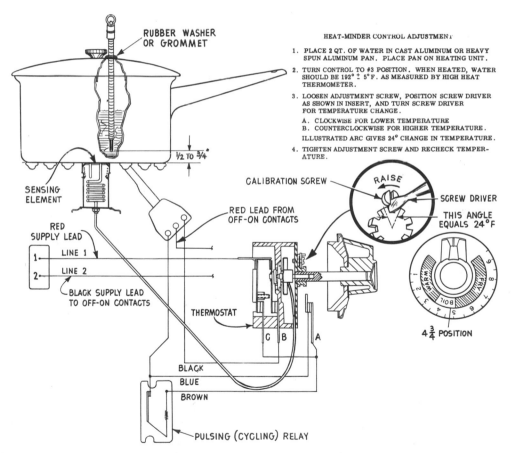

HEAT-MINDER CONTROL ADJUSTMENT

1. PLACE 2 QT. OF WATER IN CAST ALUMINUM OR HEAVY SPUN ALUMINUM PAN. PLACE PAN ON HEATING UNIT.

2. TURN CONTROL TO #3 POSITION. WHEN HEATED, WATER SHOULD BE 192° ± 5° F. AS MEASURED BY HIGH HEAT THERMOMETER.

3. LOOSEN ADJUSTMENT SCREW, POSITION SCREW DRIVER AS SHOWN IN INSERT, AND TURN SCREW DRIVER FOR TEMPERATURE CHANGE.

   A. CLOCKWISE FOR LOWER TEMPERATURE.
   B. COUNTERCLOCKWISE FOR HIGHER TEMPERATURE.

   ILLUSTRATED ARC GIVES 24° CHANGE IN TEMPERATURE.

4. TIGHTEN ADJUSTMENT SCREW AND RECHECK TEMPERATURE.

Fig. 11–10. Mechanical and electrical details of the thermostatically controlled unit shown in Figures 11–8 and 11–9. (Frigidaire Division, General Motors Corporation)

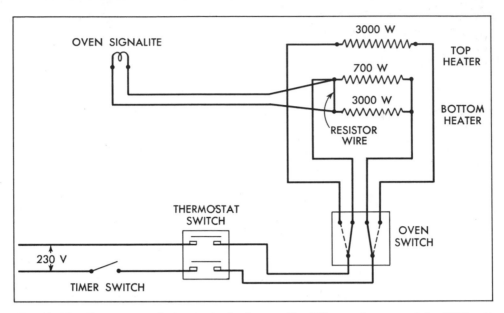

Fig. 11–11. Thermostat and electric circuit of oven. The 700-watt element and the 3000-watt element in the bottom heater function as a single unit. (Copied with permission of Westinghouse Electric Corporation)

thermostat switch are closed. Power is then supplied to the top oven unit or "top heater" only, the bottom oven unit only, or both the top and bottom units.

When the thermostat dial is set at broil, power is supplied only to the top unit. Under normal operating conditions, power is supplied continuously for this setting. If, however, the range becomes excessively hot, the broiler unit will cycle on and off as a safety provision. Power is supplied to both top and bottom units when the oven is preheating to the temperature value set on the thermostat dial. Power is supplied to top and bottom units or to the bottom unit only, depending on the model, when the oven is on after the preheat temperature has been reached.

Some ranges, notably those with push-button controls, have separate controls for preheat, bake, and broil. The bake control on modern ranges is used mostly when the oven is set for automatic operation or timed control. When the oven is on bake control, only the bottom unit cycles on and off.

A separate bake control is not an essential component of an automatic timer, and ranges without push-button controls usually do not have a separate bake control.

c. Automatic Timer

Automatic timers are clock controls which can turn oven units on and off at preselected times. Essentially, the control consists of an electric clock and a switch operated by the clock mechanism. For most automatic oven controls, the user follows three steps: she checks to see that the clock indicates the correct time of day; adjusts two knobs, one for the time oven units will go off and one for the length of time food is to cook; and adjusts the oven thermostat for the appropriate oven temperature. The oven units will go on at such a time that food placed in the oven will cook, from a cold oven start, for the length of time selected.

Precise instructions are given in user's booklets. Some booklets also suggest types of food suitable for automatically controlled cooking. Clearly, if foods are placed in an oven several hours before the food is to start cooking, some thought must be given to types of food. The types of food that should be used with caution are noted on page 147.

For many ranges, the automatic timer can be used to *stop* cooking operations only. That is, the food is placed in the oven and the timer adjusted so that the oven unit will go on immediately and will go off at the preselected time.

An oven set for timed control cannot be operated manually until the automatic timer is cleared.

The automatic timer can also control operation of an appliance outlet on the range. It operates as for oven cookery, except that the oven thermostat is not adjusted. If the appliance has a starting switch, it must also be turned to the "on" position. Appliances used in the timed outlet of a range include electric coffee makers, kitchen radios, and kitchen television sets.

11–4. USE

Conventional electric ranges are used for surface and oven cookery, including broiling.

a. Surface Cookery

The 6-inch and 8-inch surface units are provided primarily for regular and large quantities of food, respectively. (It is assumed, of course, that regular and large quantities of food will be cooked in utensils of different sizes.) Different heat settings are provided for nonthermostatically controlled surface units, in order that the user may have settings appropriate for different kinds of food and different rates of cooking. Definite heat settings also facilitate standardization in cooking procedures. If you observe that a given quantity of food placed in a particular utensil cooks in a certain number of minutes at a particular setting, you may anticipate that you will be able to repeat the cooking operation at the same

setting in approximately the same length of time.

The instruction booklets for ranges with nonthermostatically controlled surface units include recommendations of the following type: Use the highest setting to start most surface cooking operations; for example, to heat a skillet for pan-broiling or to bring water in which vegetables are to be cooked to a boil. Use the next highest setting to pan-broil and pan-fry meats, to start foods cooking in small amounts of water, and to maintain temperatures for deep-fat frying. Use the middle setting to fry chicken, fish, and griddle cakes and to make boiled icings that have a sugar-water base. Use the next to the lowest setting to finish cooking large quantities of food and to cook foods with milk and/or an egg base such as white sauce and custard. Use the lowest setting to finish cooking small quantities of food, to melt chocolate and butter, and to warm foods.

Use of thermostatically controlled surface units was discussed in section 11–3.

For best utilization of electric energy pans should fit the units. Pans with a base diameter of 5 to 7 inches "fit" 6-inch units, and those with a base diameter of 7 inches or more fit 8-inch units. Pans with flat bottoms make good contact with the unit and food is likely to cook more evenly than in pans that are warped.

When glass utensils are used for surface cooking, it is desirable to place a wire grid between the utensil and the unit if the rating of the unit is 1500 watts or more. (Wire grids should be available at stores that sell glass cooking utensils.)

b. Oven Cookery

Oven cookery includes baking cakes, cookies, biscuits, pies, and breads; roasting meat and poultry; broiling meat and other foods; and cooking casseroles.

Foods to be broiled are placed in an unheated oven.

Foods to be baked are usually placed in an oven that has been preheated to the temperature given in a recipe. That is, the oven control is set for the temperature given in the recipe and the food is put in after a signal light indicates that the oven has reached the temperature set on the control dial.

Actually, many foods will cook satisfactorily from a cold start, that is, the foods may be placed in the oven and the control turned on. But modern recipes specify certain times and temperatures, so the oven generally is preheated unless the automatic timer is used.

The results obtained in oven cookery do not depend solely on the range—preparation techniques and quality of food used are also important. On the other hand, proper adjustment of the range and proper use of the oven are important factors in obtaining acceptable products.

For both surface cookery and oven cookery the range should be level, and this should be checked when the range is installed. If it is moved, a homemaker can recheck with a bubble-type level or, less accurately, by placing a pan of water on an oven rack. If the water level is uneven, the range or rack needs leveling. Adjusting screws are provided at the bottom corners of some ranges.

The calibration of oven thermostats on home ranges is sometimes incorrect. A homemaker can check the correctness of thermostat calibration by following standard recipes, which usually indicate type of utensil to be used and time required for cooking. If foods in specified utensils consistently bake in a shorter or longer time than the recipes indicate, she should logically suspect incorrect thermostat calibration. Some user's booklets give instructions for changing thermostat calibration.

General recommendations on use of the oven are summarized below. (See also p. 147.)

If only one pan is used, place it, if possible, approximately in the center of the oven. (The pan for a large roast or fowl may have to be placed on a rack near the floor of the oven.) If several pans are used, for example, for bread, place them so they will not touch each other or any part of the oven wall or door; also, use a staggered arrangement so that one pan is not located directly above another.

Adjust the temperature or time given in the recipe when a different pan than that recommended in the recipe is used. Foods cook more rapidly in glass baking dishes than in aluminum pans of the same size; they also cook more rapidly in dark or anodized aluminum pans than in shiny ones. Warped pans are likely to produce uneven baked products.

Use a pan size such that the batter or dough fills it one-half to two-thirds full. Do not bake cookies, biscuits, or cream puffs in pans with high sides.

Roast tender cuts of meat and tender fowl in a shallow, uncovered pan. Unless the bone serves as a support use a rack under the meat. Use a properly placed meat thermometer as an indicator of doneness.

If aluminum foil is used for spillovers, use a piece only large enough to catch the possible spillover and place it on a rack below the one the food is on, unless the user's booklet indicates that foil may be placed on the floor of the oven. Bending up the edges of the foil slightly is helpful.

To broil is to cook by direct heat. For most electric ranges manufactured before 1958, the oven control is set so that only the upper unit is on and the oven door is left ajar. User's booklets for these ranges usually suggest that for high temperature or rapid broiling the broiler pan be placed in the oven so that the top of the food is close to the upper unit; for low temperature or slow broiling the pan should be placed so that the top of the food is 3 to 4 inches from the upper unit.

It is of course a matter of personal preference whether one likes one's broiled meat very dark on the outside and very rare inside or cooked uniformly throughout. The National Livestock and Meat Board recommends that the tops of steaks be about 350 F. during all or most of the broiling period.[2] This recommendation is based on experiments in which steaks were broiled at different temperatures. At moderate temperatures they cooked more uniformly and shrank less than at high temperatures.

The senior author has observed in classroom laboratory experiments that for many electric ranges a broiling temperature of 350 F at the surface of the meat can be obtained only by placing the broiler pan near the bottom of the oven and opening the oven door to its full-open position. (See Experiment 6, p. 173.) Some electric ranges are now designed for broiling with the door closed. Information on temperatures is not yet available.

In broiling as well as in baking some thought should be given to how the rack or grid is covered with aluminum foil, if foil is used. A rack or grid allows meat drippings to fall into the pan where they are protected from the direct heat of the upper unit by the meat itself. If aluminum foil covers the entire grid, the drippings will remain on it and may get hot enough to smoke and even burst into flame.

11–5. CARE

Care of an electric range is almost entirely a matter of maintaining appearance. No regular servicing is required. Once the habit is acquired, the practice of cleaning parts regularly and frequently is less tiring, and perhaps more satisfying aesthetically, than the practice of a thorough cleaning at infrequent intervals.

The principal parts to be cleaned are reflector pans and metal rings around surface units, drip trays under these units, exterior surfaces, oven linings, oven racks, covering

[2] National Live Stock and Meat Board, *Ten Lessons on Meat for Use in Schools,* National Live Stock and Meat Board, 7th, ed., 1950, Lesson Six.

and backing sheets on bottom and top oven units, broiler pan and grid, and storage spaces.

Tubular units are supposed to be self-cleaning, since food spilled on them can burn off. The other parts listed are likely to have either a metal or an enamel finish. Metal parts, except chromium-plated ones, are cleaned with soap or detergent and water, rinsed, and wiped dry. Sometimes a mild abrasive is used on oven racks. Chromium-plated parts are wiped with a damp cloth, then dried. Parts with non-metallic finishes, such as exterior surfaces, oven linings, and broiler pans, are cleaned like other glass-like materials; that is, they are wiped with a detergent-dampened or soap-dampened cloth, rinsed, and dried. Abrasives are not recommended.

Avoid applying cold water to hot porcelain parts. If a spill occurs on the surface, transfer the utensil to another unit to avoid burning food on the reflector pan. Wipe spilled foods off the cooking top as soon as practicable. Acids in milk, lemons, tomatoes, and other foods can etch the porcelain. Do not slide utensils over porcelain or synthetic enamel surfaces.

Avoid getting terminals or contacts of oven units wet. Some oven units can be removed. The oven lining is usually easier to clean if they are removed. Be sure to push them firmly back into place after the oven lining is cleaned. If a special oven cleaner is used, follow instructions on the package.

11–6. FEATURES AND ACCESSORIES

A stripped-model, conventional range might consist of a framework, enameled exterior panels, porcelain cooking top and oven liner, three or four surface units with three or five heat settings, an insulated and thermostatically controlled oven, the necessary electrical components and controls, and possibly one storage drawer under the oven. All the other parts, including trim, are features or accessories. Different features are, of course, important to different people.

A prospective purchaser who is genuinely interested can determine approximately what different groups of features cost by getting specification sheets and price information for the complete line of two manufacturers or of one manufacturer and a large mail order house. The complete line of large manufacturers may include as many as nine models of free-standing ranges, varying from the quite stripped model to the "top-of-the-line" model. A model that the manufacturer describes as deluxe is not necessarily the "top-of-the-line" model for that manufacturer. "Custom Imperial," "Customline," "Mark" with a roman numeral, are some of the special names used by manufacturers for their highest priced models.

The catalogue of a large mail order house might list as many models as the following: two 20-inch ranges, four 30-inch ranges, three 36-inch ranges, one 40-inch range, one 41½-inch range, two built-in models of surface units, and one built-in oven.

Cost information obtained by a prospective purchaser will cover *groups* of features, because different models made by one manufacturer usually differ in several features. Furthermore, different manufacturers offer different features on ranges in the same price class. That is, a range made by manufacturer A may be in the same price class as one made by manufacturer B but may have a somewhat different group of features.

Built-in surface units (and ovens) are considered deluxe appliances (Figs. 11–12 and 11–13). Overall features that make free-standing ranges deluxe include large size, finish of stainless steel, colored enamel, white or colored porcelain, and steel or chromium trim. The features associated with surface and oven cookery that are described below also make a range deluxe to varying degrees.

A mechanical or electric minute and hour minder may be provided which buzzes or chimes when the set time has elapsed. Incandescent or fluorescent lamps that illuminate the cooking top may be provided. One or two appliance outlets may be provided. Usually, if a range has two outlets, one is controlled by an automatic timer. One or more surface units may have seven heat settings. All of the surface units may have an infinite number of settings and these may be time controlled. One or more of the surface units may be thermostatically controlled. An 8-inch surface unit may be temperature-controlled for 8- and 6-inch heat patterns.

The surface and oven unit controls may be operated by push buttons (Fig. 11–1), which may have colored lights, with a different color for each setting. One surface unit may be adjustable so that it can be lowered for deep well cooking and raised for surface cooking (Fig. 11–14). A coffee percolator and a small "thawer oven" for frozen foods are available accessories for one range. A thermostatically controlled griddle may be provided. A super-speed surface unit may be provided.

A deluxe range may have two ovens, an oven and a warming compartment, or separate oven and broiler compartments. An automatic oven timer may be provided. The oven door may have a window and the oven itself may have a switch-operated interior light. Indicator lights may show when the oven is preheating, baking, or broiling. The interior lining of the oven may be chrome-plated.

A removable rotisserie with motor-operated revolving spit may be included or may be purchased as an accessory for some deluxe ranges (Fig. 11–2). Use of the rotisserie is generally for fowl, ham, barbecued ribs, and hors d'oeuvres. The broiler pan is placed under the revolving spit.

A double, "splatter-free" broiler pan is available. Water is added to the bottom, shallow pan and the food is placed in the

Fig. 11–12. Built-in or drop-in surface units. (Frigidaire Division, General Motors Corporation)

Fig. 11–13. Built-in oven with French doors. (Frigidaire Division, General Motors Corporation)

Fig. 11–14. Range with deep-well cooker. (Courtesy Westinghouse Electric Corporation)

Fig. 11–15. Oven next to built-in surface units. "Roastmeter" dial and automatic oven timer on wall above oven. (Philco Corporation)

upper, deep pan. The water in the bottom pan helps keep the fat in the upper pan cool.

A built-in oven with meat thermometer is shown in Figure 11–15. The thermometer is made up of two items. These are: a rod containing a heat-sensitive element which is placed in the meat or fowl and a dial on the wall which indicates degree of doneness of the meat or fowl.

Note: McCracken and Richardson recommend that the lowest *rack position* be about 35 inches from the floor for most built-in electric ovens and about 37 inches for most gas ovens.

B. American Standards Association Standard

The current American Standards Association standard on household electric ranges is C71.1.[3]

The purpose of the standard is to establish a uniform procedure for determining performance requirements of household electric ranges under specified test conditions and to establish certain minimum requirements. The standard covers the topics listed below and certain additional topics.

1. Definitions of terms, such as acid-resisting enamel, back splash, household electric range, and others.

2. Information to be included on nameplate.

3. Structural requirements and test procedures for checking them.

4. Safety requirements and test procedures for checking them. These requirements cover electrical and thermal characteristics. For example, "the temperature of metallic surfaces designed to be handled should not exceed 130 F, and the temperature of nonmetallic surfaces designed to be handled should not exceed 150 F, based on an ambient temperature of 75 F."[4]

[3] C71.1, *American Standard Household Electric Ranges,* American Standards Association, 1950.
[4] *Ibid.,* p. 8.

5. Performance and durability requirements and test procedures for surface units and cookers, ovens, and warming compartment.

Application of the standard for electric ranges differs somewhat from that for gas ranges. The manufacturers use the standard for electric ranges as a reference. Production models of electric ranges may be sent to Underwriters Laboratories. Ordinarily they are not sent to any other central laboratory. Underwriters Laboratories, of course, test primarily for safety and only incidentally for durability and performance characteristics. No seal comparable to the AGA blue seal for gas ranges is placed on electric ranges.

C. Experiments

Experiments 1–6 require no special electrical circuits or measuring equipment. They include experiments on inspection, uniformity of heat distribution in the oven and in the broiler, convenience of use of an electric range for different types of cookery, and oven performance at three temperatures. They may be carried out in a household equipment laboratory, in a home-management house kitchen, or in a homemaker's kitchen.

Experiments 7 and 8 require a temperature-indicating instrument such as a Leeds Northrup Temperature Indicator for use with thermocouples (Experiment 7) or an electrical circuit into which a wattmeter can be connected (Experiment 8).

Experiment 1. *Inspection*

The points to be checked are intended to be helpful in examining electric ranges prior to purchase, as well as laboratory examination. For example, nameplate information and certain seals of approval are important to a user. Overall dimensions determine whether the appliance will fit the available space. Displeasing appearance will be an irritation for a long time. Easily operated controls are desirable.

1. Is the nameplate accessible? Does it give manufacturer's name and address, total kilowatt rating, voltage rating, model or catalogue number, serial number, other information?
2. Does the range have the Underwriters Laboratories seal of approval? (The UL seal may be on the nameplate or elsewhere, for example, on the back of the range. In addition, the user's booklet will usually indicate whether the range is approved by the Underwriters Laboratories.)
3. How many inches wide is the range? How many inches high?
4. Are the controls for surface and oven units easy to grasp and operate?
5. How well constructed does the range seem to be? Do oven doors seem to be adjusted correctly? (Oven doors are *not* intended to fit tightly all the way across the top and sides on all models.) Do drawers slide smoothly? Are corners and surfaces smooth? Do surface units fit firmly? Are reflector pans and drip trays easily removed for cleaning? Do oven racks slide smoothly? Is the color of the top surface, front, and sides uniform in hue? Is toe space provided at the base of the range?

6. Is the design of the range reasonable to you? Do you like the overall appearance? Does the cooking top have a raised edge?

7. What are the sizes in inches as measured along the diameters of the rims of the surface units? What are the wattage ratings of the units? Are any of the units thermostatically controlled? Are any extra-fast heating?

8. Does the range have one or two ovens? How many inches wide, and how many inches high is each oven? (Thickness of exposed open units decreases usable height.) In how many positions will the oven door stay open? Are racks nontipping?

9. Where are broiler pan and grid stored? Are the grid and pan so made that they are easy to clean?

10. Does the user's booklet provide useful information on use and care? Are the instructions on operation of controls clear? Is information included on replacement of platform lamp, oven lamp, and appliance outlet fuse? Are there instructions for cleaning reflector pans, drip trays, oven, broiler grid? Do recipes include suggested times, thermostat settings, and placement of foods in the oven? Do they include ordinary foods as well as unusual foods? If the range has a thermostatically controlled surface unit, does the user's booklet suggest appropriate temperatures for cooking different foods on this unit?

11. Precisely what does the manufacturer's warranty promise the purchaser?

12. What special features does the range have in addition to those mentioned above? Which of these are important to you?

Experiment 2. *Uniformity of Oven Heat Distribution by Brownness of Cookies*

The uniformity of temperatures at one height in an oven may be checked by baking sugar cookies. Use a cooky mix, a favorite recipe, or the following recipe.

Sugar Cookies (about 30)

½ C. shortening	½ t. salt
1 C. sugar	2½ C. cake flour
2 eggs	(sifted before
1 t. flavoring	measuring)
1 T. cream	2 t. baking powder

Cream shortening and sugar. Blend in 2 eggs and beat with an electric mixer at high speed for about 2 minutes. Add vanilla and cream and sifted dry ingredients. Beat at low speed just long enough to work in dry ingredients (2 to 3 minutes).

Chill batter in frozen food compartment of a refrigerator or in a freezer until it can be shaped easily into a roll about 2 inches in diameter. After the batter has been molded into a roll, chill again.

Preheat oven to 375 F. Place uniform slices of cooky batter, about $\frac{3}{16}$-inch thick, on identical baking sheets. Place cookies in oven at end of fourth "on" cycle.

Bake for approximately 8 minutes on a rack placed about 7 inches from upper unit.

Remove baking sheets from oven. Place cookies on racks in same relative positions as the cookies had in the oven.

Observe brownness of tops and bottoms of cookies baked in different locations in the oven. For which locations in the oven, if any, is brownness nonuniform?

Experiment 3. *Uniformity of Broiler Heat Distribution by Brownness of Toast*

Measure area of broiler grid. Cover entire grid with slices of white bread. Place broiler pan with grid on a rack about 5 inches from upper unit. Toast bread on one side only for 6 to 8 minutes, with door ajar.

Remove broiler pan with toast. Measure area of uniformly toasted bread.

Was the area of uniform broiling central with respect to the entire broiling area? What percent of the total broiling area gave uniform broiling?

Experiment 4. *Surface Cookery*

Check convenience for low-heat surface cooking by cooking a cheese sauce or pudding mix with milk in a small utensil. Here is a suggested procedure for cheese sauce. Warm ½ cup milk and stir in ¼ pound diced processed cheese. Heat on low setting until cheese is melted, stirring occasionally with a wooden spoon. Is the product smooth and easily removed from the pan?

Check convenience for medium-heat surface cooking by cooking the following.

Meat Balls with Mushroom Sauce

1 lb. ground beef	1 can condensed mushroom soup
salt, pepper, garlic salt	

Add pepper, salt, and garlic salt to meat. Roll meat into small balls. Cook slowly in an uncovered frypan to which a *little* water has been added.

When almost done, remove meat balls from pan. Pour off excess fat. Add condensed soup to meat stock. Return meat to pan, cover pan, cook until done.

Check convenience of next-to-highest setting and simmer setting with a skillet meal. User's booklets frequently suggest recipes for skillet meals. One recipe is given below.

Skillet Meal

1 lb. round steak	4 medium-size potatoes, cut in quarters
⅓ C. flour	1 large onion cut in ½-inch slices
1 t. salt	1 can condensed tomato soup
3 T. shortening	

Cut meat into serving pieces. Dip in flour-salt mixture.

Brown in hot shortening at next-to-highest setting. Place vegetables on top of meat. Add soup. Cover skillet and cook at simmer setting for about 50 minutes.

Experiment 5. Oven Cookery

The following procedures will give an indication of the performance of the oven and the correctness of the thermostat calibration at three temperatures.

Check low-temperature performance with meringue nests.

Meringue Nests (twelve to fourteen 3-inch nests)

¾ C. egg white   ⅛ t. cream of tartar
   (6 or 7 egg whites)   1¾ C. sifted sugar
⅛ t. salt
 1 t. vanilla

Put egg whites in large bowl of electric mixer. Add salt, vanilla, and cream of tartar. Beat, adding sugar very slowly. Continue beating until mixture is stiff and will hold peaks. Spoon onto a lightly greased 10 x 14-inch cooky sheet or heavy white paper. Bake in an oven preheated to 250 F until a very light crust has formed (50 minutes to one hour, approximately).

Check medium-temperature performance with plain cake. Use a cake mix, a favorite recipe, or the following recipe.

Plain Cake (two 9-inch layers)

3 C. cake flour, sifted   1 C. sugar
2½ t. baking powder   ½ C. shortening
1½ t. salt   2 eggs
 1 t. vanilla   1 C. milk

Sift flour, baking powder, and salt. Add vanilla and sugar to shortening and cream until mixture is light and fluffy (4 to 6 minutes with electric mixer). Add 2 eggs and beat 2 minutes at high speed. Add sifted ingredients to shortening mixture in about three parts, alternating with ½ cup milk after first and second additions of shortening mixture. Mix at low speed for about ½ minute after each addition.

Bake in two lightly greased, paper-lined aluminum cake pans for 25 to 30 minutes in an oven that has been preheated to 375 F.

Test for doneness by inserting a wire cake tester or a toothpick. If the tester comes out clean, the cake is done. It should be lightly browned and should have shrunk slightly from the sides of the pan. The surface should spring back when pressed lightly with a finger.

If the cakes for the recipe given above are not done in 25 to 30 minutes, the actual oven temperature is probably less than 375 F. Other indications of too-low temperature may be coarse texture or sogginess on the bottom of the cakes. If the cakes are overbaked in 25 to 30 minutes, the actual oven temperature is probably higher than 375 F. Other indications of too-high temperature may be humping in the center, cracking on top, and dryness.

Check high-temperature performance with baking powder biscuits. Use a home-made biscuit mix, a commercial mix, or the recipe given below.

Baking Powder Biscuits

2 C. all-purpose flour, sifted	4 T. shortening
2½ t. double-acting baking powder	¾ C. milk
1 t. salt	

Sift baking powder, flour, and salt. Cut shortening into dry ingredients with a pastry blender until mixture has the consistency of coarse corn meal. Form a cavity in center of flour mixture, pour in milk, and stir with a fork. Turn out on lightly floured board and knead *gently* about 1 minute. Pat or roll dough ½-inch thick and cut with biscuit cutter. Place on a 10 x 14-inch cooky sheet.

Bake in a 450 F oven for 12 to 14 minutes.

The appearance and eating quality of the biscuits will depend to a large extent on technique in preparation. However, if the actual oven temperature is very different from 450 F an acceptable product is unlikely with any conventional preparation method.

Experiment 6. *Broiling*

Determine how far meat must be placed from the upper unit to get uniformly done beef patties, as follows.

Shape ground beef into patties about 4 inches in diameter and 1½ inches thick in a mold, if possible.

Broil different groups of patties in successive trials at several distances from the upper unit, with the oven door at the broil position.

Cut through patties vertically to observe whether they are cooked uniformly. Observe shrinkage.

Broil patties with oven door fully open. Observe uniformity of cooking and shrinkage for patties placed at different distances from the upper unit.

Experiment 7. *Accuracy of Thermostat Calibration with Leeds Northrup Temperature Indicator*

1. Adjust instrument according to directions in indicator instruction booklet or on indicator case.
2. Install five insulated thermocouples in a central plane in the oven as follows: one at the center, one midway between the center and the right rear corner of the oven, one midway between the center and the left rear corner, one midway between the center and the right front corner, and one midway between the center and the left front corner. (The thermocouples can be fastened to a rack with paper clips; however, the junctions of the thermocouples should not contact the rack.)
3. Connect the free ends of the thermocouples to the temperature-indicating instrument through a selector switch.
4. Set thermostat dial at 400 F. (The oven should be at room temperature when the test is started.)

5. After the thermostat has opened the circuit four times, record oven temperatures at half-minute intervals for three cycles. That is, record temperatures for the last three of six "on-off" cycles after preheat temperature has been reached.

6. Average the five readings taken at half-minute intervals. Using these averages compute the overall average of the three maximum and three minimum temperatures during the three cycles for which temperatures were recorded. If the average thus found differs from 400 F by more than plus or minus 15 F, change the thermostat calibration if possible. Let the oven cool; then recheck the 400 F setting.

7. Set thermostat dial at 300 F. The oven should again be at room temperature when the test is started. Check accuracy of thermostat calibration at this setting by the procedure used for the 400 F setting. Calibration is assumed correct at 300 F if the average value found at that setting differs by not less than 90 degrees or more than 110 degrees from the average value found for the 400 F setting. For example, if the average temperature corresponding to a 400 dial setting is 405 F, the average temperature corresponding to a 300 dial setting should be between 315 F and 295 F. If not, no change should be made in thermostat calibration at 300 F, but the user should compensate for this inaccuracy by setting the thermostat dial higher or lower, according to the inaccuracy of the calibration, for recipes that call for 300 F.

Experiment 8. *Thermal Efficiency of Surface Units*

The thermal efficiency of a surface unit is determined by heating a specified amount of water in a utensil of known weight and specific heat. The change in temperature of the water and the electric energy used are recorded. The thermal efficiency expressed as a percent is

$$\frac{[\text{weight of water} + (\text{weight of utensil} \times \text{specific heat of utensil})] \times \text{temp. change} \times 100}{0.239 \text{ watts} \times \text{seconds}}$$

Weights of water and utensil with cover are in grams. The specific heat of the utensil depends on the material of the utensil. The specific heat of aluminum is 0.22. The temperature change is in degrees centigrade.

Specific procedure is outlined below.

1. Set up an electric circuit to measure watts supplied to range.

2. Weigh the utensil and lid. (Weight of thermometer is assumed negligible.) For a 6-inch surface unit, use a 2-quart utensil. The lid of the utensil should have a hole in it for a mercury-in-glass thermometer.

3. Add 900 grams of cold tap water to the utensil.

4. Place the thermometer in a cored rubber cork and place cork with thermometer in the hole in the lid. Adjust the thermometer so that the bottom of its bulb is at least $\frac{1}{8}$ inch above the bottom of the utensil.

5. Place utensil with thermometer on the surface unit whose thermal efficiency is to be measured.

6. Record temperature of water.

7. Turn control on surface unit to "high" and start a stop watch.

8. Record wattmeter reading.
9. Turn surface unit off when temperature of water reaches 90 C. Record number of seconds required.
10. Compute thermal efficiency.

If the thermal efficiency of an 8-inch unit is to be measured, a 3- or 4-quart utensil and 1800 grams of water should be used. If the material of the utensil is not aluminum, get the specific heat of the material from a table in a handbook.

CHAPTER 12

Electronic Ranges

At the present time the number of household electronic ranges in use is very small in relation to the number of conventional electric ranges. One reason is that the electronic range is a new appliance. Production models became available for sale through distributors only in 1956. Another reason is that electronic ranges cost four or more times as much as stripped conventional ranges.

The appliance is called an electronic *range* because it can be used satisfactorily for some types of cookery ordinarily done on the surface of a range. For example, water can be heated in the appliance quickly, bacon can be cooked in the appliance in a very short time, and so on.[1] On the other hand, manufacturers and other persons who anticipate that the appliance will be used with surface units, and perhaps with a conventional oven as well, call it an electronic *oven*.

Construction-wise, an electronic range resembles an oven (Fig. 12–1). The overall dimensions of one model (Tappan RL–1) are these: height, $26\frac{1}{2}$ inches; depth, $22\frac{7}{8}$ inches; width, $23\frac{5}{8}$ inches. Ordinarily the range will be installed in a wall-type cabinet or set on a counter.

Unlike conventional ranges, electronic ranges need only minimum insulation because, generally, *only* the food becomes hot. The range itself does not become hot unless a unit for browning foods is used.

A housing of stainless steel is available when the range is to be mounted on a counter. Interior surfaces of the model illustrated are anodized aluminum. In place of the window found in deluxe conventional ranges, the door contains a grid with holes approximately $\frac{3}{16}$ inch in diameter. This grid permits escape of steam and other volatile by-products of cooking; it also permits the user to see the food as it cooks. (The oven has some light in it when the microwave unit is on.) Three sets of shelf racks and one solid Fiberglas shelf are provided.

The electronic range shown in Figure 12–1 includes a tubular-type unit for browning meats. This "browning unit" operates independently of the microwave circuit. It is of course mounted near the top of the oven. Above it is a Vikor glass plate and between the glass plate and the oven ceiling is a four-blade, motor-operated fan. In the Tappan electronic range the fan is called a stirrer. The shaft on which the stirrer is mounted goes through the ceiling of the oven. The ceiling also has a rectangular opening to the rear of the fan through which the microwaves enter the oven.

[1] Other examples are cited in an article by Faith Fenton, "Research on electronic cooking," *J. of Home Economics,* Vol. 49, No. 9 (November, 1957).

Fig. 12–1.   Front view of electronic range. (The Tappan Stove Company)

12–1. ELECTRICAL SUPPLY AND MICROWAVE CIRCUIT

Required electrical supply characteristics for electronic ranges are similar to those for conventional electric ranges. The electronic range requires a power source supplying 208 to 230 volts at 60 cycles. Voltage compensation in the electronic circuit will actually handle voltages up to 250. Wattage input for the range illustrated in Figure 12–1 is 2400 watts at low speed and 3100 watts at high speed for the microwave unit, and 4000 watts for the browning unit. The low-speed setting of the microwave unit is used for cooking meats. The browning unit is used in addition when cooking time is so short that the meat will not otherwise brown. The high-speed setting of the microwave unit is used for most other foods.

A schematic view of a circuit for producing the microwaves is shown in Figure 12–2. The schematic illustration is included here in place

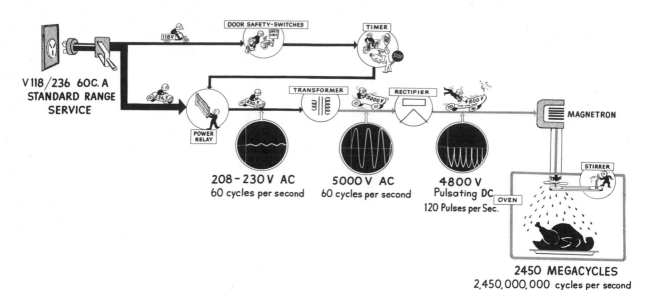

Fig. 12–2. How the microwave oven works. Schematic view of microwave circuit for electronic range. (Hotpoint Company)

of the electronic circuit, partly because a description of the actual circuit is beyond the scope of this text.

Figure 12–2 indicates electromagnetic waves with a frequency of 2450 megacycles. A frequency of 915 megacycles per second has also been approved by the Federal Communications Commission for household-size units.

The microwaves produced by the *magnetron* are diffused in all directions through the oven. Metallic surfaces either *reflect* or *absorb* the waves. Paper, glass, and china containers *transmit* the waves. Foods *absorb* the waves. The depth of penetration of the microwaves into meats, batters, vegetables, liquids, and other foods is of the order of 2 to $2\frac{1}{2}$ inches. Actually, according to theory the energy is not *all* absorbed in the first $2\frac{1}{2}$ inches, but only a very small amount of microwave energy penetrates farther than $2\frac{1}{2}$ inches.

Absorption of microwaves by food produces heat *in* the food. If the dimensions of the food are less than 5 inches by 5 inches by 5 inches, the entire food mass, except the surfaces, is cooked chiefly by heat associated with the absorption of the microwaves. If the dimensions of the food are greater than 5 inches by 5 inches by 5 inches, the *interior* of the food is cooked by heat conducted to it from the outer 2- to $2\frac{1}{2}$-inch layer or mantle of food that has absorbed the microwaves.

12–2. USE AND CARE

The "on-off" control is turned to "on." After approximately 75 seconds, the tubes of the electronic circuit will be sufficiently warm so that the *microwave control* can be turned on.

Food in or on glass or paper containers or in chinaware that has no metallic trim is placed in the range. The selector switch is turned to high or low as specified in the recipe file that accompanies the range. The timer is set to the specified cooking time, and the door is closed. When the set cooking time is up, a bell rings and the microwave unit turns off automatically. (It also turns off automatically any time the door is opened, as for turning food.) For some meats, such as steaks, the browning unit is turned on for the same length of time as the microwave unit; for roasts, the browning unit may be turned on only for the last two or three minutes of the cooking time, or not at all.

Because food is cooked by heat produced in its own outer layers rather than by transfer of heat through air in the oven, some use characteristics are quite different for electronic ranges than for conventional ranges. Cooking times are much shorter. The electronic range does not have a thermostat. Conventional cooking procedures and some recipes are modified.

The manufacturer supplies a recipe file with the range. A recipe for rolled rib roast, for example, specifies the following three factors: low speed, minutes of cooking time, and minutes browning unit should be on. The cooking times for a rib roast are six minutes per pound approximately for rare, seven minutes per pound for medium, and eight minutes per pound for well done.

An interesting difference in food preparation is the use of "standing time" after or during the time a roast is cooked. For example, after a 5-pound rolled rib roast has been cooked in the range for the time specified in the recipe, the meat is allowed to stand in or out of the range 20 to 30 minutes before carving. During this time it will increase about 20 F in internal temperature. A meat thermometer calibrated from 80 F to 190 F is provided with the range.

Recipes supplied by one manufacturer cover the following categories of food: appetizers, beverages, soups, breads, cakes, desserts, jams, meats, pies, vegetables, and miscellaneous foods. Information on cooking times and suggestions on glass utensils to be used for prepared mixes are included. Several menus are suggested, and recommendations are given regarding sequence for cooking the different foods in the menus, since usually only one food is prepared at one time in the range.

The electronic range is in many ways a more versatile appliance than a conventional oven. Foods may be reheated quickly in serving dishes. "Old" foods may be freshened in a very short time. Some frozen foods such as bread may be defrosted very quickly.

Other use characteristics might be characterized as limitations. White cakes are baked in three minutes, but the surface does not brown and the cakes "stale" faster than those baked in a conventional range. Quantity of food affects cooking time; cooking one baked potato requires about four minutes but cooking six baked potatoes may require 10 minutes. Potatoes baked in an electronic range are acceptable, but somewhat different in taste from those baked in a conventional range. Some products bake more satisfactorily in a conventional range than in an electronic range; an example is angel food cake.

A homemaker who purchases an electronic range at this time is somewhat in the position of one who purchased a home freezer when that appliance first became available. She has the opportunity of experimenting with new recipes and she may find new and convenient uses for her range. She may gain free time, because cooking times are shorter in the electronic range, and she may gain for her family and herself more varied menus.

Care of the electronic range when only the microwave unit is used consists chiefly in wiping the walls and shelf with a damp cloth after each use. In models that have a browning unit, grease may splatter on interior surfaces when the browning unit is used. In this case, the interior surfaces will need to be cleaned, *after* the range has cooled.

Gas Refrigerators

A. Construction, Use, and Care

The material in this chapter applies to gas refrigerators manufactured prior to 1956 by one company. Production of gas refrigerators was resumed in 1958 by other manufacturers. The newer models are functionally similar to those described in this chapter.

The gas refrigerator (Fig. 13–1) is constructed of an exterior shell and an inner liner with Fiberglas or mineral wool batts between the two. The shells are joined by a nonheat-conducting plastic material. The door also consists of two shells with insulation between. The outer shell is finished in a synthetic enamel.

The shelves are made of steel and have a rust- and stain-resistant finish. Some models have roll-out shelves and most current models have adjustable shelves. All but the smallest model have shelves in the door.

The cooling system of the gas refrigerator has no moving parts. It is quiet, as there is no starting and stopping of a motor.

The refrigeration system in the gas refrigerator depends upon the force of gravity for successful operation; hence it is essential that the refrigerator be level. The refrigeration unit itself is held in place by a rigid steel frame. Leveling screws on the bottom of the refrigerator make the task of leveling easier. There must also be proper air circulation for the cooling of the condensing coils and for the proper operation of the gas burner. Figure 13–2 shows the line of air flow. Air enters the burner compartment at the lower front of the refrigerator, and the louvered section on top of the refrigerator serves as the outlet for it.

13–1. ABSORPTION SYSTEM

The main functional parts of the gas refrigerator consist of a sealed-in refrigerating unit and a burner which supplies the heat to operate it.

The refrigeration system in the gas refrigerator is known as an absorption system. It has three cycles within one closed system. They are often referred to as the ammonia cycle, the hydrogen cycle, and the water cycle. Ammonia is the refrigerant; as it evaporates it absorbs heat from the interior of the refrigerator. Hydrogen is used to keep the pressure such that the ammonia will evaporate consistently in all kinds of weather and operating conditions. Water is used to separate the ammonia and hydrogen after they have passed through the evaporator. Figure 13–3 is a simplified drawing showing the relationship of these three cycles in the one system.

As the ammonia in liquid form passes through the evaporator, it is changed into a gas by the heat from the interior of the refrigerator. More or less hydrogen gas is allowed to go through with the ammonia, depending upon the operating conditions. Together, the ammonia and hydrogen are heavier than air; hence, due to gravity, they fall to the absorber where they meet the water. The ammonia will mix with the water and form a weak ammonium hydroxide solution. The hydrogen does not mix. Furthermore, hydrogen is lighter than air, so when it is separated from the ammonia, it continues upward in the system to the evaporator and is then ready to repeat its cycle. The water and ammonia are carried to the generator where the heat from the gas flame is applied. The heat vaporizes the ammonia, and as the vapor rises it carries water up the percolator tube. The vapor continues to rise while the water, due to the force of gravity, falls, returns to the absorber, and is then ready to repeat its cycle. The ammonia in vapor form passes through tubes known as condensing coils in an air-cooled finned unit. The condensed ammonia then repeats its cycle.

13–2. GAS BURNERS

Gas burners are made for the various types of gases which may be used. The correct burner must be used for the type of gas available, and it is the job of a qualified service man to install the correct one or change the burner if a family moves and uses a different type of gas as fuel.

The heat input of the burner must be properly regulated, and this should be done by a qualified service man when the refrigerator is installed. The gas burner has a safety valve on

Fig. 13–1. The gas refrigerator. (American Gas Association, *Woman's Home Companion*)

it which is essentially a bimetallic disk thermostat. When the burner goes out, the disk contracts and the gas valve closes. Relighting the burner involves an operation similar to that

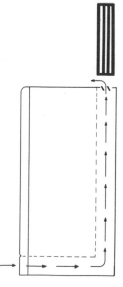

Fig. 13–2. Line of air flow in the gas refrigerator. (Copyright, 1956, by Servel, Inc. Reproduced by special permission of the copyright owner.)

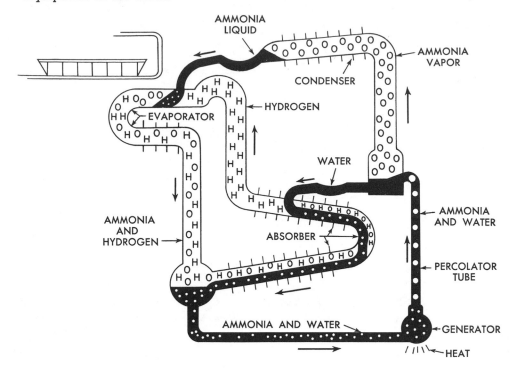

Fig. 13–3. The absorption cooling system. (Copyright, 1956, by Servel, Inc. Reproduced by special permission of the copyright owner.)

described for relighting safety pilots on gas range ovens (Chapter 10, p. 144).

The burner flame burns continuously, becoming higher or lower as the thermostat signals that it should. The minimum flame on the burner keeps the safety valve open, keeps the flues warm to maintain proper draft, and keeps the refrigerant solution at the correct minimum working temperature.

13–3. SPECIAL FEATURES

On the more deluxe models of the gas refrigerator, a device called the ice maker makes ice cubes automatically. This eliminates the problem of remembering to put water in the ice cube trays to freeze. The ice maker can be shut off by two procedures: one is to lift the signal arm and leave it fastened on a hook provided for that purpose; the other is to shut off the water supply to it.

The first ice cubes (circles) made after the refrigerator is installed or has been left turned

off a while should be thrown away, as the ice may have an "off" flavor from the stale taste of the water or impurities in the water line. After the refrigerator is in use, the ice circles need to be discarded only if stored for a long time, because they may absorb flavors from foods in the refrigerator.

When a tray full of ice circles has frozen, a sensitive element next to the ice circle at the back of the refrigerator signals a small motor to begin operation, and at the same time heater coils beneath the tray are heated. The combination of heat and force eject the ice circles into a plastic basket. This is done so quickly that the ice circles melt very little; they are held at the top of the tray for an instant to dry. They do not stick together unless left in the freezer for long periods of time. When they have been ejected, the heat is turned off and the water valve opened. This is an automatic device in which water pressure operates to keep a measured amount of water coming into the tray. This is a timed operation; at the end of the period, the water is shut off and the freezing cycle begins.

The ice maker operates continuously until the plastic basket which catches the ice circles is filled. The signal arm which rests on the circles is raised by this process and the automatic procedure stops until the basket is emptied of some of the circles, thus lowering the signal arm.

Models of the gas refrigerator which contain the ice maker require connections to gas, electricity, and water. The ice maker is self-cleaning. While it is possible to make colored ice circles, one may have colored ice circles for quite some time thereafter.

Any model, with or without the ice maker, may be used as a built-in model if properly installed. Air enters at the base of the refrigerator and flows upward and out at the top of the refrigerator into the room in which the refrigerator is located. Air pressure may vary slightly from one location to another.

The refrigerator can be built in to make a complete unit with a built-in oven and surface burners.

13–4. USE

Refrigerators have become such a common and necessary piece of equipment that factors which make for efficient use may often be neglected or ignored. No matter how splendid the design and manufacture of a piece of equipment, it will give its best service only when used as the manufacturer intended.

The refrigerator should be located conveniently to the other work centers in the kitchen. It is also highly desirable that it be reasonably close to the eating areas, as many foods are served directly from the refrigerator to the table.

Excessive opening of the refrigerator door will cause the frost accumulation on the evaporator to be greater than necessary. It is well to think before opening the door and then remove several foods for a meal at one time. In sum-

mer the door may be opened frequently because of the popularity of cold drinks. Generally it will then be necessary to defrost more often because of the extra openings of the door, higher room temperature, and the storage of many foods with a high water content. A colder setting of the control dial is usually desirable in warm weather.

Refrigerators with separately insulated freezer compartments which maintain near-zero temperatures can be used in a manner similar to a home freezer. Figure 8–2 shows this type of refrigerator. To make most efficient use of the freezer section there should be a turnover of stored foods rather than storage of foods for long periods of time.

Small quantities of food may be frozen at one time, but a refrigerator freezer is not designed to freeze quickly a large amount of food at one time. The coldest setting on the control dial should be used when making ice cream, for freezing foods, or for fast freezing of ice cubes.

The shelves on the door are useful for bottled beverages, pickles, olives, certain cheeses, and many other small items that seem to collect in the refrigerator. This door storage makes it easy to locate small items.

13–5. CARE

Refrigerators actually require very little care in comparison to the amount of service they give, but regular care should be a part of every homemaker's routine if the refrigerator is to remain in tiptop operating condition all the time.

The exterior should be kept clean by washing with lukewarm water and a mild detergent, rinsing with clear water, and drying with a soft cloth. Abrasives should not be used on either the exterior or interior of a refrigerator.

The interior of the refrigerator should be washed with a solution of warm water and baking soda. Excessively hot water should not be used on plastic parts; if water is not too hot for the hands, it is not too hot for the plastic parts.

The condensing coils must be kept clean and free from excessive accumulation of dust if the refrigerant is to cool and condense quickly. On top of the refrigerator is a louvered grille which should be kept uncovered and free from dust. If it is covered by a cloth or articles are stored on top of the refrigerator, the burner will not operate properly, and consequently the cooling operation will be impaired.

The cold control compartment should also be cleaned occasionally, as it will get dusty after a period of time.

The gasket on the door should be kept clean. From time to time it may need washing with a mild soap in warm water, followed by rinsing with clear water. If the user is careful not to place her hands on the gasket as she uses the refrigerator, the gasket will tend to wear longer. Oil and soil from the hands may have a deteriorating effect on the material of the gasket. Should it lose its resiliency, it is wise to have it replaced, as the refrigerator cannot be adequately cooled under these conditions. To check the door seal, place a 100-watt bulb in the interior of the refrigerator, using a flat extension cord with it, shut the door, and check for leaks of light. If light can be seen, the gasket may need to be replaced or the door may need to be adjusted by a service man.

The various models of gas refrigerators are equipped with different types of defrosting: automatic, push button, or manual. In refrigerators with automatic defrosting the defrosting takes place automatically once every 24 hours. It is only necessary to set the timer at the correct time of day when the refrigerator is installed or after any period when the electricity has been off. Defrosting takes place during the night, and the defrost water drains into a plastic cup which empties into an evaporating pan at the back of the refrigerator. Occasionally this plastic cup should be removed and cleaned.

In refrigerators which have automatic defrosting and a special freezer section, the freezer is treated much like a home freezer and defrosted only at infrequent intervals. Complete defrosting must be done manually. Frost accumulation can be removed by scraping with a dull-edged instrument, such as a bevel-edged plastic scraper.

In warm and humid weather, refrigerators with push-button defrosting should be defrosted two or three times a week or even daily. Push-button defrosting is much like automatic defrosting, except that the user must remember to start the defrosting process and empty the meat storage tray which catches the defrost water. If defrosting is done as often as recommended, it does not take long and frozen foods stored in the freezer do not have time to thaw.

Manual defrosting has been the conventional method of defrosting as long as mechanical refrigerators have been on the market. The cold control dial is turned to "off" and the water is allowed to drip into the emptied meat storage tray. When the frost is melted the evaporator is washed and dried, the tray emptied and cleaned, and the cold control dial reset. Defrosting can be hurried by placing trays of warm water in the evaporator. It is not advisable to use extremely hot water, as it may remove the special finish used on the trays. It stands to reason that all ice cubes should be removed from the freezing compartment before defrosting begins. If the ice cubes are to be saved until defrosting is completed, they should be wrapped in several layers of newspaper and left in the refrigerator. Any frozen food in the evaporator should be treated in the same manner.

B. Experiments

Experiments 1, 2, 3, and 5, pp. 201, 202, 203, Chapter 14, may be used here with minor changes. Experiments 1 through 3 require no special measuring devices. Experiment 5, p. 203, requires a gas meter and thermocouple equipment.

Experiment 1. *Inspection* (Suggested Additions)

1. Check for the American Gas Association seal of approval and for the British thermal unit input of the burner on the nameplate.
2. Is an ice maker included as one of the special features?

Experiment 2. *Energy Consumptions and Temperatures for No-Load Tests* (Suggested Changes for Experiment 5, p. 203)

Install three thermocouples in the cabinet at locations specified in the ASA standard for different types of refrigerators. Connect their free ends to a recording temperature instrument for an extended test or to a temperature indicator for a test of two hours or so. Refrigerator must be connected to a gas line in which a gas meter has been placed.

After temperature equilibrium has been established for a particular thermostat setting, according to the recommendations given in Experiment 4, p. 203, note the time, read the gas meter, and start observing temperatures. When the test is complete, again note the time and read the gas meter.

Record the average temperature indicated by the three thermocouples over each cycle. Subtract the initial reading of the gas meter from the final reading and calculate cubic feet of gas used per 24 hours.

CHAPTER 14

Electric Refrigerators

Refrigerators are used primarily to store fresh foods, other foods that stale or develop "off" flavors, and frozen foods. Such foods as watermelons and certain beverages are also stored in a refrigerator because we enjoy eating or drinking them when they are cold. Fresh foods are stored in a food storage compartment or food compartment and frozen foods are stored in a frozen food storage compartment or frozen food compartment.[1] Stand-

ard-type refrigerators also are used for making ice cubes and for freezing small quantities of foods.

The widespread dual use of the refrigerator by homemakers—storage of fresh and frozen foods and freezing of foods—has led refrigerator manufacturers to make combination refrigerators (refrigerator and freezer) in addition to standard-type refrigerators. The combination refrigerator is assembled in a single cabinet that includes two refrigerating systems and one motor-compressor unit.

---

[1] A few models, planned for use with freezers, do not have a separate frozen food compartment.

Average design temperatures in the food compartment and in the frozen food compartment of both standard and combination refrigerators vary for different models. The design temperature in the food compartment is determined primarily by its use requirements for storage of fresh foods. Fresh foods are refrigerated because refrigeration retards the growth of the microörganisms which cause food spoilage. An average temperature under normal operating conditions between approximately 33 F and 48 F appears to be accepted by manufacturers as most practicable. Higher temperatures might not preserve the quality of many foods for reasonable lengths of time; lower temperatures would cause some foods to freeze and would increase the operating cost of the refrigerator.

Under normal operating conditions average temperatures in the frozen food compartment of standard-type refrigerators usually range from approximately 10 F to 15 F. Average temperatures in the freezers of different combination refrigerators range from near zero to approximately 8 F, but some combination refrigerators maintain average temperatures below zero in the freezer.

A. Construction, Use, and Care

14–1. CONSTRUCTION

Standard refrigerators currently available come in free-standing or built-in models. Combination refrigerators come in free-standing, built-in, or hanging-wall models. The latter type is mounted on a wall in somewhat the same way as a wall cabinet. Sizes of refrigerators and combination refrigerators are quoted in interior volume to the nearest 0.1 cubic foot. The volume quoted is the sum of the volumes of the food compartment, the frozen food compartment, and the ice-freezing compartment, if a separate ice-freezing compartment is provided. The volume occupied by the cooling unit is not included.

Sizes of free-standing models offered by one manufacturer are 4.4, 6.1, 7.6, 9.1, and 11.0 cubic feet for standard refrigerators and 8.4, 10.3, 11.2, 11.5, and 15.0 cubic feet for combination refrigerators. Sizes smaller than 8 cubic feet are usually purchased only for special purposes, such as recreation rooms or summer cabins. Built-in and hanging-wall models are still so new that typical sizes cannot be cited.

Certain parts common to all refrigerators and combination refrigerators are described below. A knowledge of basic construction is helpful in evaluating sales literature and is an aid in understanding why certain use and care procedures are necessary.

a. Cabinet and Door

The shell of the cabinet is usually a welded steel structure which supports the inner food compartments, the door, and the refrigerating mechanism (Figs. 14–1 and 14–2). The steel shell is usually treated chemically, as by Bondcrizing, to increase resistance to rust. Exterior panels on the shell are generally baked-on synthetic enamel.

The insulation between the shell and the liner or liners of the food compartments is from 2 to $3\frac{1}{2}$ inches thick on different models, with the thicker insulation usually used in larger models. Materials used for insulation include Fiberglas, mineral wool, and Styrofoam. (Styrofoam is one of the newer insulating materials for refrigerators.) The insulation is installed so as to permit any moisture vapor that gets into it from the outside air to migrate to the inside of the cabinet. Plastic breaker strips cover the front surfaces of the insulation.

The insulation in the door is installed between the curved, outer steel panel of the door

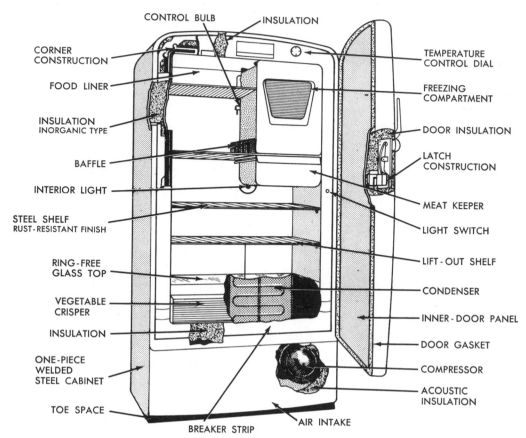

CONTROL BULB — INSULATION — TEMPERATURE CONTROL DIAL

CORNER CONSTRUCTION

FOOD LINER

INSULATION INORGANIC TYPE

BAFFLE

INTERIOR LIGHT

STEEL SHELF RUST-RESISTANT FINISH

RING-FREE GLASS TOP

VEGETABLE CRISPER

INSULATION

ONE-PIECE WELDED STEEL CABINET

TOE SPACE

BREAKER STRIP

AIR INTAKE

FREEZING COMPARTMENT

DOOR INSULATION

LATCH CONSTRUCTION

MEAT KEEPER

LIGHT SWITCH

LIFT-OUT SHELF

CONDENSER

INNER-DOOR PANEL

DOOR GASKET

COMPRESSOR

ACOUSTIC INSULATION

Fig. 14–1. Cutaway view of refrigerator. (Copied with permission of Westinghouse Electric Corporation, copyright 1952)

and an inner plastic panel. A flexible door gasket fits over the outer edges of the plastic panel.

Part of the inner plastic door panel and the strips on the front of the cabinet serve as breaker strips between the steel door and the steel cabinet. In current models, breaker strips are usually colored.

Usually refrigerators are supplied with a right-hand door—that is, a door hinged on the right side. For many models a left-hand door can be obtained by special order.

The cabinet of a combination refrigerator may have one or two outside doors. If two are provided, one is for the freezer and one for the refrigerator. If one outside door is provided, the freezer has an interior door.

b. Storage Compartments

As stated earlier, practically all refrigerators have a food compartment and a frozen food compartment. Until the last few years, the frozen food compartment was always located above the food compartment in standard refrigerators, and the freezer was located above the food compartment in combination refrigerators. In some new models, the frozen food compartment of standard refrigerators and the freezer of combination refrigerators is located below the food compartment.

If the frozen food compartment is near the top of the refrigerator, it is a U-shaped compartment on smaller and less deluxe models and a substantially full-width compartment on

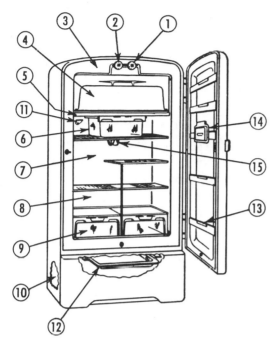

Fig. 14–2. Refrigerator with automatic defrost. (Reprinted from the *Air Conditioning Refrigerating Data Book*, Design Volume, 1955–56, 9th edition, published by The American Society of Refrigerating Engineers.) 1. Temperature control. 2. Defrost control. 3. Breaker strip. 4. Frozen food compartment. 5. Insulated baffle. 6. Meat storage drawer. 7. Bottle storage space. 8. Food compartment. 9. Vegetable storage space. 10. Unit compartment. 11. Drain. 12. Water evaporator pan. 13. Door shelf. 14. Butter storage compartment. 15. Food compartment light.

larger and more deluxe models. The U-shaped frozen food compartment was formerly called, and is sometimes still called, the evaporator compartment, or simply the evaporator.[2]

The food compartment usually has three or more rust-resistant racks. Models with a U-shaped frozen food compartment usually have one half-width rack and two full-width racks. In models with a full-width frozen food compartment, all the racks may be full width or one or more may be half-width. One or more plate-glass shelves may also be provided for special purposes.

[2] Technically, the word *evaporator* refers to that portion of the refrigerating circuit in which the refrigerant evaporates (see p. 192).

The frozen food compartment commonly has one or more solid metal shelves. A few combination models have racks in the freezer.

The finish usually used on liners of storage compartments is an acid-resistant porcelain enamel. However, synthetic organic finishes may be used.

Various special sections or compartments may be provided. One is a meat storage section maintained at a temperature close to freezing and at a high relative humidity. Compartments, drawers, or covered pans are provided for leafy vegetables. These are also high-humidity compartments, since in a closed container the cooling surface is the entire surface of the container. Shelves on the inside of the door are becoming increasingly common. Usually, these are used for storage of small containers, beverages, eggs, etc. A compartment with heating coils may be provided inside the refrigerator cabinet to maintain butter at suitable spreading temperatures.

c. Ultraviolet Lamp for High-Humidity Food Compartment

An ultraviolet lamp is usually provided in a food storage compartment designed to operate at high relative humidity. A high-humidity food storage compartment, in contrast to a high-humidity vegetable compartment, is a rather deluxe feature. The high humidity permits storing foods uncovered. They do not dry out because the moisture in the air reduces the rate of evaporation from their surfaces. The function of the ultraviolet lamp is to retard bacteria and mold growth in food stored in the moist air. In addition to its bactericidal action, the ultraviolet lamp generates some ozone which reduces or at least changes cabinet odor.

d. Baffle and Damper

An insulated baffle is provided between the bottom of the frozen food compartment and the top of the food compartment in some refrigerators that have the frozen food compartment at the top. The baffle permits a greater temperature differential between the frozen food compartment and the food compartment than would otherwise be the case.

Some models do not have an insulated baffle but do have a narrow damper or deflector under the frozen food compartment, at the rear. This may be a plastic strip hinged to the back of a meat drawer or to the bottom of the frozen food compartment. The damper usually will be flat, that is, parallel to the bottom of the frozen food compartment in the winter and vertical in the summer. When the damper is vertical, the air in the fresh food compartment can move to contact cold evaporator coils. Thus the fresh food compartment is colder when the damper is vertical or open than when it is flat or closed.

On some models the user adjusts the damper manually; on others the damper is opened or closed automatically, according to the setting of the thermostat control.

Some refrigerators have neither a baffle nor a damper.

14–2. REFRIGERATING MECHANISM

Electric refrigerators may have a compression refrigeration system or systems with a motor-compressor unit or an absorption refrigeration system with an electric heating element. In the United States the compression system is the usual electric type. Only this type is described in this chapter. The refrigeration mechanism of the absorption system is the same as that for a gas refrigerator, described in Chapter 13.

a. Functional Parts

The principal functional parts of a compressor-type refrigerating mechanism are these: motor-compressor assembly, condenser, restrictor or expansion device, evaporator, refrigerant tubing, refrigerant, and thermostat control.

The motor-compressor assembly frequently is called the unit. The compressor is operated by the motor, and the two parts (compressor and motor) are assembled in an air-tight housing supported externally by rubber or spring mountings. In current models of free-standing refrigerators, the unit is near the bottom of the refrigerator as shown in Figures 14–1 and 14–2. The compressor may be a reciprocating type or a rotary type. The motor is an induction type—split-phase start and induction-run or capacitor-start and induction-run. The nominal rating of the compressor motor is commonly $1/4$ horsepower for combination refrigerators and between $1/6$ and $1/9$ horsepower for standard models.

The condenser on most free-standing refrigerators is installed on the back of the cabinet and, unless it is a wire-type, is likely to have a curved metal panel surrounding it. Three types are commonly used. One is finned, steel tubing, brazed or welded to a plate; the second is wire-type tubing spot-welded to vertical rods (Fig. 14–3); and the third is a pair of plates formed to provide passage for the refrigerant between them. Some of the new compact or streamlined refrigerators have the condenser at the bottom of the cabinet to permit installation of the cabinet flush to the wall.

Generally condensers are designed for free or natural air circulation. When the condenser is on the back of the cabinet, the curved panel and/or spacing bolts insure free space for air circulation. When the condenser is mounted at or near the bottom of the cabinet, louvered plates or grilles may be provided near the bottom and top of the refrigerator for natural air circulation. On a few models, a fan is provided for forced air circulation.

The restrictor or expansion device is a capillary tube installed in the refrigerating circuit between the condenser and the evaporator.

Evaporators may consist of tubing fastened to sheets, tubing alone, or two plates formed

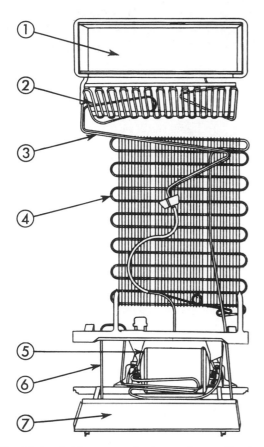

Fig. 14–3. Refrigerator with wire condenser. (Reprinted from the *Air Conditioning Refrigerating Data Book*, Design Volume, 1955–56, 9th edition, published by The American Society of Refrigerating Engineers.)
1. Frozen food evaporator.   2. Food compartment evaporator.   3. Capillary tube—suction tube heat exchanger.   4. Wire-tube condenser.   5. Motor compressor.   6. Discharge tube from compressor.
7. Water evaporator pan, plate—discharge gas heated.

to provide refrigerant passages between them. The evaporator tubing is usually located in or under the U-shaped, frozen food compartment or the full-width, frozen food compartment. For certain deluxe models called cold-wall models the evaporator tubing is installed in the frozen food compartment and the walls of the fresh food compartment.

The two refrigerants used are Freon-12 (dichlorodifluoromethane) and Freon-114 (dichlorotetrafluoromethane). Freon-114 is used in refrigerators with rotary compressors

only; Freon-12 is used with rotary and reciprocating compressors.

A thermostat-type control, described below, is used to start and stop the compressor motor.

b. Refrigerating Cycle

General principles of two types of refrigerating cycles are described here. The various auxiliary components found in actual refrigerators are considered in specialized texts on refrigeration.

Figure 14–4 shows schematically the path of the refrigerant for a one-evaporator mechanism. From the compressor, hot refrigerant

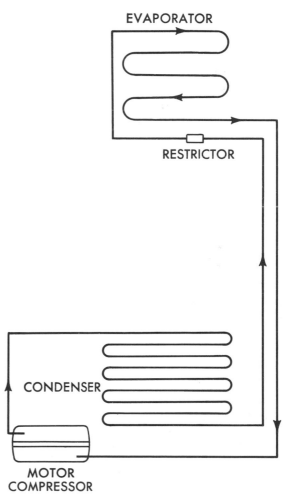

Fig. 14–4. Schematic diagram of path of refrigerant in a one-evaporator system.

vapor goes directly to the condenser where it cools, by giving up heat to the air in the room, and liquefies. The liquid refrigerant moves up through capillary tubing to the restrictor, which actually may be a narrowed portion of the capillary tubing. When the liquid refrigerant passes through the restrictor, it expands and thus enters the evaporator at reduced pressure. In the evaporator, the liquid refrigerant absorbs heat from the food in the cabinet and thus cools the food. As heat is absorbed, the liquid vaporizes. The cold refrigerant vapor moves down to the inlet or suction side of the compressor. In the compressor the vapor is compressed and heated. The cycle then starts again.

Figure 14–5 shows schematically the path of the refrigerant for one model of a Dual Temp refrigerator that has a freezing compartment and a high-humidity food compartment, with a single temperature control. The heat-sensitive element ("feeler tube" or capillary bulb) is clamped to the refrigerating coils or "humid cold plate" of the food compartment. The difference in temperature between the food compartment and the freezer is accomplished by a restrictor tube between the cooling coils of the two compartments. A change in setting of the temperature control changes the temperatures in both compartments.

An alternative design for the refrigerating mechanism of combination models has two temperature controls—one for the freezer and one for the food compartment. A two-control system may be so designed that a change in setting of the control for one compartment (freezer or food) does not noticeably change the temperature in the other compartment.

c. Thermostat Control

The thermostat control consists of a capillary bulb and bellows unit connected to a spring-controlled mechanical linkage of levers. The mechanical linkage brings together or sepa-

rates electrical contacts, thereby closing or opening the electrical circuit of the compressor motor (Fig. 14–6). The "setting" of the spring that controls the levers is itself controlled by the setting to which the user turns the thermostat dial.

The capillary bulb and bellows are filled with a heat-sensitive liquid. Cycling of the motor-compressor assembly is determined by the temperature of the bulb. For standard-type refrigerators the bulb is usually mounted near the evaporator.

The bulb temperatures at which electrical contacts open are as follows for one manufacturer's line of standard-type refrigerators.[3]

Control Setting	Contacts Open	Contacts Close
Warmest	$18° \pm 2°$ F	$29° \pm 2°$ F
Normal	$11° \pm 1°$ F	$22° \pm 1°$ F
Coldest	$4° \pm 2°$ F	$15° \pm 2°$ F

In some standard refrigerators that defrost automatically during each cycle of operation, and in at least one model of combination refrigerator, the thermostat dial setting determines only the temperature at which contacts open. The temperature at which they close is fixed at some value higher than 32 F; for example, the contacts may close at 39 F. Such a control may operate as follows: at normal setting, the compressor motor runs until the bulb temperature is 0 F. Then the electric circuit of the compressor motor opens, remaining open until the bulb temperature increases to 39 F. During the time required for the thermostat bulb to warm up to 39 F, the evaporator defrosts. The contacts again close and remain closed until the bulb temperature falls to 0 F; the process then repeats.

As stated above, combination refrigerators may have one or two thermostats. Operation of the thermostats varies for different models. Furthermore, design is currently being changed somewhat on successive models. Thus a pro-

[3] Hotpoint 1956 Refrigerator service manual.

spective purchaser who is interested in the temperature control or controls for a particular model would have to study the manufacturer's specifications for that model.

From a practical point of view the prospective purchaser is interested in knowing if the temperature in the food and frozen food compartments is appropriate for the use which will be made of these compartments, and if operating costs are reasonable. Experimental work on the effect of controlled temperature fluc-

tuations in a home freezer and on storage of foods in the frozen food compartment of household refrigerators indicates that a requirement of "constant" zero temperature for storage of some frozen foods is not essential, provided length of storage time is reasonable.[4]

d. Defrosting

In normal operation, frost collects on the evaporator because cold air contains less moisture than warm air. The evaporator is the coldest part of the refrigerator and air that passes across it gives up moisture to it. This moisture freezes.

In refrigerators with no means for automatic defrosting, the user is instructed to defrost the refrigerator when the frost on the evaporator builds up to a thickness of about ¼ inch. Some refrigerators have a defrost setting on the thermostat dial. Instead of unplugging the refrigerator, the user sets the dial at defrost. For this setting, the compressor motor will stay off until all or most of the frost has melted; then the refrigerator is ready for normal operation again. In fact, the refrigerating

[4] Florence Ehrenkranz, Harriet Roberts, and Enid Sater Ross, "Stored Foods in a Home Freezer Operated at Fluctuating Temperature," *J. of Home Economics*, 1952, *44:* 6, 441–442. Florence Ehrenkranz and Mary S. Pickett, "Energy Consumption, Temperatures, and Palatability of Foods Stored in Electric Refrigerators with Automatic Defrosting," *J. of Home Economics*, 1955, *47:* 3, 185–188.

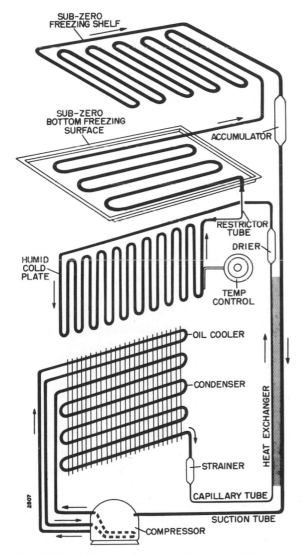

Fig. 14–5. Schematic diagram of path of refrigerant in a Dual Temp refrigerator. (Admiral Corporation)

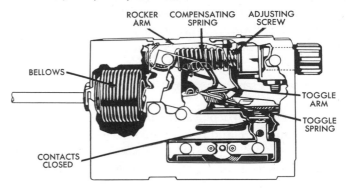

Fig. 14–6. Cutaway view of refrigerator thermostat, contacts closed. (Copied with permission of Westinghouse Electric Corporation)

cycle resumes, on some models, as though the dial were at normal setting.

Means for more automatic defrosting were introduced in about 1949. Currently, the expression "automatic defrosting" is usually used for clock-controlled defrosting, defrosting according to rate of frost collection, push-button defrosting, and defrosting during each cycle of operation.

Clock-controlled defrosting utilizes a clock-switch arrangement in the electric circuit of the refrigerator to interrupt the circuit to the motor once every 24 hours. In addition to interrupting the circuit to the motor, the clock-switch usually completes a circuit to a heating element. The heat supplied by this heating element speeds up the defrosting. Regular operation may resume either after a set time or when the evaporator reaches a set temperature.

Defrosting according to rate of frost collection starts automatically after a set number of door openings or after a set total length of time in which the door has been open. As in the clock-controlled method, a heating element is usually installed near the evaporator. Defrosting stops when the evaporator reaches the appropriate temperature range.

In push-button defrosting, the user depresses a push-button which closes an electric circuit to a heating element. The circuit containing the heating element remains closed for a preset time; then it opens automatically and the refrigerator resumes regular operation.

Defrosting during each cycle of operation was described earlier (see p. 193).

14–3. USE AND CARE

User's booklets include instructions on use and care and recipes for frozen desserts. Booklets for combination refrigerators include, in addition, instructions on preparation of foods for freezing. Often a page or two covers most of the essential points on care.

Recommendations on installation, placement of foods, and care are summarized below. The objective of the recommendations is to maintain quality of stored foods, to keep operating cost down, and to avoid unpleasant refrigerator odors.

a. Installation

The exact minimum clearance for a given model often is specified in the user's booklet. The needed ventilation above built-in refrigerators sometimes is taken care of by a ventilated above-the-refrigerator wall cabinet. Compact, free-standing models have recessed hinging of the door so that the door opens within the width of the appliance. Also, as stated in section 14–2, they have front grilles and/or a fan for circulation of air across the condenser. Such refrigerators sometimes may be installed between cabinets or next to a wall.

Other models should be installed to allow a minimum clearance of ½ to 3 inches on each side and 4 to 6 inches on top. The ½ inch minimum side clearance will provide reasonable "breathing space" for certain models but is likely to prevent a full 90-degree door opening. If one side of the refrigerator is completely exposed, less clearance is needed on the other side. To permit a 90-degree opening, a refrigerator installed in a corner requires a clearance slightly more than the thickness of the door between the hinged side of the door and the wall.

If possible, refrigerators should not be close to radiators or ranges and should not receive the direct rays of the sun.

The National Adequate Wiring Bureau recommends that refrigerators be installed in a small-appliance circuit. If an extension cord is used, the wires in the extension cord should not be less than No. 12 gauge.

For best service the refrigerator should stand level. Many refrigerators have leveling screws at two corners. These should be adjusted when the refrigerator is installed or moved to compensate for any unevenness in the floor.

b. Thermostat Settings

For normal use conditions the thermostat dial is turned to the normal setting, or to a designated number for dials marked in numbers. When the weather is cool or the refrigerator has a light load, a warmer setting may be satisfactory. When the weather is hot, when the refrigerator contains a heavy load, or when the door is opened frequently, a colder setting may be needed. The coldest setting, however, would ordinarily be used only when ice cubes or frozen desserts are to be made quickly.

Occasionally a thermostat may be calibrated incorrectly. This in itself is not important if the refrigerator maintains quality of fresh and frozen foods and freezes foods satisfactorily.

If the refrigerator has a damper between the frozen food and food compartments, it usually should be open in the summer and closed in the winter for the reasons given on page 190 and page 191. Check instructions in the user's booklets.

c. Placement of Foods

When specialized compartments are provided, placement of certain foods will of course be in accordance with the function of the compartments, to the extent that they are adequate. Examples are butter in the butter compartment, meat in the meat compartment, etc. Placement of foods in a combination refrigerator is essentially similar to that in a standard refrigerator; however, the amount of frozen foods that can be stored is greater for the combination refrigerator.

Store all fresh and cured meat in the coldest part of the refrigerator. Remove market paper from fresh and cured meat that is not prepackaged and rewrap loosely in waxed paper. Loosen the wrapper on fresh meat prepackaged by the dealer, before placing the meat in the refrigerator. Store cured meat and sausage that have been prepackaged by meat packing companies in the original packaging. Suggested maximum days of storage for best quality of some meats are these: two days for sliced liver, heart, cooked sweetbreads, and ground beef; two to three days for pork sausage; three to four days for chops; three to five days for steaks; three to eight days for roasts.[5]

Cooked meats should also be stored in the coldest part of the refrigerator but package them tightly to prevent drying of surfaces.

Cook fish within 24 hours or freeze it. It is of course necessary to wrap fish tightly to prevent odor transfer.

Store ice cream and sherbet in the coldest part of the refrigerator, of course. Milk and cream are stored near but not in the coldest part of the refrigerator. Good storage for cheese depends on the kind of cheese. Some connoisseurs prefer not to store certain aged cheeses in the refrigerator at all. Cream cheese, on the other hand, is usually stored near the coldest part of the refrigerator. Processed cheeses are stored on any convenient shelf in the food compartment; cut surfaces should be covered closely with aluminum or other freezer paper. Eggs should be removed from paper cartons and stored in a container on any convenient shelf.

If the refrigerator does not have a high-humidity food compartment, store green or leafy vegetables, carrots, and radishes in the crisper or in a tight-closing, moistureproof wrap on a shelf. If the refrigerator has a high-humidity food compartment, these foods can be stored without wrapping on shelves in the food compartment. Store fruits on the lowest convenient shelf in refrigerators that have the frozen food compartment at the top of the cabinet, or on a top shelf if the frozen food compartment is at the bottom of the cabinet. Spread berries on a plate and cover lightly with waxed paper; they should not be washed or stemmed until they are to be used. Do not

[5] Martha Logan, *Food News and Views*, 1954, Bulletin No. 110, January 1954, Swift & Company.

block air circulation in the fresh food compartment of the refrigerator by overcrowding.

d. Maintenance

Normally, the only maintenance required for refrigerators is defrosting, where automatic defrosting is not provided, and cleaning.

Frost on the evaporator acts as an insulator. As stated in section 14–2, frost should be removed whenever it has built up to $\frac{1}{4}$ inch, or the thickness of a lead pencil. This amount is likely to build up every few weeks in the winter and every few days in hot summers.

Practically all combination refrigerators require manual defrosting of the freezer compartment, even though the fresh food compartment defrosts automatically. Normally, defrosting the freezer of a combination refrigerator is necessary only two or three times a year. The usual indications for need of frost removal are a frost thickness of $\frac{1}{2}$ inch or a thickness that interferes with placement of foods.

Some user's booklets suggest use of pans of hot water to hasten defrosting of the freezer. If this suggestion is followed, the pans should be placed precisely where specified. Do not use hot water unless this suggestion is given in the user's booklet. In some models excessive refrigerant pressure may build up and cause difficulty when the compressor starts.

All refrigerators, whether automatically defrosting or not, need to be cleaned occasionally to prevent odors. Walls, shelves, and other interior parts are cleaned with a solution of baking soda in water—2 or 3 teaspoons of soda to a quart of water—rinsed, and dried. Rubber door gaskets are cleaned with a solution of mild soap and water, rinsed, and dried. The exterior surfaces of the cabinet are wiped with a damp cloth. To preserve appearance, it is desirable to wax the exterior surfaces once or twice a year with a product recommended by the refrigerator manufacturer.

The condenser of some refrigerators should be cleaned once or twice a year with a long-handled brush or a vacuum cleaner attachment, while the refrigerator is disconnected.

Tightness of fit of the door gasket can be checked with a dollar bill or a piece of paper toweling. The paper or bill should not pull out readily. A gasket that fits poorly should be replaced by a service man.

If a refrigerator is to be unused for an extended period, it should be unplugged, emptied, cleaned, and the door propped open.

For most refrigerators, the mechanism should be bolted to cross members when the refrigerator is transported in a van or railroad car. The shipping bolts are then loosened before the refrigerator is placed in service at the new location.

e. Kilowatt-Hours per Month

The electric energy used by refrigerators depends on construction characteristics, size of storage compartments, capacity of motor-compressor unit, room temperature and humidity, control setting, frequency and duration of door openings, and fresh and frozen food loads. Any refrigerator will use more electric energy in a home where installation conditions, ambient temperature, humidity, and use conditions are not optimum.

One manufacturing company, on the basis of factory tests and records of its models installed in homes in different localities throughout the United States, cites the following figures as normal ranges.[6]

Standard Models	*Energy Used*
8.1 cubic feet	25–40 kilowatt-hours
10.0	30–50
Combination Models	
11.0	40–80
12.0	50–90
14.0	55–100

[6] Service manual for 1956 General Electric Refrigerators, General Electric Company, Major Appliance Division.

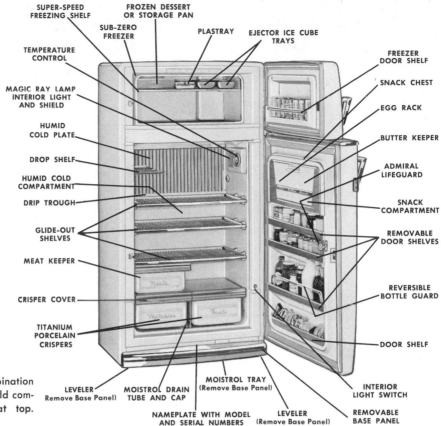

SUPER-SPEED FREEZING SHELF

FROZEN DESSERT OR STORAGE PAN

SUB-ZERO FREEZER

PLASTRAY

EJECTOR ICE CUBE TRAYS

TEMPERATURE CONTROL

FREEZER DOOR SHELF

SNACK CHEST

MAGIC RAY LAMP INTERIOR LIGHT AND SHIELD

EGG RACK

HUMID COLD PLATE

BUTTER KEEPER

DROP SHELF

ADMIRAL LIFEGUARD

HUMID COLD COMPARTMENT

DRIP TROUGH

SNACK COMPARTMENT

GLIDE-OUT SHELVES

REMOVABLE DOOR SHELVES

MEAT KEEPER

REVERSIBLE BOTTLE GUARD

CRISPER COVER

TITANIUM PORCELAIN CRISPERS

DOOR SHELF

LEVELER (Remove Base Panel)

MOISTROL DRAIN TUBE AND CAP

MOISTROL TRAY (Remove Base Panel)

INTERIOR LIGHT SWITCH

NAMEPLATE WITH MODEL AND SERIAL NUMBERS

LEVELER (Remove Base Panel)

REMOVABLE BASE PANEL

Fig. 14–7. Deluxe combination refrigerator with humid cold compartment and freezer at top. (Admiral Corporation)

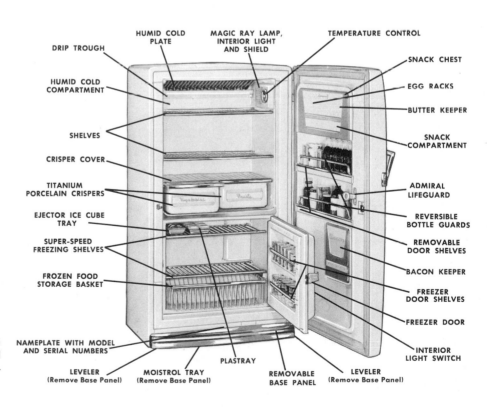

DRIP TROUGH

HUMID COLD PLATE

MAGIC RAY LAMP, INTERIOR LIGHT AND SHIELD

TEMPERATURE CONTROL

HUMID COLD COMPARTMENT

SNACK CHEST

EGG RACKS

BUTTER KEEPER

SHELVES

SNACK COMPARTMENT

CRISPER COVER

TITANIUM PORCELAIN CRISPERS

ADMIRAL LIFEGUARD

EJECTOR ICE CUBE TRAY

REVERSIBLE BOTTLE GUARDS

SUPER-SPEED FREEZING SHELVES

REMOVABLE DOOR SHELVES

BACON KEEPER

FROZEN FOOD STORAGE BASKET

FREEZER DOOR SHELVES

FREEZER DOOR

NAMEPLATE WITH MODEL AND SERIAL NUMBERS

INTERIOR LIGHT SWITCH

LEVELER (Remove Base Panel)

MOISTROL TRAY (Remove Base Panel)

PLASTRAY

REMOVABLE BASE PANEL

LEVELER (Remove Base Panel)

Fig. 14–8. Deluxe combination refrigerator with humid cold compartment and freezer at bottom. (Admiral Corporation)

14–4. FEATURES

Evaluation of different features is to a large extent personal and depends on use habits and financial resources of the prospective purchaser. The experience of the authors is that homemakers seldom complain about having refrigerators with too large a capacity. But, good management of the homemaker's time and the family's equipment money may call for a more deluxe model when the family does not own a separate freezer and a more stripped model when it does own one.

An extensive array of features may be found on very deluxe models—especially those top-of-the-line models to which the manufacturer gives a special, distinctive name. Some of those currently available are illustrated in Figures 14–7 through 14–14.

Figure 14–7 shows a deluxe combination refrigerator with humid cold compartment, "magic ray" or ultraviolet lamp, leveler, and many other features. The freezer is at the top of the cabinet. Figure 14–8 shows a deluxe combination refrigerator with two super-speed shelves in the freezer and many other features. The freezer is located at the bottom of the cabinet.

Figure 14–9 shows a refrigerator planned for specialized and visual storage of foods similar to that in a self-service store. The space under the half-shelf is suitable for storage of half a watermelon.

Figure 14–10 shows revolving-type shelves in the fresh food compartment. This refrigerator also has a "magnetic door" that closes automatically.

Figure 14–11 shows a refrigerator with adjustable shelf supports, automatic twin juice fountain, and other features. The automatic juice fountain is an accessory feature that requires plumbing to a water supply line. This fountain mixes juice concentrates with water. Juice is mixed a glassful at a time and is

Fig. 14–9. Refrigerator with specialized storage areas. (Sears, Roebuck and Co.)

aerated because water is added under pressure.

Figure 14–12 shows a 17.7-cubic-foot combination refrigerator that has 9.2 cubic feet of

Fig. 14–10. Refrigerator with revolving shelves. (General Electric Company)

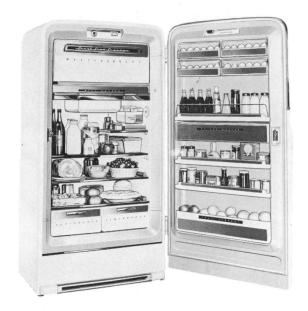

Fig. 14–11. Refrigerator with automatic twin juice fountain. (Courtesy Westinghouse Electric Corporation)

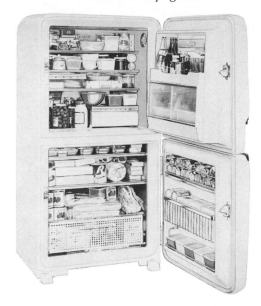

Fig. 14–12. 17.7-cubic-foot combination refrigerator (Maytag Company)

refrigerator space and 8.5 cubic feet of freezer space.

Figure 14–13 shows a wall combination refrigerator located above two under-counter freezers. Figure 14–14 shows a built-in combination refrigerator that has an all-plastic body and steel doors. It has a 9-cubic foot refrigerator compartment at top and a 4-cubic-

foot freezer underneath.

Some additional features which are not illustrated in Figure 14–14 include the following: a safety-type door that can be opened from the inside, adjustable shelf spacing obtained with a lever, and various devices that allow for the easy removal of ice cubes from trays.

B. American Standards Association Standards

The current American Standards Association standards that apply to mechanically operated household electric refrigerators are B38.1 and B38.2.[7]

The purpose of B38.1 is to provide a uni-

[7] B38.1, *American Standard Method of Computing Food-Storage Volume and Shelf Area of Automatic Household Refrigerators,* American Standards Association, 1955. B38.2, *American Standard Test Procedures for Household Electric Refrigerators* (Mechanically Operated), American Standards Association, 1944.

form method for determining food storage volume and shelf area. The standard first defines terms, for example, inside depth, width of cooling unit space, and so on. The uniform method for determining volume and area then follows from the definitions. Specifically, the total storage volume is the product of the inside depth, width, and height minus the volume of the cooling unit space plus the volumes of the ice-freezing compartments and the frozen food storage compartment.

Fig. 14–13. Wall combination refrigerator located above two under-counter freezers. (General Electric Company)

Fig. 14–14. Built-in combination refrigerator. (Courtesy Westinghouse Electric Corporation)

The net shelf area is the sum of the areas of the shelves, bottoms of suspended containers, bottom of the liner, and the shelf areas in the frozen food storage compartment.

The purpose of B38.2 is to provide a uniform procedure for determining performance of mechanically operated household refrigerators under specified laboratory test conditions. The standard first prescribes certain general requirements to be observed in the tests. For example, when the test code is used for determining conformity with purchase specifications, the refrigerator tested shall be selected either from stock or from routine factory production.

A no-load test and an ice-making test are specified. The no-load test determines the electric energy consumption per 24 hours and the percent operating time of the unit for specified average cabinet-air temperatures and ambient (room) temperatures.[8]

The ice-making test, as the name implies, determines the time required to freeze water. A test condition that might interest users is that the surfaces of the cooling unit on which the ice trays are placed should be wetted in order to insure good contact of the ice trays with the surfaces.

[8] Percent running time is related to the capacity of the refrigerating mechanism. For example, a refrigerator that runs 100 percent of the time to maintain an interior temperature of 40 F when the room temperature is 85 F could not be expected to maintain 40 F at the same thermostat setting when the room temperature is 100 F.

C. Experiments

Experiments 1 through 3 require no special measuring devices. Experiment 4 requires a stop watch or other accurate timer. Experiment 5 requires an appropriate kilowatt-hour meter and thermocouple equipment.

Experiment 1. *Inspection*

The points to be checked are intended to be helpful in examining electric refrigerators prior to purchase, as well as examination in a laboratory.

1. Is the nameplate accessible? Does it give manufacturer's name and address, model, voltage rating, amperes, serial number, other information? Does the refrigerator have the Underwriters Laboratories seal of approval?
2. Is the total capacity in cubic feet marked on the refrigerator or stated in the user's booklet? What is the capacity of the frozen food compartment? The food compartment? What is the net shelf area? How many shelves in the frozen food compartment have evaporator coils?
3. What are the overall exterior dimensions? How is the door hinged—right or left side? Are the hinges recessed?
4. How well constructed does the refrigerator seem to be? Does the door fit tightly? (Check for tightness with a dollar bill or a piece of somewhat rough paper, such as paper toweling.) Does the door close automatically? Does the hardware appear to be well made and nonrusting? Are means provided for leveling the refrigerator? Is toe space adequate? (Check with specification sheet or user's booklet to ascertain whether a Bonderizing agent or other chemical treatment that prevents rusting was applied.)
5. Is the design of the refrigerator reasonable to you? Do you like the overall appearance?
6. What are the specifications on temperature in the frozen food compartment for different thermostat settings?
7. How is the refrigerator defrosted? What are the provisions for handling defrost water? If a heating element is used for defrosting, what is its wattage?
8. What are the special features?
   a. Specialized storage spaces: meat keeper, vegetable crisper, door storage? Are these such that they would fulfill reasonable needs for storage? For example, how many slots are provided for eggs? Is storage space so specialized that inadequate space is available for half-gallon cartons, quart-size glass bottles, etc.? Would the specialized storage spaces be easy to clean?
   b. Are shelves adjustable? Are divided shelves provided for occasional storage of large items such as a ham, large fowl, or watermelon? Do the shelves slide out? Do they rotate? If the refrigerator has a sliding shelf or shelves, are stops provided to prevent tilting?

    c. What are the special characteristics—special finish, ice ejector, etc.—of the ice cube trays?

    d. What special features does the refrigerator have in addition to those mentioned? How would you rate these features?

9. Are instructions on use and care in the user's booklet clear?

10. Precisely what does the manufacturer's warranty promise the purchaser?

Experiment 2. *Effectiveness of Storage*

1. Store three similar heads of lettuce in the refrigerator as follows: one uncovered on a shelf, one in a moistureproof wrap on a shelf, and one in the vegetable crisper or other closed container. Observe appearance after two, three, four, and five days.

2. Store several pints of one flavor of a good-quality ice cream in the frozen food compartment. (Chocolate or strawberry may be more sensitive for this test than vanilla.) Use the original cartons without overwrap. Observe flavor and graininess after varying lengths of storage, such as one, two, three, and four weeks. For test purposes remove a fresh package each week.

    Store two ½ gallons of ice cream, if practicable, in the frozen food compartment. Use the original cartons. For one package, cover the exposed surface with aluminum foil, after some of the ice cream has been used. Do not use foil for the other package. Sample the ice cream from the two packages after different intervals of storage. Does the foil help?

3. Store similar patties of frozen ground beef prepared from a single lot of ground meat in the frozen food compartment. Broil patties after different lengths of storage such as one, two, three, and four weeks. Note appearance, flavor, texture, and juiciness.

Experiment 3. *Menu Project*

1. Obtain a weekly market order from a homemaker who does planned, once-a-week shopping except for occasional items. Purchase the foods that need refrigeration or improvise packages similar to those in which the foods are usually sold. (Empty cartons and bottles can be used, for example.)

2. Can all the items that will be used in one week and that require refrigeration be stored in their correct locations in the refrigerator? Is the food compartment too closely packed? Can the items be stored so they are readily accessible?

Experiment 4. *Cycling Characteristics*

    The percent "on" time of the compressor motor and the average durations of the "on" and "off" parts of a cycle are most easily measured by installing a recording ammeter or wattmeter in the electric circuit. They can also be measured by listening for the "on" and "off" sounds of the motor and using an accurate timepiece such as a stop watch.

Before the test is started, the refrigerator should have been operated for a sufficient length of time to establish thermal equilibrium. ASA standard B38.2 prescribes a 12-hour period of stabilization when the ambient temperature has changed and a 6-hour period when dial setting, but not ambient temperature, has changed. The no-load test procedure also requires that data be taken for a period of 12 hours. This is practical when a recording instrument is available, but not otherwise.

If the stop-watch method is used, data might be recorded for two hours or an interval of approximately two hours which covers a whole number of cycles.

Experiment 5. *Energy Consumption and Temperatures for No-Load Tests*

1. Install three thermocouples in the cabinet at locations specified in the ASA standard for different types of refrigerators. Connect their free ends to a recording temperature instrument for an extended test or to a temperature-indicator through a selector switch for a two-hour test. Install a kilowatt-hour meter that reads to 0.01 kilowatt-hours in the electric circuit of the refrigerator.
2. After temperature equilibrium has been established for a particular thermostat setting, according to the recommendations given in Experiment 4, note the time, read the kilowatt-hour meter, and start observing temperatures. When the test is complete, again note the time and read the kilowatt-hour meter.
3. Record the average temperature indicated by the three thermocouples over each cycle. Subtract the initial reading from the final reading of the kilowatt-hour meter, and calculate kilowatt-hours per 24 hours.

An alternate test procedure is to use a refrigerator that contains foods. It is of interest in such a test to install thermocouples in the foods, as well as in the air in the cabinet. Room temperature, of course, should be recorded during the test.

CHAPTER 15

Home Freezers

Home freezers are designed to store foods for longer periods than frozen food compartments of standard refrigerators. Some foods can be stored satisfactorily in home freezers for periods up to 8 to 12 months or even longer. Home freezers are also designed for freezing larger quantities of food than frozen food compartments of standard refrigerators.

The average temperature of the storage section of a home freezer is approximately 0 F. Furthermore, if a separate freezing section is provided in the freezer, it may operate at an average temperature lower than 0 F when the section is used for freezing.

A. Construction, Use, and Care

Two types of cabinets are available: a chest type with a top-opening lid, and an upright type with a front-opening door. The overall size of both types is quoted in interior volume to the nearest 0.1 cubic foot, or in nominal pounds of food that can be stored in the storage and freezing sections. The food-weight rating is equal to the volume rating times 35. Thus a 10.0 cubic-foot freezer has a *nominal* capacity of 350 pounds; but a cubic foot will not store 35 pounds of irregularly shaped foods such as poultry or lightweight foods such as cakes.

Available sizes range from approximately 4 cubic feet to 25 cubic feet and larger. According to information collected by *Electrical Merchandising,* about 23 percent of the freezers manufactured in 1955 were in the 9- to 12-cubic-foot size, 46 percent were in the 13- to 17-cubic-foot size, and 24 percent were in the large sizes of 18 cubic feet or more.[1]

When a freezing section is provided, its capacity is also stated in cubic feet or in pounds of food. The pound rating in this case indicates the number of pounds of compact packages that can be placed in the freezing section. The actual time required to freeze a given quantity of food varies for different models.

15–1. CONSTRUCTION

Component parts, refrigerating mechanism, and construction features are similar for freezers and refrigerators, except as the colder interior temperatures of freezers require differences. The temperature control, for example, is similar to that on refrigerators except that it is designed for temperatures suitable for freezers. Some manufacturers do 100 percent testing of temperature controls to insure as far as possible that the calibration of the control on every freezer sent from the factory is correct.

The refrigerating mechanism of freezers is designed so that the difference between maximum and minimum temperatures during a cycle of operation is less than for refrigerators. Freon-12 and Freon-22 are the refrigerants commonly used. Insulation may be heavier than in refrigerators, because the temperature difference between room air and the interior of the appliance is greater for freezers.

Additional differences in construction include the following: (1) The evaporator coils of a freezer may extend around the entire cabinet and also along interior shelves in upright freezers or along vertical dividers in chest freezers. (2) The condenser of some freezers is mounted on the back of the cabinet as on most refrigerators; more often it is installed under a storage or freezer section in a space provided for it and for the motor-compressor

[1] *Electrical Merchandising,* Statistical and Marketing Issue, McGraw-Hill Publishing Company, January, 1956, p. 297.

unit. (3) The interior panel of the lid of chest freezers and the door of upright freezers is usually a laminate rather than the plastic sheet used on the interior of a refrigerator door.

Construction characteristics of chest and upright freezers are illustrated in Figures 15–1 and 15–2. The lid or lids of chest freezers are counterbalanced to insure their staying open

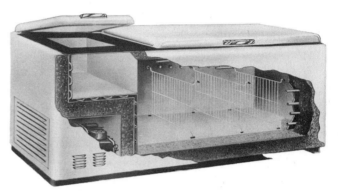

Fig. 15–1. Cutaway view of "Quickfreezer" chest freezer. (Victor Products Corporation)

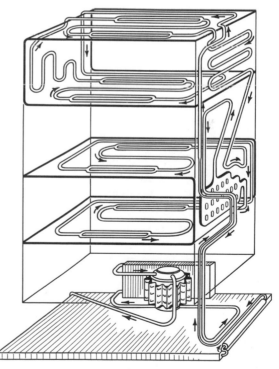

Fig. 15–2. Schematic view of refrigerating system of an upright freezer. (Frigidaire Division, General Motors Corporation)

when food is added or removed. The chest freezer shown in Figure 15–1 has a separate freezing section located on the left side above the machine compartment. This section has evaporator coils at one side and at the bottom. The storage section has evaporator coils on bottom, back, front, and right side and the lower portion of the left side. Three grid-type dividers are provided.

The schematic view of the refrigeration system for the upright freezer (Fig. 15–2) shows that in this freezer three shelves, the upper left side, the ceiling, and the right side have evaporator coils. The arrows indicate the path of the refrigerant from the unit at the bottom of the cabinet through the evaporator coils.

Starting at the top of the condenser, the liquid refrigerant passes through a drier filter, up the right side, across the top of the freezer-liner at the rear, and down into the top shelf.[2] After circulating through the top shelf, it flows up the left side to the top front of the freezer-liner, then down the right side to the middle shelf. From there it flows to the bottom shelf and empties into a waffle-type accumulator on the right side between the bottom and middle shelves.

Up to this point the refrigerant has been in a liquid state. When it enters the accumulator it is changed into low-pressure vapor, which passes out through the top of the accumulator and then down the suction line to the bottom of the compressor. From here it goes into the condenser where it is condensed to a liquid, and the cycle starts over again.

NOTE: The refrigerant can remain liquid in the evaporator, provided that the flow of the liquid in the evaporator equals the rate at which the condenser liquefies the gaseous refrigerant.

Different models differ in various aspects. Some differ in the spacing of evaporator tubing around the liner and in the number of in-terior shelves (upright) or dividers (chest) that have evaporator tubing. Some uprights have evaporator tubing in the interior floor and ceiling; others do not. Some models have refrigerated plates rather than tubing, with passageways for the refrigerant formed in them. These differences affect the quantity of food that will freeze in a given length of time.

Actual refrigerating mechanisms also vary for different models. Some have special sections designated as freezing sections; others do not. Foods placed to contact freezing coils in a separate freezing section or in a storage section will freeze in a reasonable length of time. A separate freezing section is useful for easy separation of stored frozen foods and fresh foods to be frozen.

Because freezers maintain lower temperatures than standard refrigerators, they are more likely to "sweat"; that is, moisture is more likely to condense on the outside surfaces, as on the outside surface of a glass of ice water or on cold water pipes whenever the relative humidity is high. Some freezers are so designed that the amount of condensed moisture is limited. Different means are used; one manufacturer uses a heating wire around the front of the freezer cabinet; another uses a shell-type condenser.

An indicator light or a buzzer may be provided. Again, different models have different types. Some manufacturers provide a battery-operated buzzer, which sounds when the temperature in the freezer rises to about 15 F.[3]

15–2. USE AND CARE

As for other appliances, the user's booklet or folder gives instructions on use and care. In addition, an extra booklet on freezing foods for storage may be supplied, or suggestions on freezing may be included in the booklet on use and care.

[2] *Frigidaire Service Tech-Talk,* October, 1955, p. 96. Frigidaire Division, General Motors Corporation.

[3] Desirable features of a freezer alarm system are discussed in *Home Freezers—Their Selection and Use,* Home and Garden Bulletin No. 48, USDA.

a. Installation

A freezer should be installed level and the manufacturer's recommendations on clearances should be followed. These recommendations vary with different models, depending in part on the location of the condenser. Minimum or maximum adjustment of leveling screws may be specified to insure proper air circulation across the bottom of the freezer. Manufacturers provide bolts on the back of some models to insure adequate clearance between the freezer and the wall.

Operating costs are likely to be less when a freezer is installed in a cool location, such as an unheated basement. However, a cool location may not be convenient. Some models must not be placed in a location where the temperature falls below freezing, while the operating mechanisms of other models are not affected by below-freezing temperatures. If possible, the freezer should not be installed close to a source of heat such as a radiator or where it receives the direct rays of the sun.

Because freezers have a starting wattage that is high relative to operating wattage, the National Adequate Wiring Bureau recommends that they be connected to an individual-equipment circuit protected by a fuse with an appropriate current rating. If a freezer is installed in the same circuit as other appliances, the circuit may be overloaded each time the freezer motor starts.

b. Temperatures

For normal use conditions, a correctly calibrated thermostat dial is turned to the normal setting. When large loads of food are to be frozen, turning the dial to the coldest setting may accelerate the freezing process.

Placement of frozen foods in freezers is entirely a matter of convenience. Although temperatures usually are not uniform throughout a freezer, the temperature in any part of the freezer recommended for storage of frozen foods is likely to be satisfactory. When freezing foods, on the other hand, as many packages as possible should be placed to make contact with freezing coils (see p. 208).

c. Management

Good use of a freezer calls for good packaging of foods that are to be frozen and a working philosophy that the freezer is a cold-storage pantry for foods that will be used in a reasonable length of time. General recommendations on packaging are considered in the section on freezing, p. 208. Use of a freezer as a cold-storage pantry is considered here.

Probably freezers do not save money for most families when all the costs associated with operating them are considered. They may save money if a great deal of home-grown food is frozen or if a family practices extremely good management in purchasing large quantities of foods—that the family likes—when prices are low. They may also save money if fewer market trips are made, especially if such trips are limited to planned shopping with little impulse buying.

On the other hand, families that own freezers can have better and more varied meals throughout the year; they can also have many foods on hand that are ready to be prepared. Management of the freezer therefore should be planned toward better meals and an assortment of foods on hand. A well-used freezer might be used daily.

Freezer use is simplified by organizing the foods in sections for meat, vegetables, fruits, desserts, and breads. Some complete meals are stored as a matter of convenience, even though this is likely to use more space than storing the components of the meals. As new foods are added to the freezer, some rearranging may be desirable to place foods already in the freezer near the front or on top. Packages should of course be labeled with date and content. Keeping a record of the foods in the freezer helps prevent overlong storage of items.

Individual users can usually work out the type of records easiest for them.

Jewel Graham suggests a five-way use of a freezer.[4] (1) Freeze and store fresh foods. (2) Store commercially frozen foods. (3) Freeze foods cooked in quantity; that is, prepare large recipes of favorite dishes that require long preparation and freeze in meal-size portions. (4) Freeze baked goods; that is, make several cakes or pies at a time and freeze some of them. (5) Freeze and label complete meals that can be ready in 20, 40, and 60 minutes.

Two additional points for new owners of freezers might be added to those made by Graham. One is this: after food has been defrosted, treat it as though it were fresh food. For example, ground beef frequently is cooked from the frozen state. If, however, it is defrosted and not used immediately, refrigerate it as you would fresh ground beef. The other point is this: don't plan to refreeze thawed foods. Certain foods that have thawed only partially can be refrozen safely, but this procedure does not give the best final product.

d. Freezing

The extension departments of many state colleges and the Agricultural Research Administration of the United States Department of Agriculture distribute bulletins on freezing containing information on what foods to freeze; instructions on preparation for freezing, such as scalding times for various vegetables; suggestions on varieties of fruits and vegetables that freeze successfully; and suggestions on preparing meat for freezing.

General rules to follow in freezing foods include the following:

1. Freeze good-quality products when possible.

2. Prepare food for freezing when it is at its best. For example, vegetables and fruits should be firm and fully ripe.

3. Use good packaging materials, and package tight to exclude as much air as possible.

4. Package with minimum area; for example, stack steaks one on top of another rather than side by side, with sheets of freezer paper between individual steaks.

5. Follow reliable instructions on scalding and cooling of vegetables.

6. When freezing liquid or semiliquid foods leave ½ inch of free space, or more, at the top of the container to allow for expansion during freezing.

7. Freeze meal-size amounts of meat, vegetables, etc.

8. Have an experimental attitude about foods for which freezing instructions are not available; also, accept the fact that not all foods may be frozen satisfactorily with currently available techniques.

9. As far as possible, place foods to be frozen so they contact freezing coils. If more food is to be frozen at one time than can be placed against freezing coils, interchanging the positions of the packages during the freezing process accelerates freezing for some freezers.[5]

10. Do *not* leave air gaps between packages; instead use square or rectangular packages or containers that contact each other.

e. Packaging Materials

The word *vaporproof* as used for freezing materials usually implies that there will be no significant loss of moisture from foods so wrapped. Loss of moisture causes drying out of fruits and vegetables and "freezer burn" in meats and poultry. In addition to providing a barrier to movement of water vapor out of foods, good packaging materials provide a barrier to movement of oxygen from the freezer air into the package. This characteristic is especially important in packaging

---

[4] Jewel Graham, "Your Home Freezer 'Super Market' Deluxe," *Iowa Farm Science*, August, 1955, pp. 6 ff.

[5] Florence Ehrenkranz, Jeanne Banister, and Reba Smith, "Capacity Load Freezing Time in Home Freezers," *Refrigerating Engineering*, June, 1954, pp. 63 ff.

materials used for meat, poultry, and fish to prevent rancidity of the fat in these foods.

Packaging materials include wrappings and containers. Heavy freezer-weight aluminum foil and polyethylene wrappings furnish excellent protection and are reusable. Sheets of both can be molded to the food. Polyethylene bags can be twisted at the ends and then secured with rubber bands or small pieces of wire sold for that purpose. Freezer-type cellophane and pliofilm are not reusable. They should be heat-sealed and an overwrap such as stockinette used to protect against punctures and tears. Laminated sheets combine paper and another material such as cellophane, aluminum foil, or plastic coating. Ordinarily, when these wrappings are used the paper should be on the outside. Waxed locker papers usually cost less and are recommended for shorter storage periods than the wrappings just discussed.

Glass freezer jars provided with screw-on, rustproof metal caps, polyethylene containers, and heavy-weight aluminum boxes offer excellent protection and are reusable. Waxed space-saving cartons with plastic liner bags and waxed tub-type containers with waxed lids are usually altogether satisfactory for fruits, vegetables, and small portions of cooked foods.

f. Care

For most freezer models the only care required is defrosting and cleaning. The rate of frost accumulation depends on use conditions. Frost should be removed when it interferes with placement of food in the freezer and probably should be removed in any case when it has hardened to a layer of ice. Light and fluffy frost may be removed without disconnecting the freezer motor by using a rubber, plastic, or wooden scraper. Strategically placed paper or towels can collect the frost as it is scraped down.

Ice or dense frost must be melted. When this is necessary, the freezer should be disconnected and the frozen foods removed and wrapped in several thicknesses of paper so that they will not thaw while they are out of the freezer.

In ordinary use, the interior of a freezer does not need to be cleaned as frequently as the interior of a refrigerator. The interior is cleaned with a baking soda solution, rinsed, and wiped dry. As for refrigerators, rubber gaskets are cleaned with a cloth dipped in a soapy solution, rinsed, and dried. Exterior surfaces may be polished or waxed with a product recommended by the dealer or manufacturer.

For models that have an exposed condenser attached to the rear of the freezer, the user may also be instructed to clean the condenser once or twice a year with a brush or vacuum cleaner attachment. The freezer should be disconnected when the cleaner attachment is used. Where the condenser is enclosed or partially enclosed, the user is usually not instructed to clean it.

If a freezer is to be unused for a long period of time, it should be disconnected, emptied, cleaned, and the door or lid propped open.

The proper procedure in case of failure of the power supply or mechanical failure of the freezer depends on the probable duration of such a failure, construction of the freezer, interior temperatures of the frozen foods, amount of food in the freezer, ambient temperature, and other factors. Freezers that contain a large quantity of food will maintain safe temperatures longer than those which contain only a small quantity. Some manufacturers now guarantee to the purchaser a limited cash refund in case of spoilage of food within a certain number of hours after failure. Dry ice—*not* ordinary ice—placed next to or on top of the frozen foods may be a worthwhile precautionary measure in some cases. A freezer thermometer, especially one with the indicating portion mounted outside the freezer, is helpful in deciding whether and when special measures are necessary.

NOTE: Some packages of food in a freezer remain in a thawing range (about 25 to 31 F) for many hours, while other packages thaw quite rapidly.

g. Kilowatt-Hours per Month

Considerations similar to those for electric refrigerators (see page 196) determine how much electric energy freezers use per day or month. Sears, Roebuck and Co. gives the following figures for three fully loaded chest freezers at a room temperature of 70 F.[6] (The figures appear to be based on laboratory rather than home conditions.)

Size of chest freezer	Kilowatt-hours per day
10 cubic feet	1½ to 2
15 cubic feet	2 to 2½
20 cubic feet	2½ to 3

On the basis of factory tests and records of freezers installed in homes in different localities throughout the United States, the General Electric Company gives the following values as normal ranges for two upright freezers.[7]

Size of upright freezer	Kilowatt-hours per month
13 cubic feet	85 to 105
15 cubic feet	90 to 110

15–3. FEATURES

A less extensive array of features is available on home freezers than on refrigerators. This may be associated with the following facts: (1) Refrigerators have been widely used for a much longer time than home freezers and time has thus been available to develop features. (2) Purchase of a refrigerator is at present often a replacement-purchase for an old refrigerator, while purchase of a freezer is still, in most cases, a new purchase; therefore, a prospective purchaser may not seek a large number of special features in a freezer.

The three principal considerations for a prospective purchaser of a home freezer are perhaps these: size, chest versus upright style, and convenience features with respect to storage.

The appropriate size of freezer to purchase is probably best decided by the use the family will make of it. Logically, consideration will be given to the amount of freezer space available in a combination refrigerator, if the family owns one, and to the practicability of renting freezing space outside the home. In many sections of the country, plants known as "lockers" are in operation, where frozen food compartments may be rented. It is generally conceded that locker space, though less convenient than a home freezer, is cheaper; hence, it may be reasonable to think in terms of owning a home freezer and renting some locker space. A family that plans to store 200 to 350 pounds of meat in the freezer twice a year may want one or two freezers with a capacity of 20 to 35 cubic feet; a family that plans to store only small quantities of meat may find one with a capacity of 12 to 15 cubic feet adequate. A family living in a small apartment may have floor space for only a 4- to 5-cubic-foot freezer.

Whether a chest or upright should be purchased is essentially a matter of personal preference. Since an upright occupies less space than a chest of similar capacity, adequate space might be available for an upright when it is not available for a chest. The chest type has the advantage that, since cold air is heavier than warm, less moisture-laden warm air enters the chest when the lid is raised than

---

[6] Sears, Roebuck and Co., 1956 Fall and Winter Catalogue, p. 1039.

[7] Service manual, General Electric Food Freezers HU 13 and HU 18 models. General Electric Company, Appliance and Television Receiver Division.

Fig. 15–3. 4.1-cubic-foot chest freezer with vertical divider. (Sears, Roebuck and Co.)

Fig. 15–4. 5.0-cubic-foot under-counter freezer with drawer storage. (General Electric Company)

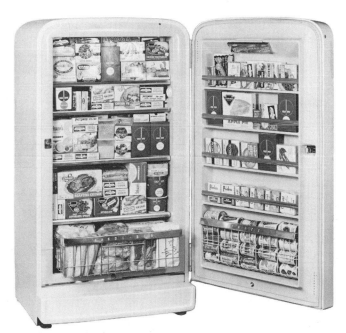

Fig. 15–6. 14.2-cubic-foot upright freezer. (Sears, Roebuck and Co.)

Fig. 15–5. 15.0-cubic-foot chest freezer with separate freezing section. (Sears, Roebuck and Co.)

enters an upright when the door is opened for the same period. For the same reason, an upright may cost slightly more to operate than a chest of the same capacity.

Whether chest or upright is the more convenient to use depends partly on features of particular models. For example, sliding baskets in a chest may facilitate reaching the back part of the bottom. Compartmentalized storage in an upright may obviate the need for reaching behind front packages.

Current models of freezers with characteristic types of storage conveniences are illustrated in Figures 15–3 through 15–7. Figure 15–3 shows a 4.1-cubic-foot freezer with one vertical divider and Figure 15–4 a 5.0-cubic-foot, under-counter freezer with drawer storage. Figures 15–5 and 15–6 show a 15.0-cubic-foot chest and a 14.2-cubic-foot upright made by the same company. Note that the chest has a freezing section at the right above the machine compartment and the storage section has baskets to facilitate organization of stored foods. The upright has door storage and refrigerated shelves with unequal spacing for packages of various sizes.

Figure 15–7 shows a 25.0-cubic-foot upright with evaporator coils in four shelves, ceiling, and floor.

A feature not illustrated that is now available on some upright freezers is a safety-seal door that opens easily from the inside.

Fig. 15–7. 25.0-cubic-foot upright freezer. (Maytag Company)

B. American Standards Association Standard

The current American Standards Association standard for home freezers is B38.3.[8] It prescribes methods of testing and rating home freezers.

The body of the standard and the appendix include several definitions. A home freezer is defined as a self-contained refrigerator for home or farm use in storing frozen foods or in freezing and storing frozen foods. A compartment is any space within a freezer completely surrounded by walls or refrigerated surfaces, or a combination of both, that helps to make up the storage volume. A section is a compartment or combination of compartments designed for specific use, as for storage or freezing. The food storage volume rating is the total number of cubic feet recommended for storage of frozen foods and for freezing, minus the volume of permanently fixed shelves and partitions. The food storage weight is the food storage volume times 35; it is given to the nearest pound.

The temperature at any given point in a freezer is the average of air temperatures at that point during a cycle of operation. The average temperature in a compartment is the average of the air temperatures measured at specified locations in the compartment. The average freezer temperature is the average of

[8] B38.3, *American Standard Methods of Rating and Testing Home Freezers,* American Standards Association, 1955.

the compartment or section temperatures, weighted according to their respective volumes.

Three tests are outlined. These are no-load, pull-down; no-load; and storage-load tests. For the no-load, pull-down test, the freezer is placed in an ambient temperature of 110 F and kept inoperative for 24 hours or longer, with all compartment doors open. Then the control is short-circuited to insure continuous operation of the compressor motor. The actual test consists in recording the number of hours for the average temperature in the freezer to reach 0 F or equilibrium, if equilibrium temperature is higher than 0 F.

The no-load test is conducted at an ambient temperature of 90 F. The freezer is operated until an equilibrium temperature is reached; then the kilowatt-hours per 24 hours and the

percent running time of the compressor motor are determined from observations taken over two 6-hour periods or one 16-hour period.

The storage-load test uses rectangular, vaporproof fiber cartons of 1 quart or smaller size, filled with wet hardwood sawdust to give a total weight of 35 pounds per cubic foot. The freezer storage space is filled with these cartons and thermocouples are installed in their geometric centers at specified locations to give load temperatures. The test is conducted at an ambient temperature of 90 F, and the freezer is operated until an equilibrium load temperature is reached. Then, as in the no-load test, the kilowatt-hours per 24 hours and the percent running time of the compressor motor are calculated from observations taken over two 6-hour periods or one 16-hour period.

C. Experiments

If a recording ammeter or wattmeter and a temperature-recording instrument are available, experiments can be carried out to determine kilowatt-hours used and percent running time for empty and loaded freezers, similar to the tests described in the ASA standard B38.3. In addition, experiments can be carried out to determine kilowatt-hours used for freezing loads of different weights, loads packaged in different wraps, loads of different kinds of food, and so on.

The experiments outlined below require no special measuring equipment and can be carried out in regular laboratory periods.

Experiment 1. *Inspection*

The points to be checked are intended to be helpful in examining freezers prior to purchase, as well as in a laboratory. Part A applies to chest and upright types. However, some points are handled differently for the two types. For example, a prospective purchaser should check on overall dimensions of an appliance to be sure it will fit into the space planned for it. For a chest freezer this involves determining vertical height with the lid at full-open position.

Part B applies particularly to chest types and part C to upright types.

A. Chest and upright freezers

1. Is the nameplate accessible? Does it give manufacturer's name and address, model, voltage rating, amperes, serial number, other information? Does the freezer have the Underwriters Laboratories seal of approval?

2. Is the total capacity in cubic feet or pounds given on the freezer, in the specifi-

cation sheet, or in the user's booklet? Is the capacity of the freezing section given separately?

3. What are the overall exterior dimensions? (Check height of chest type when lid is at full-open position.)

4. How well constructed does the freezer seem to be? Is the hardware substantial and nonrusting? Does the lid of a chest freezer open easily? Does the lid or door latch securely when closed? Is a lock provided? Are means provided for leveling the freezer? Is toe space adequate? (For an upright freezer check this while opening the door.)

Check in specification sheet or user's booklet whether a Bonderizing agent or other chemical treatment that retards rusting was applied. What provision is made for control of cabinet "sweating" in humid locations?

5. Is the design of the freezer reasonable to you? Do you like the overall appearance?

6. Is the temperature control dial readily accessible? Could it be turned accidentally? What settings are provided? Is a temperature indicator provided? Is an automatic alarm or signal light provided and if so to what operating characteristics is it responsive? (An alarm may indicate power failure and/or excess temperature in the cabinet. A signal light may indicate power failure only.)

7. Is the condenser accessible for periodic cleaning? (Check in user's booklet to determine if periodic cleaning is necessary.)

8. Are instructions in the user's booklet on use and care of the appliance clear?

9. Precisely what does the manufacturer's warranty on the appliance promise the purchaser? What is guaranteed for the food in the freezer?

B. Chest freezers

1. Is the lid counterbalanced to stay ajar at all positions?

2. Is the bottom rear portion of the interior accessible for a short person?

3. How many sides of the freezing section have freezing coils? Does the floor of this section have them? (Check on specification sheet.)

4. What special features, such as lid storage, baskets, dividers, etc., does the chest freezer have? How would you rate these features?

C. Upright freezers

1. How many shelves have freezing coils? What additional parts—walls or parts of walls, ceiling, floor—have freezing coils? (If the freezer has an enameled interior, the coils in the wall, ceiling, and floor are not visible. However, if there are coils in these locations, the specification sheet and user's booklet will usually so indicate.)

2. What provision is made for large or irregularly shaped packages? If all the shelves are refrigerated, are they appropriately spaced for large packages? Are nonrefrigerated shelves adjustable for odd-size packages?

3. If shelves of compartments are provided in the door, what type of articles might logically be stored in them?

4. What additional special features such as safety door, drawers, interior doors, etc., does the upright freezer have, and how would you rate these features?

Experiment 2. *Effect of Packaging*

1. Prepare two sets of patties from a single lot of ground beef. For one set, shape the beef into patties about 4 inches in diameter and 1½ inches thick. For the other, shape it into patties about 2 inches in diameter and ½ inch thick.
2. Package the larger patties in stacks of four, using paper disks to facilitate separation after freezing. Wrap different groups of four patties in different types of freezing paper.
3. Package the smaller patties in one layer, four or six to a package. Wrap different groups of four or six in the same types of freezing paper that were used for the larger patties.
4. Freeze and store all the meat in the freezing section or storage section of one freezer for two weeks, or a longer interval if that is more convenient. Remove the packages from the freezer, unwrap them, and note the following:
   a. Which packaging materials, if any, are associated with desiccated (freezer-burned) meat? (Look for freezer-burn at edges of patties.) If *any* freezer-burn is observed after as short a time as two weeks, the packaging materials probably are poor risks for longer storage periods.
   b. How do the 4-inch patties in the stack wrap compare with the 2-inch patties that were packaged in a single layer with its relatively large surface?

CHAPTER 16

Room Air Conditioners and Electric Dehumidifiers

A. Room Air Conditioners

Room air conditioners are air conditioners that are installed in windows or through walls and require no plumbing or duct connections. They are used in living rooms, bedrooms, dining areas, and recreation areas in the home. They are used chiefly in hot weather to decrease the temperature and humidity of the room in which they are installed. They extract heat and moisture from the room and dissipate it to the outside air by means of a refrigerating mechanism similar to that of an electric refrigerator.

The evaporator of the room air conditioner is located inside the room and the condenser is located in or outside the window or wall. The refrigerant absorbs heat from the room at the evaporator and gives it up to the outside air at the condenser.

Cooling and dehumidifying are accomplished simultaneously. Room air is caused to circulate by an evaporator blower. Since the evaporator is colder than the air in the room, room air that moves across or past it cools and gives up moisture, because cool air will not hold as much moisture as warm air.

In addition to air circulation, cooling, dehumidifying, and filtering of some dust and air-borne pollen, room air conditioners may include the following means for increasing comfort: ventilation, that is, bringing in outside air to refresh the air in the room; exhaust, that is, removing inside air for the purpose of taking out stale air and odors; and heating the air in the room, a provision ordinarily used only when outside temperatures are between 45 F and 60 F.

16–1. TYPES OF ROOM AIR CONDITIONERS

Although room air conditioners are always mounted horizontally, they are sometimes

Fig. 16–2. Snorkel-type room air conditioner. (York Corp., Subsidiary of Borg-Warner Corp.)

Fig. 16–1. Flush-mounted room air conditioner. This model has vertical and horizontal louvers in front of twin air nozzles. (Kelvinator Division, American Motors Corporation)

classified as flush-mounted and horizontal. The flush-mounted type will usually be installed so that the cabinet protrudes into the room only slightly. In the case of a window installation, draperies hang normally when the air conditioner is not in use (Fig. 16–1). The flush-mounted type can also be installed so that several inches of the cabinet protrude into the room. In practice, however, this would be done only when local ordinances or special architectural features of the house require minimum outside overhang.

The horizontal type usually protrudes 3 inches or more into the room. For example, horizontal models of one manufacturer may be installed with inside protrusion ranging in 1-inch steps from a minimum of $3\frac{1}{2}$ inches to a maximum of $16\frac{1}{2}$ inches; those of another manufacturer may be installed with inside protrusion ranging from $3\frac{1}{8}$ inches to $12\frac{1}{8}$ inches.

One manufacturer supplies a Snorkel type (Fig. 16–2) of conditioner, supported by a bracket in front of the window on the room side; the window can thus be lowered when the air conditioner is not in use. Also, since most of the air conditioner is below the window, it does not completely obscure the view through the window when it is in use.

16–2. CONSTRUCTION

Overall cabinet dimensions for household-size room air conditioners vary with different models and different manufacturers. Generally, flush-mounted models are about 21 inches high and 16 inches deep; horizontal models are approximately 15 to 16 inches high and 25 to 33 inches deep. The width of both types is usually about 25 to 26 inches. Window-mounting spacers are available with some models to permit installation in windows up to 60 inches wide. In addition to the 25- to 26-inch wide models, some manufacturers supply casement models and "portable" models.

Usually the cabinet includes these parts: (1) a steel chassis or shell on which are mounted such functional parts as the evaporator; (2) a louvered steel panel on the portion outside the window; and (3) a decorative front housing with grille or grilles for the portion inside the room. The front of the cabinet has some acoustical insulation, such as a suitable lining on the interior of the front surface.

a. Operating Components

Component parts are basically similar in all room air conditioners. Description and illustrations covering functioning of operating components of one model are given below.

The main controls for cooling, cooling with ventilation, exhaust, etc., are located behind a hinged control door in the lower left portion

Fig. 16–3. Front view of a flush-mounted type of room air conditioner. (General Electric Company)

of the front surface (Fig. 16–3). Room air enters the air conditioner through an inlet grille that covers the lower portion of the front surface to the right of the control door. Perforations allow free airflow to the evaporator fan or blower located behind the grille. The air enters or returns to the room through a polystyrene air discharge grille in the upper part of the front surface.

Outside air enters the conditioner through the lower portion of a third grille located at the rear of the cabinet (Fig. 16–4). This air cools the compressor motor, carries heat away from the warm condenser, and is then ex-

Fig. 16–4. Rear view of flush-mounted type of room air conditioner. (General Electric Company)

pelled through the upper portion of the same grille.

Two permanent aluminum-foil air filters are provided, one located behind the air discharge grille and the other behind the inlet grille (Fig. 16–5).

Fig. 16–5. Aluminum-foil air filter. (General Electric Company)

The interior of the air conditioner is divided into front and rear compartments by a steel partition or barrier. A damper and a baffle in this barrier permit introduction of outside air and removal of room air.

The front compartment contains the evaporator, evaporator blower, and control panel (Fig. 16–6). The rear compartment contains the motor-compressor unit, the condenser, and the condenser fan (Figs. 16–7 and 16–8).

The motor for the evaporator blower and the condenser fan is not part of the motor-compressor unit, but is a separate motor mounted in a housing that extends through the steel partition into the front and rear compartments. The evaporator blower and the condenser fan are mounted at the front and rear, respectively, of this motor. (The rear shaft of this motor and the condenser fan can be seen in Figure 16–8.)

Moisture from the air in the room condenses on the evaporator coils, drips into a drain pan, and passes through a drain hose into a sump. There it is picked up by a slinger ring which is part of the condenser fan and blown upward to the hot surface of the condenser where it is vaporized and carried off by atmospheric air.

16–3. CONTROLS

Room air conditioners may have mechanical and electrical controls. Mechanical controls are used to change the air flow pattern of the room air near the evaporator. The air conditioner shown in Figure 16–3 has three rotating "air directors" behind the front discharge grille, operated manually by the three controls that extend through the grille.

In a stripped model the electrical control is an "on-off" switch. In a deluxe model, the electrical controls may be push buttons, rotating parts, or parts that move in a line. The linear-type controls for the deluxe model shown in Figure 16–9 provide four "comfort" settings and ten temperature settings. The control panel has, in addition, a switch for operating the evaporator fan or blower at high or low speed and an "air freshener control." The latter is an accessory that controls "an air freshener device which consists of air freshener material in a container under pressure."

For maximum cooling the fan control is turned to high, the comfort knob is moved to the cool setting, and the temperature control is moved to one of the colder settings. With the controls at these settings, only room air is circulated, being cooled, dehumidified, and filtered as it passes across the front of the air conditioner.

All room air conditioners cool, dehumidify, and filter the room air. The temperature control provision is especially appreciated by users who operate an air conditioner for long periods at a time. Without such a control, the room will tend to become increasingly colder if outside temperature remains constant or decreases. The temperature control or thermostat controls only the "on-off" cycling of the motor-compressor unit.

The cool-vent setting of the comfort knob permits introduction and cooling of outside air; that is, when the comfort knob is at cool-vent and the temperature knob is at a num-

Fig. 16–6. Front view of room air conditioner showing evaporator fan behind aluminum-foil air filter. (General Electric Company)

Fig. 16–7. Chassis of room air conditioner. Cooling coil or evaporator is at the front. Motor-compressor unit is in the rear compartment. (General Electric Company)

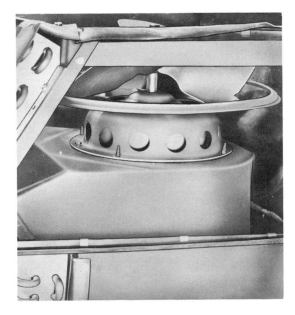

Fig. 16–8. Condenser fan with slinger ring mounted on motor shaft. (General Electric Company)

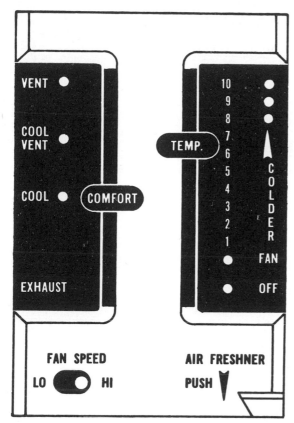

Fig. 16–9. Linear-type controls. (General Electric Company)

bered position, fresh air is introduced from the outside, mixed with the recirculated room air, cooled, and dehumidified.

For the vent and exhaust settings, the air is filtered only. In particular, when the comfort knob is at vent and the temperature knob at fan, fresh air is mixed with recirculated room air. The mixture is filtered but not cooled or dehumidified. When the comfort knob is at exhaust and the temperature knob at fan, air is drawn from the room to the outside. The motor-compressor unit is off for this setting also.

16–4. HEATING AND REVERSE CYCLE OPERATION

As indicated earlier, room air conditioners may be designed to provide some heat on cool days. The source of heat may be an electric heating element. When this is provided it operates independently of the refrigerating mechanism.

Heat may also be provided by a refrigerating mechanism designed for reverse cycle operation, that is, cooling *or* heating. In a cooling cycle, heat from the room is absorbed at the evaporator and given up to the outside air at the condenser. In a heating cycle, heat from the outside air is absorbed at the condenser (acting as an evaporator) and given up to room air at the evaporator (acting as a condenser).

Reverse cycle operation will be more readily understood by tracing the path of the refrigerant in a cooling cycle and a heating cycle. Figures 16–10 and 16–11 show schematically how reverse cycling works.

A characteristic feature of a refrigerating system designed for reverse cycle operation is a reversing valve. For cooling, the solenoid plunger (6) of the reversing valve is in its down position, as shown in Figure 16–10. Refrigerant discharge gas from the compressor passes through the reversing valve and through tube (3) to the condenser. The condensed refrigerant next passes through a restrictor into the evaporator. The vaporized refrigerant (suction gas) now moves through tube (4) to the reversing valve and leaves the reversing valve through tube (2) to enter the compressor inlet. This is a standard cooling cycle.

For heating, the solenoid plunger (6) of the reversing valve is in its up position as shown in Figure 16–11. In this case refrigerant discharge gas from the compressor passes through the reversing valve and through tube (4) to the evaporator, where it is condensed because the evaporator is now serving as a condenser. The condensed refrigerant then passes through the restrictor to the condenser where it is vaporized because the condenser is now serving as an evaporator. The vaporized refrigerant next passes through the reversing valve

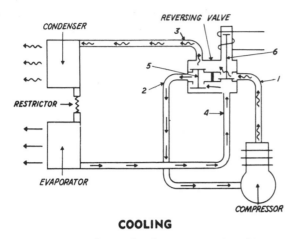

COOLING

Fig. 16–10. Cooling cycle of a reverse cycle refrigerating mechanism. *(Frigidaire Service Tech-Talk, March, 1956.)*

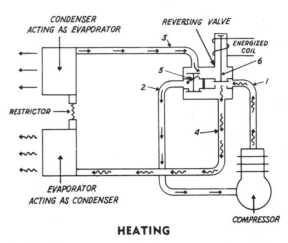

HEATING

Fig. 16–11. Heating cycle of a reverse cycle refrigerating mechanism. *(Frigidaire Service Tech-Talk, March, 1956.)*

and tube (2) to the compressor inlet. The outside air gave up heat to vaporize the refrigerant in the condenser, and this heat was absorbed by room air when the refrigerant was condensed in the evaporator.

16–5. COOLING RATINGS AND ELECTRICAL SPECIFICATIONS

Owners sometimes describe their room air-conditioners by the horsepower rating of the compressor motor. "We have a 1-horsepower air conditioner" or "we have a ¾-horsepower air conditioner." This particular characteristic may have been emphasized when the appliance was purchased. Horsepower ratings are sometimes assumed to correlate with average areas to be cooled, approximately as follows: ¾ horsepower for 300 to 400 square feet, 1 horsepower for 500 to 600 square feet, 1½ horsepower for 700 to 900 square feet.[1]

Actually, the total cooling capacity rating, that is, the number of British thermal units the air conditioner will remove per hour gives

more information on cooling than the horse-power-rating. One model of a ¾-horsepower unit may be rated to remove 6900 Btu's per hour and another model of the same horse-power may be rated to remove 7600 Btu's per hour. The first model has a cooling effect equivalent to that which would be obtained if 48 pounds of ice were melted in the room per hour,[2] or 0.57 tons per 24 hours. The second model has a cooling effect equivalent to the melting of 53 pounds of ice per hour or 0.63 tons per 24 hours.

Other ratings that apply to the performance of the room air conditioner are the recirculated air quantity rating, the ventilated air quantity rating, and the exhaust air quantity rating. These are all defined in terms of cubic feet of air per minute. (See section 16–8 on air conditioner standards.)

Electrical specifications in addition to horse-power rating affect type of electrical supply needed and operating costs. These additional electrical specifications include operating volts, amperes, and watts. Units of ½ horsepower are rated to operate at 115 volts; units of ¾ horsepower are rated for 115 or 230 volts; units of 1 or 1½ horsepower are usually

---

[1] The square feet refer to floor area. It is assumed that the room is of average height, that air circulation is unrestricted throughout the area cooled, and that the windows in the room have a north or east exposure. Usually, also, continuous 24-hour cooling is assumed.

[2] 6900 divided by 144, which is the heat of fusion of water, is approximately 48.

rated for 230 volts. Operation at rated voltage is somewhat more critical for room air conditioners than for other household appliances. Manufacturers stress that an air conditioner should not be expected to operate satisfactorily at a voltage greater or less than 10 percent above or below its rated voltage.

Power input for 90 F ambient temperature is of the order of 800 watts for ½-horsepower units, 1100 to 1300 watts for ¾-horsepower units, 1600 watts for 1-horsepower units, and 2200 watts for 1½-horsepower units.

Running currents are of the order of 7.5 amperes for ½-horsepower units, 11 amperes for ¾-horsepower units when operated on a 115-volt supply or 5.5 amperes when operated on a 230-volt supply, 7.5 amperes for 1-horsepower units, and 10 to 11 amperes for 1½-horsepower units.

Starting currents for room air conditioners are likely to be very high. The July 1956 issue of *Consumers' Research* reports starting currents from 42 to 53 amperes for the twelve 115-volt, ¾-horsepower air conditioners tested and 21 amperes for the one 230-volt, ¾-horsepower unit tested.

Electrical specifications are changing for some of the new models, partly because of the effort by manufacturers to make home models that can be used with existing wiring. Two examples are these: Some ¾-horsepower units are available with a running current of only 7.5 amperes at 115 volts; some 1-horsepower units are now available that may be operated at 115 volts.

16–6. ROOM COOLING LOAD

The cooling obtained by means of a room air conditioner depends not only upon the cooling capacity of the unit, but also upon such room characteristics as amount of window area and directions windows face, height of ceiling, type of roof on the house, floor area, number of people who customarily use the room, wattages of lights and other electrical equipment used in the room, and lineal feet of doors and arches continuously open to unconditioned space.

Wherever possible in house planning, all the usual means of maintaining comfort should be utilized in addition to air conditioning. Outside awnings over windows decrease the cooling load on the air conditioner. Insulation of walls and roof decreases the cooling load; and so on.[3]

16–7. INSTALLATION, USE, AND CARE

a. Installation

A room air conditioner should be installed in a window on the cooler side of the house, if the room has windows on more than one side and if installation on the cooler side is practical. Furthermore, the location should be such that free air circulation is possible at both the front or room part and the rear or outside part of the air conditioner.

Because the starting current is very high, a time-delay type of fuse is recommended for the electric circuit to the air conditioner. A separate circuit is desirable to insure correct voltage for the air conditioner and to avoid dimming of lights or unsatisfactory operation of other electrical devices.

Although an individual-equipment circuit is desirable, the National Electrical Code does not require one, subject to the following rules. If lighting or other appliances are in the same circuit, nameplate current for the air conditioner should not exceed 7.5 amperes for a unit connected to a 15-ampere branch circuit (number 14 wire) or 10 amperes for a unit connected to a 20-ampere branch circuit (number 12 wire). If an extension cord is

[3] An interesting discussion of living comfort is given in a research report by G. J. Everson, L. W. Neubauer, and R. B. Deering, "Environmental Influence on Orientation and House Design to Improve Living Comfort," *J. of Home Economics*, 1956, *48*: 161–167.

used, its wire should not be smaller than number 12 gauge.

Local ordinances may require grounding the unit. Whether required or not, it is desirable to ground the air conditioner by a ground type of plug on the cord.

b. Care and Use

Suggestions for care of specific models are given in user's booklets. Also, the dealer will often offer suggestions, especially on preventive maintenance. The information below covers some points that may or may not be noted in user's booklets.

Usually, the filter is clean or replaced by the user according to instructions in the user's booklet. For spun-glass filters a vacuum cleaner is used to remove excess dirt and lint. Polystyrene filters may be rinsed in cool water. Aluminum ones may be washed in hot, sudsy water. After they have been rinsed and dried, a coating of filter oil is applied; this is obtained from the dealer. The air conditioner should not be operated with the filter removed. Many models now have throw-away filters; that is, a dirty filter is replaced rather than cleaned.

Preventive maintenance at the beginning of each cooling season by a service man may include the following operations: cleaning the condenser and evaporator, if required; installing a new air filter, if required; oiling the fan motor and, for some models, the fan bearing; checking tightness of seals around the window in which the unit is installed.

Room air conditioners are designed for individual rooms and private offices. In most cases, it is not recommended that one unit be used to cool two connecting rooms.

If a room is allowed to become excessively hot, more time will be required to obtain a comfortable temperature because of heat stored in walls and furnishings. For maximum comfort, the unit should be turned on before the room becomes excessively hot so that the unit need only *maintain* comfort conditions.

During extremely hot weather it is better to operate the air conditioner at the cool rather than the cool-vent setting to avoid placing the unit under a heavy overload.

The members of the family should recognize the *usual* operating sound of the unit. If any unusual operation is noted, such as continuous "on" and "off" cycling, the air conditioner should be turned off until the reason for the unusual operation is ascertained and corrected, either by the user or by a service man. One trouble may be too high or too low voltage; another may be that the air conditioner is installed in a hot area with poor ventilation. In the latter case the location of the air conditioner may have to be changed.

When an air conditioner is moved in a truck from one house to another, the motor-compressor assembly of some air conditioners should be bolted to the supports (cross members) on which it rests. A dealer will know whether this is necessary for models he sells.

CAUTION: The shipping bolts should be loosened or removed before the air conditioner is turned on in the new location.

Perhaps the best suggestion on noise associated with an air conditioner is to listen to the operating sounds of several models before purchase and to choose one with the least objectionable noise. For most people, fortunately, the comfort obtained greatly overbalances the noise.

16–8. AIR CONDITIONER STANDARDS

Current standards that apply to room air conditioners are the ASRE Standard 16–56 of the American Society of Refrigerating Engineers and the ARI Standards 110–56 and 120–56 of the Air-Conditioning and Refrigeration Institute. The ASRE standard covers methods of rating and testing all types of air conditioners which operate with "nonfrosting" when cooling and dehumidifying. ARI standard 110–56 covers room air conditioners, and

ARI standard 120–56 is a cooling-load estimate form for room air conditioners.

ARI standard 110–56 defines a room air conditioner as a "factory-made encased assembly designed primarily as a unit for mounting in a window or through a wall, or as a console, for free delivery of conditioned air to an enclosure and without ducts for conditioned air supply or return. It includes a prime source of refrigeration and dehumidification and means for circulating and cleaning air, and may also include means for ventilating, heating, or performing other functions."[4]

This standard also prescribes that ratings for room air conditioners shall be based on

[4] ARI Standard 110–56, *Room-Air Conditioners,* Air-Conditioning and Refrigeration Institute.

tests conducted in accordance with the ASRE standard. The ratings of particular interest to prospective purchasers include the following:

1. Total cooling capacity rating in British thermal units per hour.
2. Recirculated air quantity rating in cubic feet per minute of standard air (air at 70 F dry-bulb temperature, 50 percent relative humidity, and 29.92 inches of mercury).
3. Ventilated air quantity rating, for units with means for providing ventilation, in cubic feet per minute of standard air.
4. Exhaust air quantity rating, for units with means for exhausting air, in cubic feet per minute of standard air.
5. Heating capacity rating, for units with means for heating, in British thermal units per hour.

B. Electric Dehumidifiers

Electric dehumidifiers are self-contained appliances designed to remove moisture from the air. Those used in homes are usually about 12 inches wide, 12 to 18 inches high, and 20

Fig. 16–12. Front view of electric dehumidifier. (RCA Whirlpool, Whirlpool-Seeger Corporation)

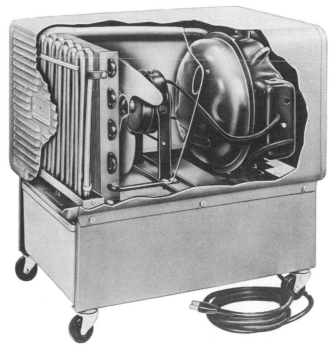

Fig. 16–13. Cutaway view of electric dehumidifier. (Kelvinator Division, American Motors Corporation)

inches or so deep (Fig. 16–12). Ordinarily, a dehumidifier would be used in the summer in a basement or a workshop.

Removal of moisture from the air retards rusting of metal parts, such as furnace parts or tools, and retards warping of wooden objects such as furniture. In addition, the space that is dehumidified is more comfortable for people who use it.

16–9. FUNCTIONAL PARTS

An electric dehumidifier contains an electric refrigerating mechanism similar to that used in an electric refrigerator or a room air conditioner. The cutaway view shown in Figure 16–13 shows many of its principal functional parts. A filter is mounted between the front grille and the evaporator or cooling coils. The condenser, suction fan and fan motor, and motor-compressor unit are mounted behind the evaporator. The suction fan draws air over the coils and the moisture in the air condenses on the coils. This moisture then drains either into a pan or pail under the coils or through a hose to a house drain.

Some models are designed to run continuously once they are turned on. In such cases the user turns the appliance off when excess humidity has been removed from the air. Other models have a *humidistat* control that starts and stops the motor-compressor unit as needed to maintain a factory-preset value of relative humidity.

16–10. ELECTRICAL AND MECHANICAL CHARACTERISTICS

The usual household models of dehumidifiers have a sealed motor-compressor unit rated at ⅕ horsepower or less and are designed for use with a 60-cycle, 110-120-volt supply. A motor-overload protective device is usually provided.

As indicated above, a humidistat control may be provided on the dehumidifier; for other models it may be purchased as an accessory. Controls are available for a range of values from approximately 20 percent to 80 percent relative humidity. A setting of 65 percent relative humidity is recommended in the literature of one manufacturer.

Dehumidifying capacity is stated either in pints or gallons of water the appliance can condense per 24 hours or in volume of enclosed space from which excessive humidity can be removed. Examples are these: a dehumidifier may be designed to remove up to 20 pints of water per 24 hours or to remove excessive moisture in enclosed areas up to 10,000 cubic feet.[5]

16–11. LOCATION AND USE

The dehumidifier should be so placed as to permit unrestricted air circulation around it. Windows and doors in the space to be dehumidified are kept closed while the appliance is operating.

Although dehumidifiers are portable appliances, a permanent type of installation may be preferred. An installation is described as permanent when a rubber hose of ½- to ¾-inch diameter is attached to the dehumidifier to provide for draining moisture into a house drain.

The filter is cleaned at the beginning of the "moist" season and as often thereafter as needed, since a dirty or clogged filter decreases the efficiency of the appliance.

The container for moisture is emptied as often as necessary. This might be twice in 24 hours on very humid days.

The fan motor is oiled according to the instructions that come with the appliance.

A final important point on use is this: Dehumidifiers are not designed for use in cool, dry weather and should be turned *off* at such times.

[5] If the space to be dehumidified is larger than 10,000 cubic feet, more than one dehumidifier will be needed.

C. Buymanship Exercises

1. Outline an inspection experiment for a room air conditioner and test the usefulness of your outline by calling at a store that sells room air conditioners. When you go into the store, have in mind the main points in which you are interested. Get some of your inspection data by looking at one or more room air conditioners and reading the manufacturers' literature that is available in the store. In addition, listen to what the salesperson says. He may supply information you did not think to ask for!

2. Carry out Exercise 1 for an electric dehumidifier.

Electric Vacuum Cleaners and Floor Polishers

Currently, electric vacuum cleaners and their tools or attachments are the most labor-saving devices available for removing dust and other soil from many of the large and small surfaces in the home.

Electric floor polishers are the most effective home tool for polishing and buffing waxed floors and hard floor coverings.

One reason for using cleaners and floor polishers is to decrease the amount of human energy expended in cleaning. An additional means of decreasing the work of cleaning is of course to keep as much dirt as possible *out* of the home. Dust and other soil enter through open windows, filter through openings around windows and under doors, filter through screens, and are carried on shoes and clothing of persons and paws and other parts of pets.

Effective mats at all entrances decrease the amount of soil carried into the house on shoes.

Good stripping around windows and doors cuts down the amount of soil that gets through openings. In home-heating systems in which a furnace filter can be used, some air-borne dust can be removed by installing one. In air-conditioned homes or rooms some dust collects on the filters in the air conditioner rather than on surfaces that have to be vacuumed frequently.

A. Electric Vacuum Cleaners

Vacuum cleaners and their attachments are used for carpets, rugs, wood floors, cement floors, hard floor coverings, ceilings, walls, and some furniture. The standard attachments are also used for lamps, lighting fixtures, pictures, drapes, books, and bric-a-brac. Special attachments are available with some models for spraying wax or insecticides and for spraying mothproofing compounds.

Vacuum cleaners and their attachments are not ordinarily used for counter tops or other surfaces on which food is handled.

Every electric vacuum cleaner has one or two fans or blowers assembled at one end of a motor. As the fan or fans rotate, air is thrown outward, creating an area of low pressure around the fan hub. This low pressure produces a vacuum or suction effect. The overall effect of the high-speed rotation of the fans is to cause air to enter the floor nozzle or other cleaning attachment, move through the fan chamber, through the bag or other filtering device, and out into the room.[1] This entering air picks up soil from the surface under the nozzle and leaves it in the filtering device. One cleaner uses a container filled with water instead of a bag to filter soil from the moving air.

As dirt collects in the cleaner, the filtering action is impeded and the efficiency of the cleaner decreases. Comments on frequency of

removal of accumulated dirt from the cleaner are given in section 17–6.

In addition to cleaning by rapid movement of air, modern vacuum cleaners make use of brushes.

17–1. TYPES OF VACUUM CLEANERS

Vacuum cleaners currently may be classified as canisters, tanks, uprights, and special-purpose types. Canisters, tanks, and special-purpose types depend primarily on rapid movement of air through the cleaner for their cleaning effect. However, the rug tool of canisters and tanks usually has a free-floating brush and/or a comb-like device in the nozzle. The device can be positioned on some models according to the type of soil on the rug or carpet to be cleaned. If the brush is positioned to make contact with the rug, it picks up threads and similar light litter as the nozzle is moved across the rug. If the brush is retracted into the nozzle, it is inoperative. This position is used when no more light litter is present on the rug.

Upright cleaners use a motor-driven brush for cleaning carpets and rugs, in addition to air movement. A cylinder or roll is mounted inside the part of the cleaner that makes contact with the rug. Different manufacturers describe the cylinder as a brush roll, an agitator, or a "Disturbulator." The roll is belt-connected to the motor used for the fan. The belt passes over the motor shaft just ahead of

---

[1] In the upright cleaner, air leaves through the bag. In the canister and tank, air leaves through blower ports after passing through the bag.

the fan and over a recessed portion of the roll. Brushes are mounted in or on the roll, either parallel to its axis or in a spiral around it. The brush roll rotates at high speed when rugs are vacuumed.

In addition to brushes, one manufacturer of upright cleaners uses a curved bar mounted spiral-fashion on the exterior of the brush roll. Its function is to beat the rug and loosen embedded dirt that is then picked up by the air current and carried into the cleaner.

17–2. CANISTER AND TANK CLEANERS

Appearance and convenience features of canisters and tanks have been changing quite a lot since about 1953, and it is likely that additional marked changes will occur in the future. Figures 17–1 through 17–6 show canister types of cleaners. Figures 17–7 and 17–8 show cleaners for which the manufacturers use special names rather than canister or tank designations. Figures 17–9 through 17–11 show tanks.

Canisters have housings that somewhat approximate vertical cylinders or rectangular boxes. The suction opening is in the top or front of the cleaner. Tanks are horizontal cylinders; their suction opening is at the front.

a. Interior Components

Interior components of the canister shown in Figure 17–4 are illustrated by the exploded views of Figures 17–5 and 17–6. Note in Figure 17–5 that the exterior housing consists of a top plate and upper and lower shells. The suction opening is in the top plate. The blower opening, through which the air leaves the cleaner, is part of a shutter assembly in the bottom shell. The bottom of the motor is mounted on a plate and the top is protected by a cap. The paper bag and ring fit into the top part of the cleaner over the motor cap.

Two fan assemblies are mounted on the armature shaft; the commutator end of the armature is mounted in a ball bearing that fits into a bracket (Fig. 17–6).

Other models of canisters have functional parts that correspond to those for the model shown in Figures 17–5 and 17–6, though the actual physical parts are different. For example, the cleaner shown in Figure 17–2 has two Fiberglas filters on the discharge side of the motor, one oil-impregnated and the other described as a "noise and microdust" filter.

Tank cleaners also have interior functional parts that correspond to those shown in Figures 17–5 and 17–6. In the case of a tank, the disposable paper bag and the cloth bag that protects it would be installed at the suction end of the cleaner, ahead of the fan. Movement of air through a tank cleaner is illustrated in Figure 17–11.

b. Hose and Extension Tubes

A hose and extension tubes to connect the cleaner with the tools are provided with canisters and tanks. A metal part at one end of the hose is assembled to the cleaner, and another metal part at the other end is connected to an extension tube or directly to a dusting tool. The hose is usually about 8 feet long. It may be made of vinyl or fabric and is always flexible. At least one manufacturer uses a hose that stretches, its advantage being that the cleaner needs to be moved less frequently when a large area is cleaned.

Two hollow extension tubes or wands, each about 20 inches long, are usual. A friction fit may be used to connect hose, wands, and tools, or mechanical locking devices may be provided. In general, mechanical devices are considered more satisfactory than a friction fit for locking tool to wand, one wand to another wand, and wand to hose.

One manufacturer provides wands that telescope; that is, one wand slides into and out of the other. Their advantage is that they are handled as one piece instead of two.

For some canisters and tanks, one of the

Fig. 17–1. Canister cleaner with dual-purpose floor nozzle. Note provision for storage of cord. (Courtesy Westinghouse Electric Corporation)

Fig. 17–3. Tank cleaner that uses water instead of a bag for filtering soil. (Rexair Division, Ward Industries Corporation)

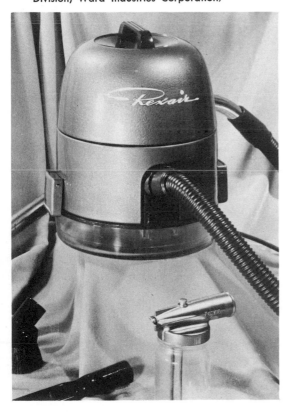

Fig. 17–2. Canister with floor tool assembled. Note large wheels and dial for suction adjustment on top of housing. (Lewyt Corporation)

Fig. 17–4. Canister with hose, wands, and tools. (Eureka Williams Corporation)

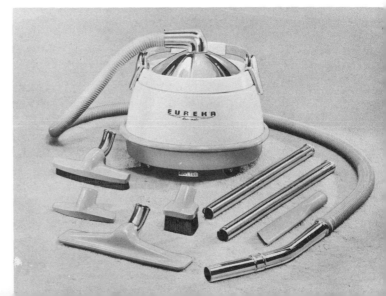

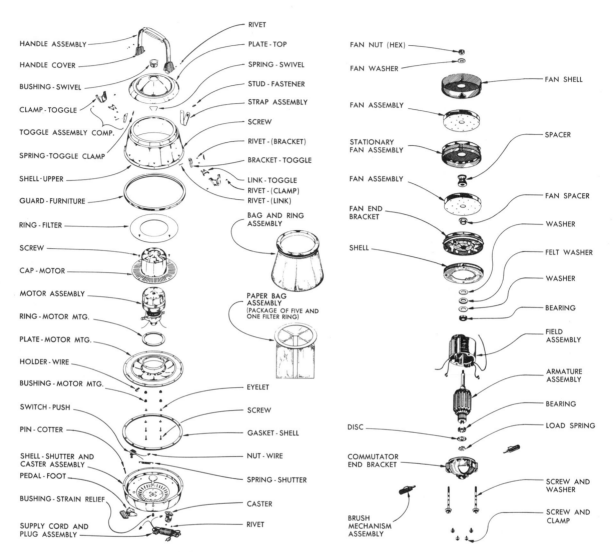

HANDLE ASSEMBLY
HANDLE COVER
BUSHING - SWIVEL
CLAMP - TOGGLE
TOGGLE ASSEMBLY COMP.
SPRING - TOGGLE CLAMP
SHELL - UPPER
GUARD - FURNITURE
RING - FILTER
SCREW
CAP - MOTOR
MOTOR ASSEMBLY
RING - MOTOR MTG.
PLATE - MOTOR MTG.
HOLDER - WIRE
BUSHING - MOTOR MTG.
SWITCH - PUSH
PIN - COTTER
SHELL - SHUTTER AND CASTER ASSEMBLY
PEDAL - FOOT
BUSHING - STRAIN RELIEF
SUPPLY CORD AND PLUG ASSEMBLY

RIVET
PLATE - TOP
SPRING - SWIVEL
STUD - FASTENER
STRAP ASSEMBLY
SCREW
RIVET - (BRACKET)
BRACKET - TOGGLE
LINK - TOGGLE
RIVET - (CLAMP)
RIVET - (LINK)
BAG AND RING ASSEMBLY
PAPER BAG ASSEMBLY (PACKAGE OF FIVE AND ONE FILTER RING)
EYELET
SCREW
GASKET - SHELL
NUT - WIRE
SPRING - SHUTTER
CASTER
RIVET

FAN NUT (HEX)
FAN WASHER
FAN ASSEMBLY
STATIONARY FAN ASSEMBLY
FAN ASSEMBLY
FAN END BRACKET
SHELL
DISC
COMMUTATOR END BRACKET
BRUSH MECHANISM ASSEMBLY

FAN SHELL
SPACER
FAN SPACER
WASHER
FELT WASHER
WASHER
BEARING
FIELD ASSEMBLY
ARMATURE ASSEMBLY
BEARING
LOAD SPRING
SCREW AND WASHER
SCREW AND CLAMP

Fig. 17–5.   (Left) Exploded view of canister shown in Figure 17–4. (Eureka Williams Corporation)
Fig. 17–6.   (Right) Exploded view of motor of canister. (Eureka Williams Corporation)

wands has a variable vacuum or suction control. This is a small hole or set of small holes in the surface of the wand and a sliding ring or cover. Moving the cover off the hole or holes permits air to enter the wand, thereby decreasing the vacuum effect of the cleaner. Some cleaners have the vacuum control in the cleaner itself or in one of the metal parts of the hose, rather than in a wand. Maximum suction (opening covered) is used when cleaning heavy rugs and carpets. Less suction (uncov-

ered or partially uncovered opening) is used when cleaning lightweight scatter rugs and dusting drapes and certain other lightweight furnishings.

c. Tools

Usually, tools are provided with the cleaner for five types of use, and additional attachments are available as accessories. Standard models of canisters and tanks may have a rug tool, a floor-and-wall tool, a dusting tool, an

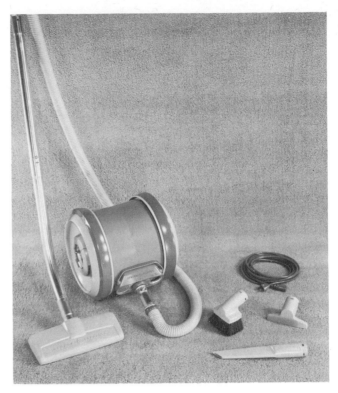

Fig. 17-8. "Roll-Easy" vacuum cleaner. (General Electric Company)

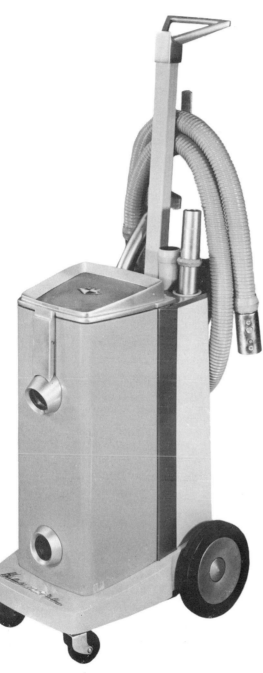

Fig. 17-7. "Ken-Kart" vacuum cleaner. (Sears, Roebuck and Co.)

Fig. 17-9. Tank cleaner with two dual-purpose tools and automatic cord winder. (Electrolux Corporation.)

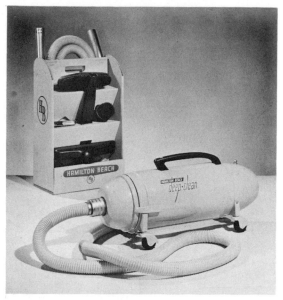

Fig. 17–10. Tank cleaner with container for storage of tools. (Hamilton Beach Company)

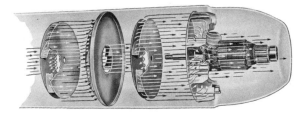

Fig. 17–11. Schematic view of movement of air through a tank cleaner. (Hamilton Beach Company)

upholstery tool, and a crevice tool. Many models have one dual-purpose, rug-and-floor tool instead of separate tools for rugs and bare floors. A dual-purpose, dusting-and-upholstery tool may also be provided as shown in Figure 17–9. Effective dual-purpose tools simplify cleaning, since fewer tools need to be removed and replaced in the wand.

As indicated earlier, the rug tool or the rug side of a rug-and-floor tool often has a two-position floating brush or comb-like device inside the nozzle for picking up light litter. The comb-like device has narrow openings to concentrate air flow through the nozzle. The manufacturer of one model states that this

concentrated air flow will pick up such fine litter as individual dog hairs.

The floor-and-wall tool or the floor side of a rug-and-floor tool usually has a brush around the nozzle, which provides a sweeping action when walls and hard floors are cleaned. The small dusting tool also has a brush around the nozzle; its bristles are generally softer than those of the brush on the floor tool. The crevice tool has no brush and the upholstery tool generally has no brush around the nozzle.

Because of its narrow opening, greater suction is obtained with the crevice tool than with any other tool. It is used for cleaning hard-to-get-at narrow spaces and drawers by means of high suction. In addition, it may be attached, by means of the hose, to the blower end of the cleaner when a strong, directed blast of air is desired—the only practical means of dislodging small particles and dirt from narrow enclosures.

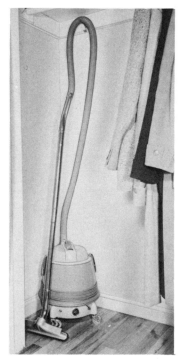

Fig. 17–12. Storage of canister cleaner with hose, wands, and rug tool attached. (Landers, Frary & Clark)

One of the newer convenience features of some models of canisters and tanks is provision for storing the tools *on* the cleaner. Tools are shown stored on the cleaner in Figures 17–2, 17–7, and 17–9. A vinyl tool holder that slips onto the cleaner may be purchased as an accessory for the model shown in Figure 17–4. This arrangement has the advantage of keeping tools immediately available when the cleaner is in use; between uses, cleaner and tools can be stored as a unit.

Canister and tank cleaners can be stored with hose, wands, and rug or other tools assembled. The hose will store vertically by looping it over a hook in a storage closet or other storage space (Fig. 17–12).

d. Accessories

Accessories include attachments for demothing and for spraying wax, paint, and insecticides. These are attached by means of the hose to the blower end of the cleaner. Usually such accessories are not expensive; logically, however, they should be purchased only if they will be used. They cannot be stored on the cleaner.

The manufacturer of the cleaner shown in Figure 17–8 suggests use of the crevice tool for demothing. Instead of adding demothing crystals to a special attachment, they may be added to a clean disposable filter bag inside the cleaner. Hose and crevice tool are then attached to the blower end of the cleaner and the motor is turned on.

The cord winder shown in Figure 17–9 is another accessory. It has a window-shade action which rewinds the cord automatically. This device keeps the cord out of the way when the cleaner is in use and provides convenient storage for it when the cleaner is not in use.

Floor polishers are available as an accessory for some cleaners. They are attached to the suction end of the cleaner. While this attachment is not inexpensive, it may be less expensive than a separate electric floor polisher.

One manufacturer has announced a "do-it-yourself" attachment that is used on the suction end of the cleaner. Assembled in a utility kit are several parts designed "to drill holes, sandpaper woodwork, wax floors, polish automobiles."

e. Specifications and Features

Specification sheets of different manufacturers differ in completeness of information supplied. The type of information found on detailed specification sheets is summarized below.

Dimensions are usually stated. These are important to the user, since they determine amount of storage space required. Weight in pounds is often specified, with or without tools, hose, and wands. For example, one cleaner is described as weighing 12½ pounds for cleaner only and 6 pounds for tools. Weight of present-day canisters and tanks is not as important a consideration as it was before they were put on wheels.

Maximum water lift is sometimes given. For canisters and tanks, water lift is usually quoted at some value between 35 and 70 inches. This is a measure of suction effect; it is the height of a column of water that can be supported by the difference between atmospheric pressure and the air pressure in the cleaner.

Input wattage is sometimes given on specification sheets and always on the nameplate of appliances that carry the Underwriters Laboratories seal of approval. Current models of canisters and tanks usually have an input rating between 550 and 750 watts, but some have higher ratings. Sometimes a model rated at 750 watts is described as a 1-horsepower cleaner. This description tends to be confusing, because horsepower ratings of motors of other appliances refer to output rather than input.

Length of cord is often noted; a usual length is 20 feet.

Reference may be made to extra filters on

the intake or discharge side of the motor, if provided.

Special features are noted, varying, of course, with different manufacturers. Those mentioned here are the ones a user might be especially interested in.

The cleaner shown in Figure 17–1 has a special recess in its shell around which the cord may be wound. Its motor circuit has a condenser to minimize radio and television interference while the cleaner is operating. It also has a series of blower holes around the bottom of the cleaner. In regular use, air does not leave the cleaner in a single blast; when the blower end of the cleaner is used the holes are closed automatically.

One manufacturer provides two wheels near the rear end of the dual-purpose, rug-and-floor tool, which tend to insure correct fit of the nozzle to the rug or floor, as well as ease of motion of the nozzle (Fig. 17–13).

The specifications will usually note provi-

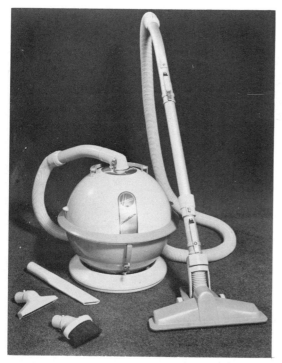

Fig. 17–13. Canister cleaner with wheels on rug-and-floor tool. (The Hoover Company)

sion for making the operating noise of the cleaner less, if such provision is made.

Finally, the specifications may give information on the disposable bag and/or the cloth bag. One tank cleaner is designed so that the disposable bag seals itself at a preset level of dirt accumulation, the motor stops, and the front cover of the cleaner opens—all three operations occurring automatically. The user is left with only the tasks of removing the bag and installing a new one.[2]

17–3. UPRIGHT CLEANERS

Fewer companies manufacture uprights than manufacture canisters and tanks, and successive models of uprights seem to change less radically than do canisters and tanks. Successive models, however, actually do change. Uprights are designed primarily for effective cleaning of carpets and rugs. Unlike canisters and tanks, they are sold with or without attachments for cleaning bare floors and furnishings.

a. Construction

The main parts of an upright that are visible when the cleaner is in operating position are the handle assembly, the bag, and the motor hood (Figs. 17–14, 17–15, and 17–16). The switch is usually in the upper part of the handle. The outer bag is made of cloth or plastic, and in newer models a disposable bag is generally inside it. The hood may have a light bulb and lens at the front—"to seek out the dirt"—and a narrow plastic strip or furniture guard that extends almost completely around the bottom.

The motor and fan are assembled in a housing or case underneath the motor hood. The nozzle for the brush roll is located at the

[2] When this feature was described in class, a freshman student of the senior author remarked: "Oh, suppose the cleaner stopped when I just had a little bit left to do!"

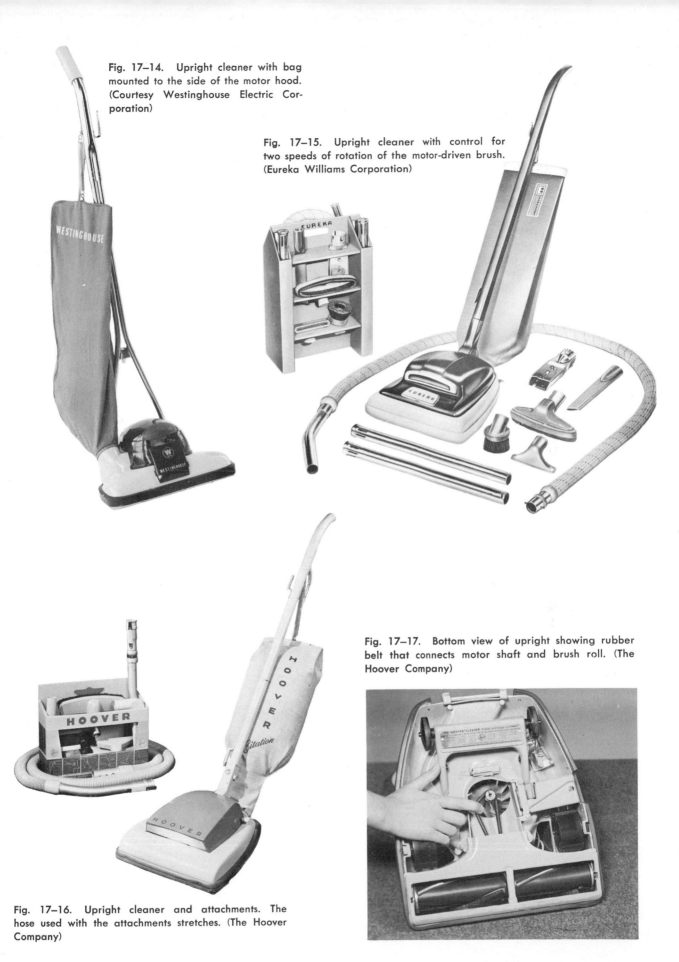

Fig. 17–14. Upright cleaner with bag mounted to the side of the motor hood. (Courtesy Westinghouse Electric Corporation)

Fig. 17–15. Upright cleaner with control for two speeds of rotation of the motor-driven brush. (Eureka Williams Corporation)

Fig. 17–17. Bottom view of upright showing rubber belt that connects motor shaft and brush roll. (The Hoover Company)

Fig. 17–16. Upright cleaner and attachments. The hose used with the attachments stretches. (The Hoover Company)

front of the cleaner under the motor hood and a rubber belt connects the brush roll with the motor shaft (Fig. 17–17).

Two front wheels are located under the hood just behind the nozzle, and two smaller wheels are located under the rear part of the hood. The wheels help make the cleaner easy to move.

A manual handle control or pedal may be located at or near the back of the motor hood. This is depressed to lower the handle from the vertical used for storage to the slanting position which is usual for cleaning carpets. The handle can also be lowered to an almost horizontal position for cleaning under furniture.

b. Attachments for Bare Floors and Furnishings

The floor-and-wall tool, upholstery tool, dusting tool, crevice tool, hose, wands, and connector or converter that may be used with an upright are generally called the attachments. The connector is a device used to connect the hose to the cleaner.

On some models the hose may be assembled to the cleaner without removing the belt from the brush. The connector is placed in the opening provided for it and the hose is assembled to it. If with this arrangement the brush roll rotates when the attachments are used, one should take care not to let the cleaner stand for too many minutes at one location on a rug. On other models, the belt is disconnected before the connector is installed in the cleaner, and the brush roll is not rotated by the motor when the attachments are used.

c. Specifications and Features

The information on specification sheets for uprights is somewhat similar to that for canisters and tanks. Some characteristic differences are summarized here. Wattage input is less than that for canisters and tanks; for uprights, a rating between 350 and 450 is usual. Maximum water lift may not be specified, but is substantially less than that for tanks and canisters. The relatively low water lift or suction is adequate for cleaning carpets and rugs with the motor-driven brush, but is sometimes disadvantageous for above-the-floor cleaning. One new upright is designed to use 420 watts for rugs and 620 watts with attachments.

Some uprights provide for two speeds of rotation of the brush roll, according to the setting of the "on-off" switch. Automatic adjustment of nozzle height to rug thickness or pile may be provided by use of a spring mounting in the support for the rear wheels. (Ideally, the nozzle lips *just* clear the top of the pile and the brushes make contact with the pile.)

Uprights may also have a mechanical device for lowering the roll to compensate for wear of the brush bristles. When mechanical adjustment is no longer possible the entire brush roll is replaced, or the brushes only are replaced for models that have replaceable brushes.

If positive means are provided to prevent spillage of dirt when the bag is removed from the cleaner, this feature will probably be noted in the manufacturer's literature.

17–4. SPECIAL-PURPOSE CLEANERS

Figure 17–18 shows a cleaner that can either be hung over the operator's shoulder by a strap or carried by hand. This cleaner is intended primarily for above-the-floor cleaning. It is also useful for cleaning automobile interiors.

Figure 17–19 shows a lightweight (6¾ pounds) upright. The base of this cleaner is designed for vacuuming rugs, bare floors, and furnishings. The cleaner is held upside down for above-the-floor cleaning. The bag does not have to be removed to empty accumulated dirt. Instead, dirt that collects in the filtering bag is shaken down into a dirt cup on the right side of the cleaner just below the bag, and only the dirt cup is emptied.

Fig. 17–18.   Special-purpose cleaner that may be hung over the shoulder. (The Hoover Company)

17–5. USE OF VACUUM CLEANERS

Specific suggestions for the different tools or attachments are given in the user's booklets and other literature distributed by manufacturers. The discussion here covers general procedures for using a vacuum cleaner to clean a family room, living room, or den.

Without a plan for room cleaning, one is likely to take many unnecessary steps. Planned cleaning of a room, on the other hand, can be a satisfying activity. You know in advance how you are going to do the work. You know where you are in your work after unplanned interruptions, such as telephone calls. You know what you have accomplished when you are through. Finally, you may learn effective short cuts to improve your plan.

Two types of room-cleaning plans have been suggested. The first and probably the better known one is to use one tool for all the cleaning in the room for which that tool is appropriate, then to use a second tool for all the cleaning for which that tool is appropriate, and so on. The second plan is to clean a portion of a room completely, changing tools as necessary, then to clean another portion of the room completely, and so on, until the entire room is cleaned.

These two plans evolved before the introduction of dual-purpose tools. With such tools

Fig. 17–19.   Special-purpose cleaner for floor cleaning and for above-the-floor cleaning. (The Regina Corporation)

available, a modified form of the second plan seems most logical. The modification consists of using *both* parts of a dual-purpose tool in cleaning portions of a room.

In the general work plan outline given below some of the suggestions are adapted from the Hoover cleaning manual.[3]

[3] *House Cleaning and Home Management Manual,* Hoover Home Institute, 1950.

1. Pick up magazines, clothes, toys, etc.

2. Empty ash trays and set them aside for washing. Move wastebaskets to a hall or elsewhere for later emptying and replacement.

3. Divide the room, mentally, into several areas. For example, a corner might be one area. The space associated with one-half of a wall might be another area.

4. Move furniture slightly away from the wall, provided it is not too difficult to move.

5. Start in one area and clean the wall or walls, moldings, drapes, lamps, etc. Clean the front, back, top, bottom, and sides of the furniture in that area. Clean the floor register. Clean the carpet, rug, or wood floor between the back of the furniture and the wall. The floor brush of an upright, canister, or tank is the reasonable tool to use for the portion of the carpet or rug near the walls.

6. Move to the adjacent area and repeat step 5. Then move to other areas until you have gone all around the room.

7. Move the furniture back into place against walls.

8. Clean the uncleaned portion of the floor, including areas under the furniture. (There is no reason to assume that moth larvae boycott the parts of rugs that are under furniture.)

9. Empty and replace wastebaskets. Wash and replace ash trays.

10. Clean the dusting tool and the floor tool with the vacuum cleaner itself. Empty the fabric bag or replace the disposable bag, if necessary.

17–6. CARE AND MAINTENANCE OF VACUUM CLEANERS

Care of vacuum cleaners is rather simple and consists essentially of four parts. One is regular emptying of the cloth bag or replacement of the disposable bag. The second is replacement of filters when necessary. The third is regular cleaning of brushes and replacement when necessary. The fourth is replacement of the belt, when necessary, on vacuum cleaners that have a belt-connected brush roll.

As noted earlier, the efficiency of a vacuum cleaner decreases as dirt accumulates in the bag, because the dirt in the bag and that covering the interior surface of the bag offer a mechanical resistance to the flow of air through the cleaner. For maximum efficiency, the bag should be empty and the interior surfaces of cloth or vinyl bags should be clean, that is, free of clogged dirt, at the start of each use.

Many homemakers are unwilling to empty the cleaner after each use. (Emptying after use insures that the bag is empty before the next use.) A practical compromise probably is to empty a cloth bag or discard a disposable bag when it is about half full. Actually, the size of the bag may make some difference, since the larger the bag, the larger the filtering surface available. If cleaning is routine, one can learn from experience about how much cleaning can be done before the bag is half full.

Brushes on the tools should be cleaned after each use and during use for some types of cleaning. Use the suction end of the hose for this purpose.

As the brushes on the roll wear, the height of the roll should be adjusted according to instructions in the user's booklet. A test for correct length of bristles of the brush roll is to hold the edge of a small, stiff card perpendicularly across the nozzle lips and rotate the roll by hand. If the length of the bristles is correct, the bristles will just brush the edge of the card.

The belt should be replaced when the roll slips as it is driven by the motor. Another indication of need for replacement is elongation of the belt. This can be checked by laying a new belt alongside the old belt or by measuring the length of the belt when it is new and again when it looks worn. Instructions on replacement are given in the user's booklet.

If any periodic maintenance by a service man is necessary, this fact would usually be mentioned in the user's booklet. Such maintenance is not necessary for all cleaners. On the other hand, if a cleaner does not pick up threads and lint with a very few strokes, it probably is desirable to have a factory-authorized service person check the cleaner, after you have made sure that the bag is not too full.

17–7. SELECTION CONSIDERATIONS

As noted earlier, changes in canister and tank cleaners, and to a less extent in upright cleaners, have been occurring rapidly for several years. Frequent model changes benefit the consumer in that early incorporation of improvements is possible. On the other hand, frequent model changes make it difficult for a consumer to know which models have proved themselves in use.

The inspection experiment at the end of the chapter outlines some use characteristics that can be checked without a home trial.

One type of cleaner probably is not best for all homes. The best procedure at present for selecting a new cleaner seems to be to try a few models that you have inspected, according to Experiment 1, pages 243–244, or other plan, in your home. If a cleaner performs satisfactorily for a few days and is convenient to use for your type of housecleaning, it is likely that it will be adequate for the length of time you might reasonably expect to use it.

If home trials are not practical, try to visualize the cleaning tasks that you do in your home when you make your choice of model.

B. Electric Floor Polishers

As is the case with practically all other household appliances, more than one type of electric floor polisher is available. The twin-brush type uses a pair of brushes (Fig. 17–20). The brushes alone are used for scrubbing, waxing, and polishing, and pads are used under them for buffing. The single-brush type may have one scrubbing and waxing brush, one polishing brush, and disposable buffing pad (Fig. 17–21).

Brushes are assembled to the motor through a pulley and gears (Fig. 17–22). When the motor is turned on, the brushes rotate at high speed.

A motor-driven floor polisher is one of the household appliances that people seem to enjoy owning. Probably, the enjoyment is really associated with the superior results obtained when the appliance is used to polish and buff hard floors and hard floor coverings.

17–8. USE AND CARE

The floor polisher is used for four types of operation: scrubbing, waxing, polishing, and buffing.

a. Scrubbing

The scrubbing brush or brushes may be used with detergent and water to scrub hard floor coverings or concrete floors or with cleaner for wood floors.

1. Vacuum the floor to remove dust, litter, and other surface dirt.

2. Use a sponge mop to sponge a convenient area of floor, perhaps 6 square feet. Note that the recommendation is to *sponge* an area, not to flood it with water.

3. Scrub the sponged area with the polisher.

4. Rinse with the sponge mop. Then pick up as much water as possible with the mop.

5. For wood floors, a solvent cleaner or a liquid cleaning-and-polishing wax is used instead of detergent in water. Cleaner or cleaning wax can also be used for sealed concrete floors and linoleum. No extra mop is necessary.

The cleaner or cleaning wax is applied with fine steel wool, such as 00 grade. A roll of the fine steel wool is purchased in a hardware store. One user's booklet suggests cutting the steel wool into 4-inch by 4-inch strips and

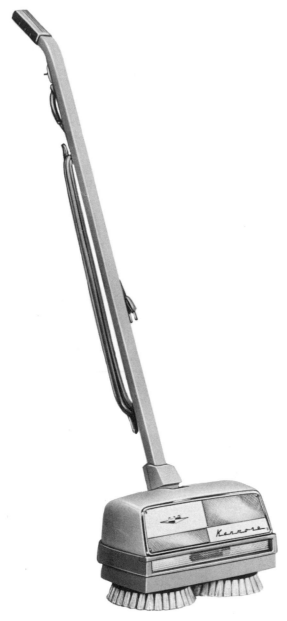

Fig. 17–20. Twin-brush electric floor polisher. (Sears, Roebuck and Co.)

pressing or embedding the strips into the scrubbing brushes of the polisher. Small puddles of cleaner are poured onto the floor, and the polisher with scrubbing brush is used to scrub. The steel wool strips are discarded as they become soiled.

b. Waxing, Polishing, and Buffing

Floors and coverings are waxed to enhance their appearance, to increase their life, and to minimize staining. To achieve these results, it is necessary to use the correct wax. So, read the label on the package, and use a type of wax appropriate for the material of the floor or floor covering. Generally, a wax that is not self-polishing and that has a naphtha-like odor is used for wood, vinyl floor coverings, sealed cork, and sealed concrete. Self-polishing wax only is recommended for asphalt and rubber tile. Either a wax that is not self-polishing or a self-polishing one may be used for linoleum floor coverings.

Self-polishing waxes should not be *applied* with an electric polisher, but the floor may be polished with the polisher after the self-polishing wax has dried.

A suggested procedure for waxing, polishing, and buffing with a floor polisher is as follows:

1. Vacuum the floor or scrub it, if necessary. Scrubbing is necessary only when the floor is very soiled or when a thick coat of wax has been allowed to build up on it. (One indication that a coat of wax is too thick is that the wax peels.)

2. Apply paste or liquid wax with fine steel wool. Paste wax may be spread on steel wool strips that are pressed into the scrubbing brush or brushes. Apply only a very thin coating.

3. Let the wax dry thoroughly on the entire floor. This will require 20 to 30 minutes or longer.

4. If the polisher was used to scrub the floor, wait until the brushes are dry before proceeding with step 5. If the polisher has an extra polishing brush, replace the scrubbing and waxing brush with the polishing brush and continue with step 5, as soon as the wax on the floor is dry.

5. Polish the entire floor with the polisher.

6. Buff the floor with wool pads or other pads provided with the polisher to give the floor a high luster. The bright look obtained by buffing means good polishing to many homemakers.

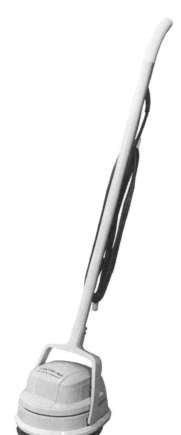

Fig. 17–21.   (Left) Single-brush electric floor polisher. (Johnson's Wax)
Fig. 17–22.   (Right) Bottom view of single-brush floor polisher. (Johnson's Wax)

CAUTION: User's booklets are likely to note that two or more very thin coats of wax give a harder, smoother, and more lasting finish than one coat. However, floors that are too slippery cause falls. Hence, a practical compromise is to use only one coat of wax and to renew it whenever necessary. It is especially important to follow this practice in households that have aged members. The appearance of a floor should under no circumstances ever be allowed to take precedence over safety in the home.

c. Care

Polishers require little maintenance. Occasional, once a year or so, oiling of a motor-shaft bearing may be specified in the user's booklet. Brushes are cleaned with water and detergent or a cleaner, as suggested in the user's booklet. The one care procedure always emphasized is to store the polisher so that the bristles do not rest on the floor. Either hang the entire polisher, using the hook provided on the handle, or store the polisher and brushes separately with brush bristles pointing up.

C. Vacuum Cleaner Experiments

Experiment 1. *Inspection of Vacuum Cleaners*

1. Are model number and manufacturer's name and address given on the nameplate? What is the wattage rating or the current and voltage ratings? Does the appliance carry the Underwriters Laboratories seal of approval?

2. Is the appliance easy to move? Check by moving the cleaner over a rug, if possible. If the cleaner is a canister or tank, move it with the hose, wands, and rug tool attached. Is the cleaner stable or does it have a tendency to tip over when it is moved? Can you lift it fairly easily?

3. Do the rug and floor tools of a canister or tank appear to be designed so as to insure correct fit to the floor when the cleaner is handled naturally?

4. Is the cloth bag easy to empty or the disposable bag easy to replace? If possible, check by emptying or replacing a bag. Does the cleaner have a positive means for preventing spillage of dirt when the bag is emptied or replaced?

5. Are positive mechanical devices provided for locking tools, wands, and hose?

6. If the cleaner is an upright, note the height of the top of the motor hood from the floor and estimate whether it will fit under furniture for under-furniture cleaning.

7. What provision is made for storing the tools? How is the cord handled when the cleaner is not in use?

8. Will the cleaner and its tools or attachments be easy to store in a closet? Approximately how many square inches of floor area will be needed for storing cleaner and tools?

9. Does the air leave the cleaner in a single stream or is the discharge air distributed over a broad area?

10. Are a specification sheet and an instruction booklet supplied with the cleaner? Does the manufacturer's literature indicate that periodic servicing is necessary? If so, where is this servicing available? Where will you obtain additional disposable bags, filters, and replacement brushes?

11. Does the manufacturer's literature indicate that some provision has been made to decrease the noise of operation? Check the effectiveness of this provision by listening while the cleaner is operated.

12. Does the manufacturer's literature indicate that the electrical circuit of the motor has some provision for minimizing radio and television interference? (If no such provision is made, radio and television reception may be poor in your neighbors' sets as well as your own when the cleaner is in operation.)

13. Are special accessories that you want available?

14. Precisely what does the manufacturer's warranty promise you?

Experiment 2. *Use of Cleaners*

1. Use several cleaners in a living room or family room, if possible.
2. Follow the plan outlined in section 17–5.
3. Evaluate the cleaners, as well as you can, in terms of dirt-removing ability and ease of use.

Do not assume you can rate cleaners on the basis of a single use in one part of one room.

CHAPTER 18

Water, Laundry Supplies, and Mechanical Water Softeners

In many areas throughout the world today, people wash their clothes without soap in a river and dry them by placing them on rocks in the sun. In contrast to these simple and uncomplicated procedures, laundering soiled articles with modern appliances involves the use of greatly increased equipment. We use water, water heaters, detergents, washers, dryers, irons and/or ironers, and, in some cases, mechanical water softeners. Other laundry supplies such as starch and bleach may also be used, in addition to soap and synthetic detergents.

Because so many appliances are used, as well as water and laundry supplies, four chapters are devoted to laundering with modern equipment. Suggested guides on washing, drying, and ironing are discussed in the sections which cover laundry supplies and different appliances.

A. Water and Supplies

18–1. WATER

From a practical point of view, hard water is usually considered to be water that contains calcium and magnesium salts. Soft or softened water does not contain these salts.

Calcium and magnesium acid carbonates produce temporary hardness in water; calcium and magnesium sulfates and chlorides produce permanent hardness in water. The relative amounts of temporary and permanent hardness in a water supply thus depend on the relative amounts of the minerals producing the two types of hardness.

Temporary hardness is removed when water is heated, because the acid carbonates are decomposed and ordinary or normal carbonates are precipitated. The precipitate, which is mostly calcium carbonate, is observed as a white or gray deposit on the utensil used for heating the water. Permanent hardness is not removed when water is heated, because the sulfates and chlorides are not decomposed by heat.

Water hardness is expressed in grains per gallon or parts per million. One-grain-per-gallon hardness is equal to 17.1 parts-per-million hardness. Water with a hardness of 1 grain per gallon contains 1 grain or 1/7000 of a pound of hardness-producing minerals per gallon of water. Water with a hardness of 1 part per million contains 1 part of hardness-producing minerals per 1,000,000 parts of water.

The average hardness of the water supply varies in different regions of the United States. Some regions, for example, most of the Eastern seaboard, have soft water. Others have very hard water. A particular location in a soft-water region may have hard water and a particular location in a hard-water region may have soft water. For example, most of the Midwest has very hard water, but some locations have a water supply of approximately zero grains hardness.

Though many municipalities now soften water before delivering it to homes through the mains, such water is not completely softened; in fact a hardness of 5 to 7 grains per gallon is often left in the water.

Hard water, even that with a hardness of 5 to 7 grains, creates some problems in laundering, as well as in dishwashing and general cleaning. These problems are primarily associated with the use of soap in water that has permanent hardness. Whenever soap is used with such water, some of it combines with the calcium and magnesium sulfates and chlorides to form a gray curd or scum. As far as cleaning is concerned, this part of the soap is lost. The scum thus formed in hard water also adheres to laundered fabrics and washed surfaces, such as washed walls.

When *syndets* (synthetic detergents) are used in hard water, the formation of curd is not usually a problem.

Although only calcium and magnesium salts contribute to water hardness as usually calculated, other minerals dissolved in the water supply may also cause problems in home laundering and dishwashing. For example, a concentration of iron greater than 3/10 parts per million may cause rust stains on washed fabrics.

18–2. LAUNDRY SUPPLIES

Laundry supplies include packaged water softeners, soaps and syndets, bleaches, bluing, sizing, antistatic agents, and fabric softeners.

a. Packaged Water Softeners

Packaged water softeners are of two types, both sold under various trade names. The precipitating type combines with the hardness-producing salts to form water-insoluble floating particles. Washing soda is an example of this type. When it is used, some of the precipitate floats to the surface and some is dispersed throughout the water. Softening is obtained whether the surface precipitate is skimmed off or not. But it is good procedure to skim off the surface scum before adding clothes to a washer, if practical. (This procedure is not practical for a front-loading washer.) The precipitating type of water softener is useful, theoretically at least, for water of any degree of hardness.

The nonprecipitating type of packaged water softener combines with the hardness-producing salts to form water-soluble compounds. The water thus does not become cloudy and no scum forms on the surface of the water. Furthermore, when enough nonprecipitating softener is used, enough active ingredient is available both to soften the water and to combine with hardness-producing minerals in a detergent buildup (unrinsed detergent) in the fabrics being washed. This type is thus useful both to soften water and to remove soap or syndet buildup in clothes. However, the nonprecipitating softeners have limited value for very hard water.

The amount of packaged water softener to be used in laundering depends on the hardness of the water and the water capacity of the washer. Suggested amounts for different hardnesses of water sometimes are given in the washer instruction booklets.

When an automatic washer is used, packaged water softeners are usually considered less convenient than running soft water, since to have soft water throughout the wash and rinse parts of the cycle a homemaker would have to add softener before the wash and before each rinse. This problem has been partially solved by some manufacturers of automatic washers. One manufacturer, for example, provides a wheel device for holding a solution of a nonprecipitating softener on the agitator. The softener is placed in the device at the beginning of the wash cycle and remains there until the first rinse, when it automatically falls into the wash tub.

b. Soaps and Syndets

Soaps and syndets are the most usual laundry supplies. Currently available soaps and syndets are classified as either mild or all-purpose. Mild soaps and syndets are considered to be less harmful to the skin than all-purpose products and hence are used for hand laundering fine articles and hand dishwashing. All-purpose soaps and syndets are used for laundering heavily soiled articles and for general cleaning.

Mild and all-purpose syndets are currently available in both liquid and granular form. Mild and all-purpose soaps are usually sold for household use only in granular form.

Ingredients used in soaps and syndets are noted below to aid in understanding some of the advertising claims on packages of the products.

The active ingredient of soap is a salt of a fatty acid, made by reacting a fat or oil, such as tallow or coconut oil, with an alkali, usually lye. A mild soap is an almost pure soap; that is, it contains an active ingredient, some moisture, and a small quantity of inorganic material.

All-purpose soaps contain a soap ingredient, builders, moisture, and frequently a fluorescent dye. The materials used for builders include soda ash, washing soda, borax, trisodium phosphate, and sodium metaphosphate. Some of these are water softeners. The fluorescent dye makes the washed articles look brighter than they otherwise would.

Syndets are chemically quite different from soaps. Their active ingredient is made from coal tar derivatives or fats and oils by a somewhat more complex chemical process than that used in making soap. Sulfonated types of syndets are made from coal tar derivatives; sulfated types are made from naturally occurring fats and oils.

Mild syndets contain an active ingredient and inorganic salts.

All-purpose syndets contain several ingredients in addition to the active one. The inorganic builders, primarily phosphates, act as water softeners. Organic builders may be included to maintain "live" suds during the washing process. An antiredeposition or whiteness-retention agent, sodium carboxymethylcellulose (CMC), is included to hold the soil in suspension in the wash water during the washing process. Sodium silicate may be added to prevent reactions between aluminum parts of the washer and the inorganic builders. Finally, a fluorescent dye or "optical bleach" or "brightener" is usually included.

The amount of suds produced by mild and all-purpose soaps and mild syndets depends to a large extent on the hardness of the water. In contrast, all-purpose syndets can be formulated to give a high, a controlled, or a low suds by use of the organic builders mentioned in the previous paragraph.

Manufacturers of wringer-type washers and top-loading automatic washers usually state that low, controlled, or high sudsing syndets or all-purpose soaps may be used, but often imply that the high-sudsing syndet is preferred.[1] Some manufacturers of front-loading automatic washers state explicitly in the washer booklet that only a low- or controlled-sudsing syndet should be used.

Suggestions on quantities of all-purpose syndet or soap per washer load are given on the packages or bottles of the supplies and in washer instruction booklets. The amounts suggested for low-sudsing and controlled-sudsing syndets appear to be based on the assumption that the wash water will be hard.

[1] A package of high-sudsing syndet frequently is supplied with the washer.

Directions on the packages of high-sudsing syndets and all-purpose soaps are usually to use enough to make a good suds that lasts through the washing cycle.

Experimental work has emphasized that the amount of detergent to use should depend on the cleanliness to be obtained and on the feel or "hand" of the washed articles.[2] Excess detergent may produce cleaner clothes; but if the detergent is not free-rinsing some of it is left in the washed clothes. This is objectionable because the clothes feel and look harsh or stiff. Furthermore, articles containing detergent may scorch more easily when ironed.

Experimental work in this field thus far reported is insufficient to make broad generalizations. It appears to be true, however, that the quantities of low- and controlled-sudsing syndets currently recommended on packages of supplies and in washer instruction booklets are definitely excessive for soft water. Also, instructions for high-sudsing syndets may be somewhat misleading when soft water is used. On the other hand, the recommendation that only enough soap be used to give a lasting suds appears to be sound for soft water.

c. Bleaches

Bleaches are helpful when used as an aid (1) for retaining or restoring whiteness to fabrics and (2) for removing some stains not removed by ordinary washing procedures. Instructions in washer booklets usually do not specify use of bleach as part of the regular washing procedure. Nevertheless, good washing procedure and careful and restrained use of a bleach are more likely to produce brightly washed articles than good washing procedure alone.

Care and restraint in bleaching require following instructions on the bottle or package

[2] F. Ehrenkranz, V. W. Hyatt, and M. Beale, "Soap in the Home Clothes Washer," *Soap and Sanitary Chemicals,* 1954, *30:* 2, 97.

of bleach, bleaching only those articles that need it, and thoroughly rinsing the bleach. If chlorine bleach is added at the start of the wash period, it inhibits the action of the fluorescent brightener that is part of most all-purpose detergents. Hence, *diluted* chlorine bleach is best added to an automatic washer a few minutes after the start of the wash cycle.

Liquid chlorine bleach has been a well-known laundry supply for many years. It is an effective aid in laundering white and colorfast cottons and linens and white nylons, Dacrons, and Orlons. It should not be used on silk, wool, acetate or most resin-treated materials. Also, it should not be used if the water supply contains iron.

A dry "chlorine-type" bleach is available which is described as having the same bleaching ability as chlorine bleaches. This bleach is recommended only for fabrics for which liquid chlorine bleaches may be used and in water that is free of iron. However, the dry bleach is said to release the active ingredient more slowly than the liquid bleach; hence less care is necessary in using it.

Diluted hydrogen peroxide can be used for silk, wool, and acetate. Only small quantities should be purchased at a time, because the compound decomposes on standing.

The usual powdered bleaches on the market at the present time are either sodium or calcium perborate bleaches. These bleaches are mild, and the instructions on the box usually indicate that they are safe for fabrics and colors that hot water will not harm. Thus they are safe for resin-treated cottons. Because they are mild, they are most effective when used each time articles are washed. For example, a nylon article may stay bright if such a bleach is used each time the article is washed; but one that has acquired a dingy look will probably not be greatly improved in appearance by one or two washings with sodium perborate bleach added.

d. Bluing, Sizing, Antistatic Agents, and Fabric Softeners

Bluing is used to make articles look white or bright. Liquid and solid bluings contain a dye material. They are used in the last rinse. To avoid streaks, liquid bluing must be thoroughly mixed with, or solid bluing completely dissolved in, the rinse water. Bead and flake bluings contain a detergent (syndet or soap) in addition to the blue coloring matter; hence, they are used in the wash water.

The usual sizing agent in home laundering is starch. It is used to give "body" to a limp fabric or to give a smooth finish that improves the appearance of an article and may make subsequent washings easier. Liquid starches are more convenient—and for large loads more expensive—than lump or powdered starches which are heated in water before use. Starches labeled "cold-water starches" are generally used only when rather stiff starching is desired, as for collars. Plastic starches that last through several washings are preferred by some homemakers for certain articles.

Washer booklets suggest procedures for starching complete loads in the washer. If only a few articles are to be starched, it may be more convenient to starch them in a utensil rather than in the washer. The articles should be thoroughly wet but not dripping wet when placed in the starching solution. To get the same finished appearance, articles that will be dried in a dryer need to be starched two to three times more heavily than articles that will be dried on a line. Starched articles should be dried completely, dampened, and allowed to season before they are ironed. (As used here, the expression "to season" means to become uniformly damp as a result of remaining in a plastic bag or being rolled up in a turkish towel for several hours.)

Antistatic agents for nylons are sold under different trade names. Some of them are used in the last rinse. One-half teaspoon of white vinegar per gallon of rinse water is also sometimes recommended as an antistatic agent.

Fabric softeners, available under different trade names, are sometimes added to the last rinse water to give a soft "hand" or feel to the washed articles. Fabric softeners that contain quaternary ammonium salts are reported to function also as antistatic agents for some of the newer synthetic fabrics.[3]

B. Mechanical Water Softeners

18–3. CONSTRUCTION AND SOFTENING MECHANISM

Modern, mechanical, home water softeners are cylindrical or rectangular tanks that contain no moving parts except controls. Water passing through them is softened by an ion exchange process. Inside the tank a bed of exchange material rests on a bed of gravel or on

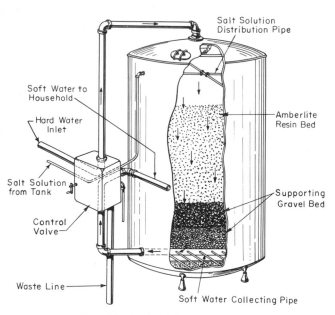

TYPICAL SOFTENER IN OPERATION

Fig. 18–1. Schematic sketch of a mechanical water softener. (Rohm and Haas Company)

a screen (Fig. 18–1). The exchange material consists of natural zeolites, bead-like granules known as synthetic ion-exchange resin, or a mixture of natural zeolites and synthetic resin. The synthetic material has a higher exchange capacity than natural zeolites; hence less is needed to soften a given amount of water. The

synthetic material usually has a trade name which sometimes is marked on the tank.

When hard water falls from the top to the bottom of the bed of exchange material, the material gives up sodium ions and takes on calcium and magnesium ions. Water leaving the tank thus contains sodium salts rather than calcium and magnesium salts and is therefore softened water. This exchange of ions goes on until the exchange material becomes exhausted, that is, saturated with calcium and magnesium ions. The resin or zeolite is then regenerated by a brine solution.

The actual process of regeneration involves the following three steps: backwashing, addition of the brine solution, and rinsing. In the backwashing, water is made to flow from the bottom to the top of the tank. This removes dirt and sludge from the granules and prevents compacting of the bed of exchange material. In the second step, the brine solution of water and ice cream salt or water softener salt passes down through the exchange material. As this occurs, the resin or zeolite gives up calcium and magnesium ions and takes on sodium ions. In the final or rinsing step, water is flushed through the tank to the waste line to remove the brine solution, which now contains calcium and magnesium salts rather than sodium salts.

Note that the ion-exchange process does not of itself take care of iron in the water supply. In fact, Calhoun and Hetherington state that "concentrations of iron greater than about two parts per million can cause difficulty in the

[3] H. L. Ward, "Textile Softeners for Home Laundering," *J. of Home Economics*, 1957, *49:* 2, 122.

softener."[4] Some forms of iron content in the water are handled best by means of a special filter in the supply line to the softener.

18–4. CHARACTERISTICS AND FEATURES

Home softeners deliver softened water at rates of from 4.5 to 17 gallons per minute, depending on the model. Generally, home softeners are designed to operate properly for a water supply pressure greater than 20 pounds per square inch. If the pressure is less, as is sometimes the case in suburbs of cities, special provision must be made for satisfactory backwashing.

a. Capacities

Softeners are rated in "grains capacity." This is the total hardness in grains the softener will remove between regenerations. Home softeners of one manufacturer have ratings of 27,000, 30,000, 44,000, 55,000, and 80,000 grains. Amount of salt per regeneration ranges from 25 pounds for the 27,000-grain softener to 60 pounds for the 80,000-grain softener. Between regenerations, the 30,000-grain softener will soften approximately 1000 gallons of water that had a hardness of 30 grains per gallon, or 6000 gallons that has a hardness of 5 grains per gallon, or other combinations of gallons times grains per gallon that total 30,000 grains.

The larger the grains capacity of the softener, the longer can be the time between regenerations; but softeners of larger capacity cost more initially, and regeneration takes longer. The grains capacity required depends on the water consumption practice of the family and the hardness of the water supply. Ordinarily the softener purchased will be one that requires regeneration every two to four weeks, for nonautomatic models.

[4] W. D. Calhoun and Richard Hetherington, "ABC's of Home Water Softeners," *Plumbing and Heating Journal*, April through August 1954 issues.

b. Features

One-tank and two-tank softener models are available (Figs. 18–2 and 18–3). The one-tank model is more common. The softener is regenerated by pouring salt directly into an opening in the top of the tank. In the two-tank model, one tank is the softener and the other is a container for storing the brine solution.

Both types are available with various degrees of automation. For the one-tank type, the backwashing and rinsing may be controlled by manual manipulation of valves or by a mechanical or electric timer. For the two-tank type, backwashing, addition of salt solution, and rinsing may be controlled by a single electric switch. Addition of salt to the tank in which the brine solution is stored is not automatic.

Filters for iron, manganese, and hydrogen sulfide are available for use with some models. An analysis of the water supply should be given to or made by the dealer so that he can check with the manufacturer, if necessary, on the probable utility of any filter that might be included with the softener installation.

18–5. INSTALLATION AND MAINTENANCE

Various installation arrangements are used for softeners. One accepted arrangement is to direct the water from the hard water supply to the house through three pipes—one to the softener, a second to the toilet flush boxes, and a third to taps used for sprinklers outside the house. This arrangement provides soft water for all cold and hot water taps in the house and hard water for toilet flush boxes and outside sprinklers. A modification of this arrangement is to provide also for one cold hard water tap inside the house. Whatever arrangement is used, a by-pass line should be provided around the softener so that water will be available in the house while the softener is being regenerated.

Pipe of a size recommended by the manu-

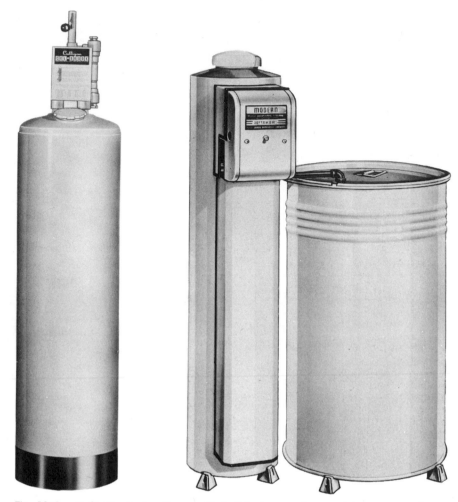

Fig. 18–2. (Left) One-tank softener with built-in by-pass for supplying water to house lines during regeneration. (Photograph courtesy of Culligan Soft Water Institute.)
Fig. 18–3. (Right) Two-tank softener with automatic, electrically controlled regeneration. (ServiSoft, Division of George Getz Corporation)

facturer should be used, and the material of the pipe should be one that is known to give satisfactory service for the particular water supply. (The dealer may be able to supply this information on the basis of an analysis of the water supply.)

Drain lines from the softener should of course meet local plumbing requirements in areas where there are such requirements. If no requirements are imposed by local ordinance, recommendations can be requested of the dealer.

Perhaps the two most important points to observe for good maintenance are these. (1) Follow instructions carefully when regeneration is done manually. If for any reason an excessively long time elapses between regenerations, consult the dealer on the procedure to follow. Generally, a longer backwashing than usual will be necessary. (2) Use the type of salt recommended by the softener manufacturer.

It is worth noting that owners of home softeners usually consider that the advantages of softened water outweigh any inconvenience associated with the necessary regeneration.

CHAPTER 19

Gas and Electric Water Heaters

A. Gas Water Heaters

19–1. CONSTRUCTION

The main parts of a gas water heater are the tank, the burner with its thermostatic control, the flue, the insulation and exterior shell, and the relief valves.

It has been stated that the life of the tank is the life of the water heater. The material from which the tank is made should be able to resist corrosion and withstand the water pressures to which it may be subjected. Some of the materials in use for tanks of gas water heaters are galvanized steel, Monel metal, copper, aluminum alloy, and glass-lined steel.

The useful life of a water heater depends on the material of the tank, the kind of water heated in it, and the temperature to which the water is heated. With use, tanks of all materials become lined with carbonates if the water supply is hard. A small deposit of hard water scale serves essentially as an extra finish on the interior of the tank; a thick deposit may be expected to increase the operating cost of the heater. Tanks of certain materials corrode when the water supply is corrosive. Water that has acid in it or a high dissolved oxygen content is likely to be corrosive. Dissolved solids, too, may contribute to the corrosive effect.

Galvanized steel is more likely to corrode than the other tank materials listed above. For this reason, in a water heater that has a galvanized steel tank a magnesium rod is sometimes used to "direct" the corrosive action to the rod rather than to the zinc lining of the tank, as discussed below. The magnesium rod is not effective for all types of water.

A magnesium rod coupled with a dissimilar metal and placed in water will develop electrical energy. The magnesium will corrode and destroy itself while protecting the other metal. The protection a magnesium rod supplies in a water heater tank takes place in three ways: (1) The corrosion takes place on the magnesium rod rather than on the metal of the tank; (2) the tank walls are covered with a protective film; and (3) the water in the tank is chemically conditioned so that less corrosion will take place.

Magnesium protective devices may be installed on new equipment or they may be added to water heaters already in use. The rod may be solid and rigid or a link type.

The life of a water heater is prolonged by using a thermostat setting only as high as needed for the hot water demand in the home, since the reactions that wear the tanks are accelerated at high temperatures. The walls of glass-lined tanks, however, are not corroded as are most metal tanks without anticorrosion rods.

Most gas water heaters use the Bunsen type of burner which has a primary air inlet, a mixing tube, and a burner head with ports. There may be one burner or a cluster of burners. Smaller size, automatic storage water heaters have less gas input than larger ones. The orifices used may be of the fixed or adjustable types. The burner flame should not touch the bottom of the tank or any other surface within the burner compartment. Burners designed to be used with liquefied petroleum gas have fixed orifices.

The door or doors to the burner assembly should fit tightly. If a door is warped or is not closed as tightly as it should be, excess air and drafts are admitted, which may cause the pilot to go out. It may also cause a loss of heat when the burner is not in operation. Doors should be large enough so that the pilot is easily accessible and the burner can be removed for servicing, if necessary.

An automatic pilot is a safety device which stops the flow of gas to the burner if the constantly burning pilot should go out. In the 100 percent shut-off type, gas supply to both the pilot and main burner is shut off should the pilot go out. In many water heaters the operation of the automatic pilot depends on a thermomagnetic effect.

In the thermomagnetic type of safety cutoff, two dissimilar metals are joined together, and the junction is placed in the pilot flame. This produces a small amount of electricity. When the flame goes out, no electricity is produced, the magnet controlling the gas valve is deënergized, and the flow of gas is stopped.

The pilot should remain on at all times. The flame should be high enough to maintain heat to operate the automatic gas shut-off. It should be adjusted so that the main burner will ignite rapidly.

The thermostat controls the temperature of the water in the storage tank by controlling the flow of gas to the burner. The heat-sensitive part of the thermostat is located in the water tank. Many thermostats for gas water heaters are actuated by a copper tube (expanding element) over an invar rod (nonexpanding element).

The thermostat may operate on a snap-acting, throttling, or quick-acting principle. In snap-acting thermostats the valve controlling the flow of gas moves from open to closed, or

vice versa, very rapidly. In throttling thermostats the valve is wide open, allowing a full
flow of gas to the burner when the water in
the storage tank is cold. As the water is heated,
the main valve gradually closes until the
thermostat setting is reached, at which time
the main valve is completely closed. A by-pass
or minimum flame is used on this type, because
of the problem of ignition on slow-opening
valves. Quick-acting thermostats react much
more rapidly to changes in water temperature.
This type of thermostat is much like the throttling type of thermostat, but because the action
is more rapid little or no by-pass gas is required.

Tank corrosion usually does not affect an
immersion type of thermostat, but the copper
part of the thermostat can cause galvanic corrosion on the tank adjacent to the control. The
copper may be covered with a plastic sheath to
prevent this reaction.

The gas burner in the automatic storage
type of water heater is placed below or underneath the water tank (Fig. 19–1). The heat
from the burner and from the gases surrounding the tank must be kept close to the tank. A
liner may be used around the tank which will
allow the passage of the hot gases at the correct
speed (Fig. 19–1). Flue liners must be made
of heavy enough material so that they will not
lose their shape. It is important that there be
equal flue space around the tank.

A center flue may be used in the tank, with
baffles in it to regulate the rate of flow of the
hot gases.

Good insulation is necessary in an automatic storage type of water heater to keep the
stored water from cooling too rapidly. In the
type of heater using the outside flue, insulation
is placed between the liner and the outer shell
(Fig. 19–1). In the center-flue type, insulation is placed between the tank and the outer
shell. Spun glass or rock wool are the insulating
materials usually used.

Relief valves for a gas water heater are a

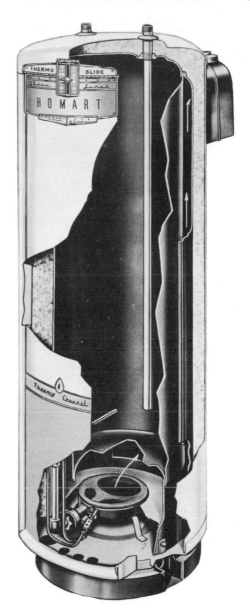

Fig. 19–1. Automatic storage water heater—glass
lined tank, underfired. (Sears, Roebuck and Co.)

pressure-relief valve and a temperature-relief
valve or the two combined into one.

Water heater tanks may be subjected to
pressures much higher than ordinary city water
pressure. A sudden closing of a faucet can
cause a momentary high pressure, or there
may be increased pressure in the street main.

The pressure-relief valve should preferably
be located on the cold water line. This valve

unseats slightly when excessive pressure occurs within the tank and allows water to run out, thus relieving the strain on the tank.

A pressure-relief valve is not always required on open-water piping systems. It is, however, a very wise precaution, as an open-water piping system can become a closed system without warning. It is quite possible to have excessive pressure within the water tank and not have high temperatures. The reverse may also be true. Pressure-relief valves in a closed system may drip continuously during heating periods.

The temperature-relief valve is designed to prevent excessively high temperatures of water within the storage tank. It does not relieve high pressures nor does the pressure relief valve relieve high temperatures.

The temperature-relief valve usually acts at about 205 F: a fusible plug melts and the overheated water can escape. The plug must then be replaced. Location of temperature-relief valves varies. Manufacturer's instructions and city plumbing codes govern their location.

A combination pressure- and temperature-relief valve may be used. This combined valve may be installed in the hot water line, near the hot water outlet connection at the tank. Manufacturer's instructions and local ordinances should always be checked.

19–2. TYPES OF GAS WATER HEATERS

Gas water heaters may be manually operated or automatically controlled. Water heaters in use today include the automatic storage, nonautomatic storage, adjustable recovery, automatic circulating tank, and automatic instantaneous types. Instantaneous heaters and the larger circulating tank heaters are generally used for multifamily homes, institutions, recreational centers, and industrial buildings.

Water is heated and stored in both automatic and nonautomatic storage types of water heaters. The nonautomatic storage type does not have a thermostat; the user must regulate the temperature of the water by controlling the source of heat. The automatic storage type is thermostatically controlled and is probably the more common type of water heater used in the home. The British thermal unit input rating for these heaters must be under 50,000 Btu's per hour. The automatic storage type is designed for uses in which the demand is not greater than the recovery capacity of the water heater. Recovery capacity is the amount of water that can be heated through a 100-degree rise in temperature per hour.

The automatic storage type of water heater has the heater, storage tank, insulation, and controls all incorporated into a single unit. The design is such that it can be installed in the kitchen, recreation room, or utility room if desired (Fig. 19–2).

The American Gas Association defines a fast-recovery heater as any heater having a burner input of at least 1000 Btu's per hour for each gallon of storage tank capacity.[1] From a practical point of view a fast-recovery heater is one that will raise the temperature of a full tank of water 100 F in a little more than an hour. This type gives the most complete kind of hot water service. The size of storage tank is not as important in fast-recovery heaters as in the slow-recovery type. Thirty- and 40-gallon sizes are widely used for home installations.

Slow-recovery heaters have much lower gas input rates per gallon of storage tank capacity. From three to ten hours is required for a slow-recovery heater to recover the storage tank capacity. A 30- to 40-gallon storage tank, slow-recovery heater may be satisfactory if the amount of hot water used per day is not over 50 gallons. Once the hot water is used there is no quick way of getting more. The biggest disadvantage of slow-recovery heaters is the in-

[1] *Gas Appliance Service Water Heater Manual*, 4th ed., American Gas Association, 1953, p. 3.

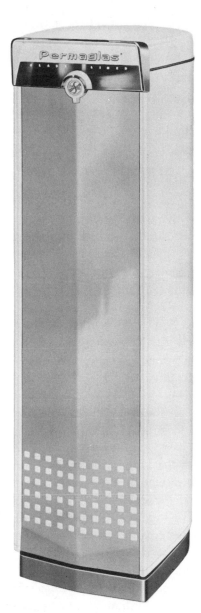

Fig. 19–2. Automatic storage water heater. (A. O. Smith Corporation, Permaglas Division)

ability to meet occasional heavy demands during short periods of time.

Most automatic storage water heaters deliver water at one temperature only. However, two-temperature water heaters are available which can supply water to the dishwasher and washer at a higher temperature than that supplied to bathroom and lavatory faucets. Plumbing connections must be planned for use with the two-temperature heater. The hotter water is taken out at the upper level of the storage tank; the tempered (less hot) hot water is a result of mixing hot water with some of the water from the cold water inlet line before the tempered water is drawn off.

Adjustable-recovery heaters are either a type that is adjustable by the consumer or one that is adjustable when installed. In the former type, anticipated heavy demands can be met by manually turning on additional burner capacity. In the latter type, this adjustment is made by a change in the input burner. Usually the latter change would be made only for continued increased demand for hot water.

Adjustable-recovery heaters have the advantage of the higher service efficiency of slow-recovery heaters during ordinary use plus the ability to meet occasional heavy demand. The type of adjustable-recovery heater which is adjusted at the time of installation does not have this flexibility, but it can be changed if continued demands for hot water should change.

The heat input in circulating tank water heaters ranges from about 15,000 to 30,000 Btu's per hour. Larger heaters than these are used for multifamily, institutional, and commercial installations. This type of heater is sometimes called a *sidearm* or *tank* heater. The storage tank is usually not insulated in those that are manually controlled, so storage of unused hot water is not economical. Because the coils carrying the water are directly above the burner, precipitation of salts from hard water is accelerated. In time, the circulation of water between the heater and the tank is impaired. This type of water heater is not generally recommended because people may forget to turn the burners off, tanks and piping are not usually insulated, and more water may be heated than necessary.

Some circulating tank heaters may be controlled automatically. These are similar to manually controlled circulating tank heaters;

the difference is that these operate automatically. The installed cost of these heaters is usually not much less than for a galvanized automatic storage heater that is all in one unit.

Natural, manufactured, or mixed gas or liquefied petroleum gas may be used as fuel for gas water heaters. Water heaters designed to be used with liquefied petroleum gas should be plainly labeled. It is possible to change a burner designed for use with other gases for use with liquefied petroleum gas, but this is not recommended.

a. Sizes and Shapes

Size of water heater should be determined by the needs of the household for hot water. Shape is usually determined by the place where it will be installed and by the size needed.

Sizes commonly available in the automatic storage tank types are 20, 30, 40, 45, 50, and 60 gallons. A small tank and fast recovery will often supply more hot water for peak demands than a large tank with slow recovery.[2]

A water heater that is too small for the use required of it will literally be overworked and will not last as long as an adequate size water heater which is not overworked.

Future uses, anticipated and perhaps not yet dreamed of, should be considered when deciding upon the size water heater to install.

The American Gas Association lists the following factors as some of the more important points to be considered in choosing the correct size of water heater. The number, sex, and age of people in the house, including the number of servants, is one consideration. How the dishes are washed, how the laundry is done, the number of baths or showers taken daily, and the number of times h ds are washed— all these factors influence the demand for hot water. Leaky hot water faucets and the distance from the hot water tank to the faucet also influence the amount of water that needs

to be heated. The size of the faucet and the water pressure are also factors. How the water was heated previously is considered important in the correct sizing of a water heater for the home.

The more people there are in a home, the more baths, the more clothes to wash, and the more dishes there are to do. Many families do not use 1000 gallons of hot water per month; other families use much more. Many tests conducted in various parts of the country estimate that the average hot water consumption is between 7 and 12 gallons per day per individual.[3]

Water heaters may also be sized according to the number of rooms in the home, the number of bathrooms, and the appliances that use hot water. A five- to six-room house with one or one and a half baths would probably need a 30-gallon automatic storage water heater. If an automatic washer were added a 40-gallon water heater would be recommended.[4]

The temperature rise through which the water must be heated also helps to determine the size water heater to purchase. In northern sections of the United States, the lowest temperature at which water is supplied to the water heater might be around 40 F. If water is heated to 140 F this would be a 100 F rise. Water delivered at 60 F would require no more fuel to be heated to 160 F.

The common shape of a gas water heater is a cylinder approximately 60 inches high and 14 to 25 inches in diameter. Some water heaters have an all-over exterior covering that fits to the floor (Fig. 19–2). Others are supported on legs several inches off the floor. Some models have the exterior shell in a rectangular shape. Cabinet models are also available. Cabinets have the appearance of kitchen base cabinets and may fit nicely into the kitchen cabinet installation.

---

[2] John M. Lyle, in a personal communication, Ruud Manufacturing Company, August 1956.

[3] *Gas Appliance Service Water Heater Manual, op. cit.,* p. 13.

[4] John M. Lyle, *op. cit.*

19–3. INSTALLATION AND CARE

An insulated, automatic storage water heater that is underfired and approved by the American Gas Association may be located as close to the walls of a room as 2 inches. It should be located near a good flue and have plenty of air around it. Gas water heaters should not be located in closets or cubbyholes, unless one side is permanently open to provide good ventilation. Water heaters located in any confined space require special venting. The American Gas Association describes the specifications for these openings.[5] Water heaters should not be installed in bathrooms or bedrooms.

Preferably the water heater should be not over 15 to 20 feet from the place where hot water will be used most often—usually the kitchen sink. The correct diameter of the hot water pipe depends partly on the number of faucets it will supply. A larger diameter than necessary results in unnecessary heat loss. When practical, copper pipe is preferred over iron pipe because it is thinner and therefore has less area to cool. Insulation around the hot water pipe also helps decrease loss of heat from the pipe.

Draft hoods should be used, as they help to regulate the draft or speed with which the heated gases pass around or through the water heater. They also serve to divert any back drafts. Back drafts may cause the pilot to go out or interfere with combustion of the gas. If the heated gases pass over the water heater too quickly, they do not give up as much heat as they should, and the fuel bill goes up.

A water heater should be level and on a solid fixed base. It should be easily accessible for operation, maintenance, and servicing.

a. Care

Water heaters actually require very little care. Pressure- and temperature-relief valves

[5] *Gas Appliance Service Water Heater Manual, op. cit.,* pp. 18, 19.

should be checked occasionally by a service man. Corrosion or sediment around the seat or fusible metal of the valve may keep it from operating as it should.

If the automatic storage type of water heater is used in a soft water system, very little or no flushing of the tank is needed. If the heater is to be used in areas where the water is very hard it should have a hand-sized, clean-out hole, as it is almost impossible to flush out the deposits of precipitated solids. Occasionally, perhaps once a month, the drain cock should be opened and at least a bucket of water drawn off. If the house is to be closed during cold weather, the supply of cold water to the tank should be turned off and the tank completely drained.

The outside of the heater can be kept clean by wiping with a damp cloth and occasionally washing with a detergent, followed by a rinse of clear water.

Leaky faucets should be repaired, as they may be the reason for high fuel bills. A water faucet leaking at the rate of 60 drops per minute will waste about 200 gallons of hot water per month. If it leaks twice as fast it will waste enough water to supply an average family with hot water for 11 days.

Do not attempt to relight a gas pilot or burner that has been extinguished accidentally until after the gas has been turned off, the lighting door opened, and the room adequately ventilated for at least ten minutes.

19–4. AMERICAN GAS ASSOCIATION STANDARDS

The American Gas Association has set up standards for the construction and performance of gas water heaters for all types of gases. These standards have been approved by the American Standards Association.[6] A gas water

[6] Z21.10.1 Gas Water Heaters and Z21.10.2 Side Arm-Type Water Heaters, American Standards Association, 1956.

heater that carries the blue star seal of approval of the American Gas Association will give safe and efficient performance and be of substantial and durable construction. Construction and performance may be better than American Gas Association standards, which are minimum standards.

B. Electric Water Heaters

Some construction, use, and installation factors are the same for electric and gas water heaters. Other factors are, of course, quite different.

19–5. CONSTRUCTION

Electric water heaters, whether of cylindrical or table-top form, contain an interior tank and an exterior shell with insulation between tank and shell (Fig. 19–3). Materials currently used for tanks of electric water heaters include galvanized steel, steel with glass fused on the inside surface, Monel, and copper. The material of the shell is steel and the exterior surface of the shell is usually baked-on synthetic enamel. The finish on the tops of table-top heaters may be porcelain enamel.

The cold water inlet is at the bottom of the tank. A cold water baffle may be welded to the interior of the tank above the cold water inlet. Its function is to direct the incoming cold water to the bottom of the tank, thereby minimizing mixing of cold and hot water when hot water is drawn off. The hot water outlet is at the top of the tank. The outlet pipe usually has a curved or gooseneck shape. This curve prevents cool pipe water from moving down into the tank when hot water is drawn off.

A drain faucet is provided near the bottom of the water heater to enable the user occasionally to drain water from the bottom of the tank into a pail. (Draining from the bottom of the tank removes sediment.)

Factors that affect the useful life of a water heater were considered earlier (see p. 253).

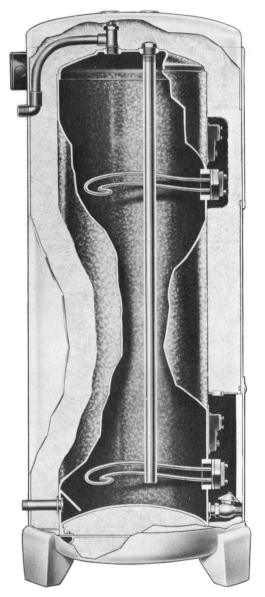

Fig. 19–3. Phantom of electric water heater with immersion-type heating units. (Frigidaire Division, General Motors Corporation)

a. Tank Capacities and Wattages

Electric water heaters are available with gallon capacities of 30, 40, 52, 66, 80, 110, 120, and 140 gallons. Some manufacturers also supply intermediate capacities such as 33 and 44 gallons. For many years the wattage of the heating unit or units was related to capacity; that is, certain tank capacities were associated with certain wattages and the larger the tank, the larger the wattage of the heating unit or units. For example, an 80-gallon tank would have one heating unit of 4000 watts near the bottom of the tank or a heating unit of 2500 watts in the upper part of the tank and another of 1500 watts near the bottom. A 66-gallon tank would have one or two heating units totaling about 3250 watts.

Currently, quick recovery electric water heaters with units of rather high wattage are also available. For example, one manufacturer's line of electric water heaters includes a 9000-watt, 40-gallon cylindrical model and a 9000-watt, 44-gallon table-top model. Each has a 4500-watt upper unit and a 4500-watt lower unit.

The quick-recovery type of electric water heater is reported to compare with gas water heaters in quantity of hot water that can be supplied. Also, a consumer can get a large quantity of hot water with a tank approximately comparable in size to that used for gas heaters, provided the house is suitably wired and the local power supplier permits use of the high-wattage heater.

The unit or units of standard models are either immersed in the water in the tank (Fig. 19–3) or wrapped around the tank under the insulation (Fig. 19–4). The units of the quick-recovery heaters are of the immersion type.

Factors to be considered in choosing the size of water heater to be purchased were discussed on page 258. A reliable local dealer is likely to be a useful person to consult.

Fig. 19–4. Glass-lined, electric water heater with wrap-a-round heating units. (A. O. Smith Corporation, Permaglas Division)

19–6. OPERATING CHARACTERISTICS AND RELIEF VALVES

The operation of a single-unit heater consists simply in the electric circuit to the unit being open or closed according to the thermostat setting and the temperature of the water in the tank. The operation of water heaters with two units is slightly more complex. The units may be connected separately or in parallel, if the local power supplier permits a parallel connection. Usually, water heaters that have two units are connected so that only one unit is on at a time, and the major part of the water in the tank is heated by the lower unit.

The cycle of operation is as follows. Assume that the tank is filled initially with cold water. The upper unit operates and heats about the top fourth of the tank. When the water in the upper part of the tank reaches approximately 150 F, a double-throw thermostat switch opens the circuit to the upper unit and closes the circuit to the lower unit. The lower unit now operates until *all* the water reaches approximately 150 F; then a single-throw thermostat switch opens the circuit to the lower unit.

As hot water is drawn from the top, cold water enters at the bottom, and the single-throw thermostat of the lower unit closes the circuit to the lower unit again. The upper unit ordinarily will operate only when most of the hot water in the tank has been replaced by cold water.

a. Relief Valves

Relief valves that will open the tank or the water line to the air in case of unsafe water pressure or temperature in the tank are provided with electric water heaters or are available as accessories. Requirements of the local power supplier and local plumbing ordinances may specify the type of relief valves to be used.

A pressure-relief valve is usually considered to supply minimum effective protection. The pressure-relief valve is installed in the cold water supply as close to the water heater as possible.

Protection against excessive water temperature is obtained with either a cutout switch or a temperature-relief valve. A temperature cutout switch is essentially a thermostat so in-

stalled that it opens the electric circuit to the heater if the outside of the tank reaches a too-high temperature. A temperature-relief valve gives protection against excessive temperature by opening the tank to the air if the water in the tank becomes excessively hot.

Sometimes a combination temperature–pressure-relief valve is used; it will usually be installed in the top of the tank.

19–7. INSTALLATION AND SUGGESTIONS ON USE

Many of the considerations here are the same for electric and gas water heaters. The heater should be installed as close as possible to the place where hot water is used most frequently. Ideally, the water heater should be next to the kitchen sink or directly under it in the basement. Frequency of use rather than volume of hot water used is the criterion because after each withdrawal of hot water, the water in the pipe cools, due to radiation.

Water pipes to all hot water faucets and water-bearing equipment, such as a washer, should be as short as possible. In fact, if the house has a very large area, it may be better to have two water heaters rather than one in order to have short hot water lines. The considerations that determine the diameter and material of the hot water pipe are given on page 259.

a. Suggestions on Use

Three recommendations are usually emphasized for electric water heaters. (1) It is important to repair leaking faucets. (2) Remove sediment from the bottom of the tank occasionally. This is done by placing a pail under the drain faucet and turning the faucet on. If a clean-out plate is provided, it may be possible to clean sediment from the inside of the tank with a brush. (3) Use a thermostat setting only as high as needed for the hot water demand in the house. (The factory setting of 150 F can be changed; for some heaters this is done most conveniently when the heater is installed.)

19–8. AMERICAN STANDARDS ASSOCIATION STANDARD

The current standard that applies to electric water heaters is C72.1.[7] This standard applies to electric storage-type heaters of not less than 30-gallon capacity. The purpose of the standard is to establish a uniform procedure for determining performance under specified test conditions and to establish certain minimum requirements.

Introductory material includes definitions and ratings. The fourth section deals with "general standards," some of which are summarized below.

Parts intended to be serviced shall be reasonably accessible. Water service connections to the heater shall permit use of standard pipe or tube fittings. Provision shall be made to install temperature- and pressure-relief devices effectively. A data nameplate conveniently accessible for observation shall be attached to the heater.

The setting of the thermostat or thermostats shall be 150 F. "The upper limit of the range of adjustment of any thermostat shall be 194 F or less." The secondary unit of a two-unit heater shall be located so as to heat effectively the top 25 percent of the actual tank capacity. "Under normal operating conditions, a water heater shall not cause a temperature higher than 194 F to be attained at any point on surfaces near or upon which it may be mounted in service when operated at the highest thermostat setting."

Section five prescribes test conditions and procedures. These cover sturdiness of the complete heater, strength of tank, recovery characteristics, rate of delivery of hot water, and other performance aspects. The user is interested, of course, in durable construction. On the performance side, the following two recommendations are of particular interest to the user: (1) The efficiency of heating water in the tank, as determined by the specified test procedure, shall not be less than 90 percent. (2) At least 90 percent of the actual tank capacity can be withdrawn before the temperature of the delivered water drops 30 F.

[7] C72.1, *American Standard Household Automatic Electric Storage-Type Water Heaters,* American Standards Association, 1949.

CHAPTER 20

Laundry Area, Washers, and Washing Guides

A. Laundry Area

The appliances and accessory equipment used for washing, drying, and ironing household textiles may be assembled either in a single laundry area or in several places in the home.

A complete laundry area is one planned for prelaundering tasks and for washing, drying, and ironing. But family needs or preferences for use of space may be such that a complete, single laundry area is not provided. For example, a homemaker may prefer to do such prewashing tasks as sewing torn articles in a sewing room or in a living room; she may wish to vary the room in which she irons according to other activities taking place in the home at a given time.

Whether a complete center is planned or not, the washer and dryer should be located close to each other, since they are usually used together. Cabinet or shelf space should be provided near the washer for storage of laundry supplies. Some well-lighted counter space should be provided for prewashing treatment of heavily soiled parts and for folding articles after removal from the dryer.

20–1. LOCATION

If a laundry area is provided, available space in the home tends to determine its location. For many years, part of the basement has been used for the laundry area. In ranch-

Fig. 20–1. Laundry area for washer and dryer. (Hamilton Manufacturing Company)

Fig. 20–2. Laundry area with sink, counter, and water heater. (Hotpoint Company)

style houses with no basement, the laundry area is of course on the first floor. The currently popular split-level houses are likely to have the laundry area in the basement level.

Laundry equipment is sometimes installed in the kitchen. A washer only or a washer and dryer may be placed along the "fourth wall," that is, the wall not used for the kitchen work area. Alternatively, if the kitchen includes a peninsula of cabinets and appliances, a washer, dryer, and ironer sometimes can be installed on the side that faces away from the food preparation and cleanup area. This use of space in the kitchen can be one way of meeting the recommendation that an area be provided in the kitchen for activities appropriate to the family.

A somewhat unusual location is near the bedrooms. This is convenient from the point of view that soiled bed linens, towels, and clothes are "picked up" in bedrooms and bathrooms. But if the bedrooms are on the second floor and the kitchen on the first, the homemaker is likely to have to do some walking up and down stairs, just as she does when the laundry is in the basement.

Figures 20–1 and 20–2 show two arrangements of laundry equipment. Note that in both illustrations the dryer is located to the right of the washer. This is usual because most present-day dryers have the door hinged on the right. If the dryer door were hinged on the left, the dryer could be installed to the left of the washer as shown in the picture of a built-in installation in Figure 20–12. Placement of the dryer at the left of the washer permits the right-to-left work sequence that is normal for a right-handed person.

A separate sink, as shown in Figure 20–2, is most useful in a laundry area.

B. Washers

Currently, the most widely used washers may be classified in two ways. One is to classify them as wringer washers, spinner washers, or automatics. The other is to classify them as agitator-type, cylinder, or oscillating-tub washers.

The first classification differentiates between washers partly on method of extraction of water. In wringer washers washed clothes are passed between two rolls. In spinner washers and automatics water is extracted from washed clothes by centrifugal action; that is, rotation of a spin basket or tub causes excess water to squeeze through and spin off the clothes. In the spinner washer, washing takes place in one tub and extraction of water and rinsing in another. Since the user must transfer clothes from wash tub to spin tub, operation of the spinner washer is not automatic. In automatics, one tub assembly is used for the entire process. Fill, wash, extraction, and rinse operations are all controlled by moving one or more dials or levers at the beginning of the fill part of the cycle.

The second classification differentiates washers according to washing method. Agitator-type washers include wringer washers, spinner washers, and automatics that have an agitator or pulsator. A special type is one in which the agitator rotates around the tub continuously in an off-center circle. Cylinder washers are automatics that have a cylinder with interior projecting baffles instead of an agitator or pulsator. This cylinder rotates about a horizontal or inclined axis. The oscillating tub washer has a tub or basket that oscillates about a vertical axis.

The washing action of agitator-type washers is due primarily to water currents produced by back and forth movement of an agitator or up and down movement of a pulsator. The water currents flex the clothes and cause them to turn over and move around in the detergent-water solution.

In cylinder washers the washing action consists in clothes tumbling through a detergent-water solution. They are carried up from a bottom position by the rotating cylinder, fall and tumble through the detergent-water solution, and the process repeats.

In the oscillating-tub washer clothes move up, down, over, and around in the tub.

20-2. WRINGER WASHERS

Currently, the number of automatics sold per year in the United States exceeds that of wringer washers. Nevertheless, large numbers of wringer washers continue to be sold each year, so clearly some homemakers prefer them. One consideration is availability of water. With wringer washers wash and rinse waters can be reused for several loads. Another consideration is laundering work habits. In a wringer washer eight or more loads can be washed in two hours, whereas in automatics the complete cycle usually requires 30 minutes or longer for a normal load. Some homemakers who have large quantities of laundry each week prefer to do all the washing one morning per week rather than do two or three loads every few days, even though time used for washing with an automatic is partially free time in that the user need not stay at the washer. A third consideration in determining choice of model is that stripped models of wringer washers cost less than stripped models of automatics.

a. Construction Characteristics

Wringer washers are illustrated in Figures 20-3 and 20-4. The tub in which the clothes are placed is separated from the outer shell by a dead air space which acts as a thermal insulator and helps maintain the temperature of the water in the tub. The inner tub is either finished in porcelain enamel or is made of a rustproof material such as aluminum. The exterior finish on the outer shell is usually synthetic enamel, and the more deluxe models

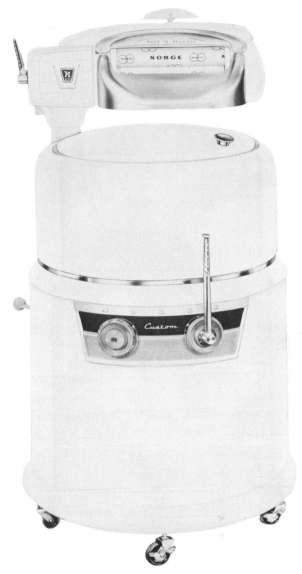

Fig. 20-3. Wringer washer with deluxe features. (Norge Sales Corp., Subsidiary of Borg-Warner Corp.)

may have a colored enamel exterior. Most manufacturers state capacities in pounds of clothes—7, 8, 9, or 10 pounds—*and* in gallons of water required to fill the inner tub. Washers rated at 8 to 10 pounds usually take about 17 gallons of water when filled to the fill line. Low-priced or stripped models are likely to have the lower capacities. However, the actual weight of clothes that should be washed at one time in a washer depends on the bulkiness of

Fig. 20–4. Wringer washer with square, aluminum tub. (Maytag Company)

the articles as well as the pound-capacity rating of the washer. (See section C on washing guides.)

Lids of washers that have a square tub may be hinged to the body of the washer. Washers that have round tubs usually have a lid with a hook that enables the lid to be hung on the side of the washer.

Aluminum and plastic agitators are used. These usually have a "positive fit" to the agitator shaft by splines and a locking cap. The agitator is formed with vanes which have a double curvature in some models. The vanes extend farthest from the axis near the bottom, curve in toward the axis, and extend out from it again near the top of the agitator, but not as much as at the bottom. One manufacturer uses vanes that spiral from the bottom to the top of the agitator.

On some washers the agitator is countersunk in the bottom of the tub so the top edges of the sides of its bottom part are flush with the tub bottom. Most agitators can be removed from their shafts by removing the locking cap, if one is provided, and lifting the agitator straight up.

A sediment trap may be provided in the bottom of the tub to catch insoluble bits of dirt. A water discharge pump for rapid emptying of the tub after use is provided as a standard feature on some deluxe models and can be obtained as an extra feature for most models. Wringer washers with pumps usually have some provision to prevent their clogging— sometimes a strainer at the location where the water is pumped from the tub.

Power-driven wringers can usually be swung through a complete circle and locked in any of several operating positions. A tension-adjustment screw may be provided at the top of the wringer. This can be adjusted for a somewhat tight fit of the rolls when thin fabric is to be wrung and a looser fit for bulky items. Some manufacturers use rolls of unequal hardness which adjust automatically—within limits —for thickness of fabric. A safety release is provided so that the user can separate the rolls quickly with one hand or even an elbow, when necessary. Tilt or feed "boards," usually aluminum, are provided on both sides of the rolls to permit the extracted water to drain back into the tub or laundry tray. Safe and correct usage requires that the user flip clothes onto a feed board, whence they will be drawn onto the bottom roll.

Controls provided on the washer vary with price and with manufacturer. A control such as a lever or button for starting and stopping the agitator is usual. Some manufacturers also provide a motor "on-off" switch. A time control may be provided which stops the agitator automatically when the preselected washing time is up. A minute indicator and bell may be provided which indicate elapsed time but do not control length of wash period.

b. Operating Components

Washers that use a gasoline engine are available for homes not wired for electricity. The usual type, however, is the washer that operates on house current and has an electric motor rated at $\frac{1}{3}$ or $\frac{1}{4}$ horsepower. A gear mechanism or transmission is used to change rotary motion of the motor shaft to the oscillating (back and forth) motion of the agitator shaft. This mechanism also provides for rotation of the extension shaft for one of the wringer rolls. Usually, the gear parts that drive the agitator shaft and the wringer roll extension shaft are permanently lubricated and sealed in a metal gear case housing. The gear mechanism and motor may be connected by direct-drive rod linkage or by pulley and belt.

The pump for removing water is separate from the gear mechanism.

c. Special Use and Care Recommendations for Wringer Washers

Particular instructions for different wringer washers are, of course, given in user's booklets. Some considerations that should be noted especially are these:

1. Dissolve the soap or syndet in the water before adding the clothes.
2. As far as possible, flip clothes onto the feed board of the wringer. Also, to minimize creases, pass clothes and other textiles one at a time through the wringer.
3. Release the tension on the rolls after washing. Whenever the washer is not to be used for some time, separate the rolls by striking the safety release.
4. Follow instructions on oiling and greasing. For example, the user's booklet may recommend that every month or so a drop of oil be applied to the bearings for the upper wringer roll.
5. Have a service man lubricate the motor at the intervals—three to five years or so—recommended by the manufacturer.

20–3. SPINNER WASHERS

As stated earlier, a spinner washer is one in which clothes are washed in one tub and rinsed and extracted in another. After a load of clothes has been washed, they are lifted from the washtub into the basket tub. Excess sudsy water is drained back into the washtub, and rinse water is sprayed over the clothes in the basket tub.

After the first load is washed, two loads can be handled at a time; that is, one load can be washed while another is being rinsed. Some care must be taken to load the basket tub uniformly.

20–4. AGITATOR-TYPE AUTOMATICS

As indicated previously an agitator-type automatic is an automatic that has an agitator or pulsator. Agitators used in automatics are similar to those used in wringer washers. A pulsator is actually used by only one manufacturer. It is somewhat similar to an agitator with flexible disks, but, unlike an agitator which moves back and forth at one height on its shaft, the pulsator moves up and down on its shaft instead of oscillating about it.

a. Construction Characteristics and Operating Components

Operating components and construction features of agitator-type automatics are illustrated in Figures 20–5 through 20–8. The construction features one sees on the outside are controls, top with lid assembly, housing or chassis, and supply and drain hoses. Inside the housing are an agitator, wash-spin tub, drain or basin tub, and a base assembly on which are mounted motor, gear mechanism, pump, valves, and other parts.

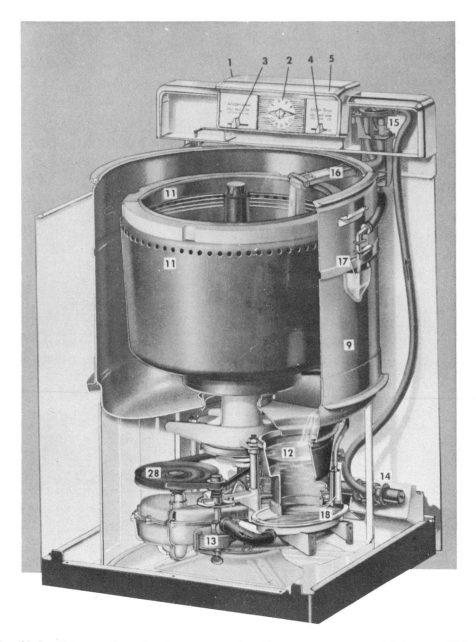

Fig. 20–5. Cutaway view of agitator automatic with pressure-type water-fill feature. (Philco Corporation)

1. Back splash
2. Dual cycle timer
3. Water-level control
4. Water-temperature control
5. Fluorescent lamp
9. Drain tube
11. Wash or spin tub
12. Drain sump or boot

13. Nonclog pump
14. Solenoid-operated water valves
15. Fill cup
16. Main fill nozzle
17. Metering fill nozzle
18. Pressure chamber
28. Transmission drive pulley

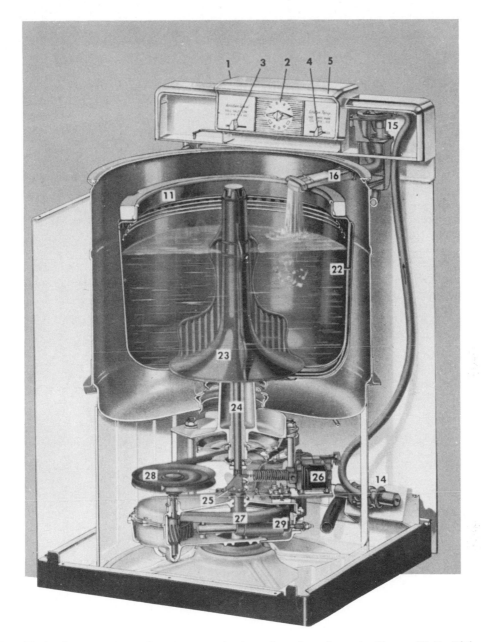

Fig. 20–6. Cutaway view of agitator mechanism of washer shown in Figure 20–5. (Philco Corporation)

22. Sediment ejector tube
23. Agitator
24. Agitator shaft
25. Agitator clutch

26. Agitator clutch solenoid
27. Transmission
28. Drive pulley for transmission
29. Rack adjustment

(Other numbers as explained in caption for Figure 20–5.)

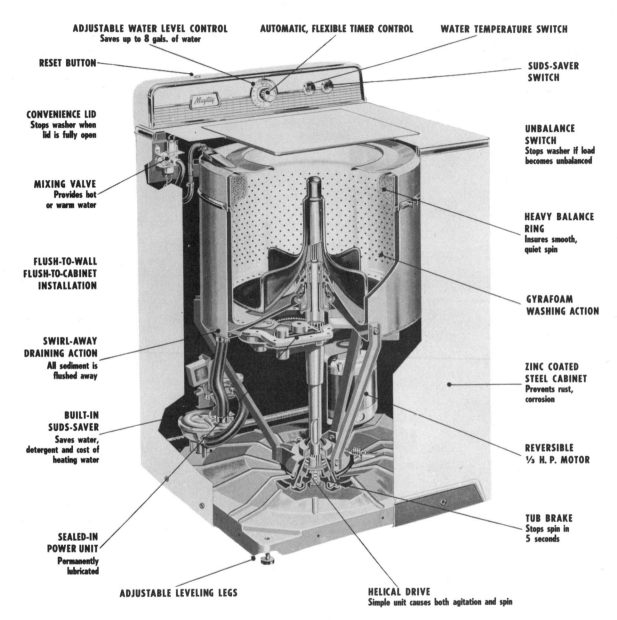

ADJUSTABLE WATER LEVEL CONTROL
Saves up to 8 gals. of water

AUTOMATIC, FLEXIBLE TIMER CONTROL

WATER TEMPERATURE SWITCH

RESET BUTTON

SUDS-SAVER
SWITCH

CONVENIENCE LID
Stops washer when
lid is fully open

UNBALANCE
SWITCH
Stops washer if load
becomes unbalanced

MIXING VALVE
Provides hot
or warm water

HEAVY BALANCE
RING
Insures smooth,
quiet spin

FLUSH-TO-WALL
FLUSH-TO-CABINET
INSTALLATION

GYRAFOAM
WASHING ACTION

SWIRL-AWAY
DRAINING ACTION
All sediment is
flushed away

ZINC COATED
STEEL CABINET
Prevents rust,
corrosion

BUILT-IN
SUDS-SAVER
Saves water,
detergent and cost of
heating water

REVERSIBLE
⅓ H. P. MOTOR

TUB BRAKE
Stops spin in
5 seconds

SEALED-IN
POWER UNIT
Permanently
lubricated

ADJUSTABLE LEVELING LEGS

HELICAL DRIVE
Simple unit causes both agitation and spin

Fig. 20–7. Phantom view of agitator automatic with water-level fill feature. (Maytag Company)

The agitator automatic shown in Figures 20–5 and 20–6 has a single wash-spin tub with one row of perforations near the top of the tub. The drain tub is sealed to the washer top with a gasket. It surrounds the washtub and extends above and below it. Water from the supply lines is mixed to the preselected temperature by valves in the base assembly and enters the washtub through a fill nozzle that extends through the drain tub at a location above the washtub. During the fill part of the cycle, a small amount of water also enters the drain tub, falling into a small pressure chamber in the base of the washer; the amount of this water is a metered fraction of the amount entering the washtub. When the washtub has the correct amount of water, the water in the pressure chamber operates a pressure switch which actuates the timer and starts the washing action. After the tub is filled, the timer controls the wash, extraction, and rinse times for the complete cycle.

During extraction the washtub rotates and water spins up and through the perforations at

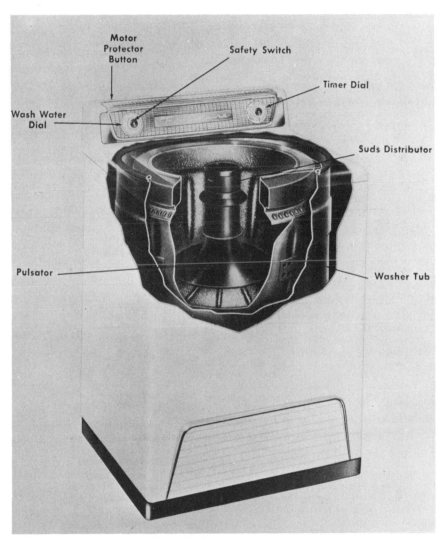

Fig. 20–8. Phantom of pulsator automatic with time-fill feature. (Frigidaire Division, General Motors Corporation)

the top of the washtub into the drain tub. From here it drains through a boot into the pump and then down the house drain.

The agitator is mounted on the agitator shaft. Oscillation is produced by the gear mechanism or transmission, which is belt-driven by the transmission drive pulley assembled to the motor shaft. The washtub is supported on a permanently lubricated ball bearing. Power for the tub spin-shaft is provided through a clutch from a spin pulley mounted on a shaft in the transmission.

The pump impeller (a bladed device similar to a fan) is driven by the same pulley that drives the transmission.

Another agitator automatic is shown in Figure 20–7. The lid of this washer contains a water-level control switch and an unbalance switch. The water-level control switch actuates the timer to start the washing action when the proper level of water is reached in the tub. The unbalance switch shuts off the motor if the wash load becomes unbalanced. The inner washtub has perforations over its entire surface —sides and bottom. A balancing ring is provided at the top of the double tub to minimize vibration when the tub spins.

Water enters at the top of the double tub through valves. Whether it is hot, cold, or warm is determined by which control lever the user has pushed. Temperatures for the hot and cold settings are the temperatures of the hot and cold water supplies. For the warm setting, the water enters the tub at a temperature of 100 F plus or minus 5 F. When the tub is filled to the preselected level (full, medium, or low) a cap on top of the agitator rises and closes the water-level control switch in the lid. As stated, this starts the washing action.

When the preselected minutes of washing time are up, the agitator stops oscillating and the washtub starts to rotate. Water spins out into an opening in the bottom of the tub basin, from where it is either drained into the house drain by a pump or raised to a set tray or fixed

laundry tub by another pump. (The second pump operates only when the sudsy wash water is to be reused.)

Automatic operation of the timer starts the spin rinse while the washtub is still rotating and water is being extracted from the clothes. Next, the washtub stops rotating and is filled or partially filled with water for the "power rinse." This rinse fill is the same as that selected for the wash; for example, if a partial fill was selected for washing, the tub will automatically have a partial fill for rinsing. The power rinse is a rinse with agitator operating. After it, the tub spins again, water is expelled, and the motor turns off. All parts of this cycle are automatic after the user has turned the timer control to a specific number of minutes for wash.

The function of the tub brake is to stop the rotation of the tub quickly.

The washer shown in Figure 20–8 differs somewhat from those just described. It has a pulsator instead of an agitator. Also, it has a *time* fill; that is, water enters the washtub for a definite time for the fill for the wash part of the cycle and the fills for the separate rinses. The level of water in the tub at the end of the time fill is correct for usual water pressures. The type illustrated is available with either a high or a conventional speed of rotation of the washtub. During the spin part of the cycle, the tub of the high-speed model rotates at approximately 1140 revolutions per minute, while the tub of the other models rotates at approximately 660 revolutions per minute.

20–5. CYLINDER AUTOMATICS

Figure 20–9 shows a front-opening cylinder automatic. The cycle of operation is controlled by a timer. Four baffles are provided on the inner surface of the rotating cylinder or tub. During the wash part of the cycle, the clothes are carried between and on the baffles from a bottom to a top position and then drop back.

This tumbling action in the detergent-water solution washes the clothes. During the spin part of the cycle, the rapid rotation of the tub causes excess water to be thrown off the clothes. Tumbling action in water rinses the clothes.

Washing, rinsing, and spinning take place in the perforated washtub mounted in an inner unit. This unit includes a front tub and a back tub which are clamped together and surround the washtub. The bearing in which the washtub shaft rotates extends through the rear surface of the back tub. The complete inner unit is suspended from the washer housing by springs. Friction devices are provided for stabilization.

In case of a severe unbalance a lever arm connected between the housing and the timer trips the timer.

A transmission is used to rotate the washtub at two speeds: about 50 revolutions per minute during the wash cycle and about 470 revolutions per minute during the spin. Belts transfer power from the motor to the transmission and from the transmission to the washtub pulley. The pump for draining water is driven by a friction wheel.

Adjustable feet are provided for leveling the washer.

20–6. FEATURES AND WATER REQUIREMENTS OF AUTOMATICS

It is likely to be true for automatic washers as for other appliances that no one model will have every feature a well-informed prospective purchaser might want. Usually, therefore, a purchaser must decide which features are most important to her.

A built-in, motor-overload protective device is a desirable feature for the following reason: A 15-ampere fuse is used in the washer circuit to take care of the high starting current, but this fuse is too large to protect the motor *after* it is running.

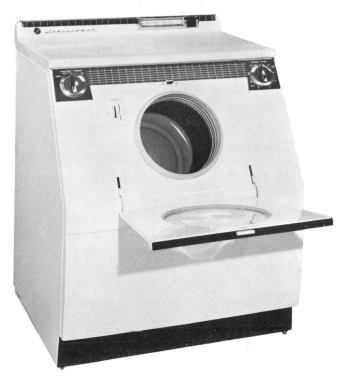

Fig. 20–9.   Front-opening cylinder automatic. (Courtesy Westinghouse Electric Corporation)

An effective balancing or stabilizing device for handling moderately unbalanced loads without excessive vibration is of course also desirable.

A brake mechanism to stop the rotation of the washtub quickly is a feature the senior author, for one, appreciates.

Features related especially to operation of the washer includes these: type of fill control, provision for removing sediment, type of rinses, and speed of rotation of the washtub during spin. A time fill may be provided, or the fill may be controlled by a pressure switch or a water-level switch. The latter two types of fill control insure correct water level in the washer, regardless of the pressure of the water supply.

The effectiveness of the provision for removing sediment, such as sand or grit, from the wash and rinse waters can best be determined by using the washer. Practically, therefore, information on this point must usually be obtained from a person who has used the washer.

Washers may have "power" or "deep" rinses and spray rinses, deep rinses only, or spray rinses only. Some models also have overflow rinses, in which enough water enters to fill the washtub and overflow into the drain basin. The purpose of such a rinse is to float off loose soil at the start of the power rinse. To date no experimental data have been published to indicate superiority of any particular combination of rinses.

Different models of cylinder and agitator automatics have different speeds of rotation of the washtub during spin. If all other construction characteristics are the same, the amount of water extracted from clothes will be greater, the faster the speed of rotation of the tub during spin. Also, within limits, the longer the spin part of the cycle, the greater the amount of water extracted.

Some washers have a special suds-saver feature. In the model shown in Figure 20–10 a set tray for saving the sudsy water for the second load of clothes is next to the washer.

As noted earlier, washers are now available with a device for automatically adding packaged water softener to the rinse water. The one shown in Figure 20–11 has a "wheel" on the agitator for this purpose.

Front-opening cylinder washers stop automatically when the door is opened. Some models of agitator automatics stop when the lid is raised; others do not. This feature might be important to a family with small children.

Simplicity of operation and appearance is desirable in controls. Overall construction that facilitates disassembly for servicing is also desirable.

Still relatively new are provisions for washing and rinsing small loads in smaller than normal amounts of water and for regular and "fine-fabric" cycles. In the fine-fabric cycle, the speed of oscillation of the agitator and the times of the wash, rinse, and spin operations are usually less than in the regular cycle.

Another relatively new feature is provision for built-in installation of washers and dryers. Here a vertical arrangement may be used, with the dryer above the washer. Horizontal arrangements provide for side-by-side installation of washer and dryer. The two appliances may be either under or on a counter (Fig. 20–12).

The total amount of water and the amount of hot water used per cycle vary for different models. If comparisons are made on the basis of full loads with maximum water requirements, cylinder automatics generally use less than agitator automatics. Among the agitator automatics, those that have overflow rinses are likely to use more water than those without them. The above statements are general and washers might be available that refute both statements. The amount of water used per cycle for a given washer is given on the specification sheet.

20–7. INSTALLATION AND CARE OF AUTOMATICS

Installation of automatic washers should be in accordance with local electrical and plumbing requirements in communities where such requirements are imposed. For maximum satisfaction in use, it is recommended that an automatic be connected to a 115-volt, individual-equipment circuit that has a 15-ampere time-delay fuse or a 20-ampere circuit breaker. Washers should be grounded; some have special provision for grounding, as in the plug; others require an external grounding wire between a metal part of the washer and an unpainted part of a cold water pipe, or other ground.

Washer supply hoses are connected to hot and cold water taps or faucets. The water pressure should be between the limits specified by the washer manufacturer, approximately

Fig. 20–10. Washer and set tray for saving sudsy water. (RCA Whirlpool, Whirlpool-Seeger Corporation)

Fig. 20–12. Built-in installation of washer and dryer. (Courtesy Westinghouse Electric Corporation)

Fig. 20–11. Washer with "wheel" on agitator for packaged water softener. (Norge Sales Corp., Subsidiary of Borg-Warner Corp.)

20 to 120 pounds per square inch. The type of house drain required may also be specified by the washer manufacturer. Some washers can be used with a floor drain, provided the local plumbing code permits this and provided also that an air gap is left between the drain hose and the back-up water in the drain system. Some washers should be drained into a fixed laundry tray or into a standpipe provided with a suitable trap.

Generally, automatics need not be bolted to the floor; however, they should stand level and leveling legs usually are provided on the washer. Sometimes the service man who in- stalls the washer places it on rubber pads or cups cemented to the floor.

a. Care

Some general points can be made for care of automatics: (1) To relieve pressure on the hoses, the supply taps or faucets should be turned off when the washer is not in use. (2) The lid or door should be left open after the washer has been used. (3) In freezing weather, if the washer is installed in an un- heated area of the house, the supply hoses should be disconnected from the water faucets and all water drained from the washer.

C. Washing Guides

User's booklets give instructions on opera- tion of controls, short cycle of operation, when one is provided, prewash or soak, starching, bluing, tinting, procedures for such special items as small rugs, pillows, electric bed cover- ings, etc.

Some guides that apply, in general, for all washers are summarized here.

1. Stains are less difficult to remove when they are fresh. In any case, articles with certain stains should not be washed in hot water. For example, articles that have blood or meat juice stains should be soaked in cold or cool water before they are laundered and those with egg stains should be treated before they are washed. Some types of stains, on the other hand, are removed by hot water or by hot water plus bleach. These include light dye stains, such as those transferred in a mixed wash, perspiration, mustard, and light scorch. But even for these stains, it is better to treat them when they are fresh rather than let the stained articles remain in the soiled clothes hamper for several days.

2. Excessively soiled areas, such as collars of shirts and blouses, should be pretreated with a brush and a thick or jelly-like solution of syndet or soap or a brush and liquid syndet.

3. Clothes and household textiles are sorted to make loads that should be washed under the same conditions, that is, at the same water tem- perature, for the same length of time, and for the same cycle of operation if the washer has two cycles. Articles that are not colorfast are washed separately. White nylons are washed only with other white articles. Heavily soiled articles are not washed with lightly soiled articles. Infants' clothing and bedding are washed separately.

4. Loads are made up not by weight alone but with some consideration given to size and bulkiness. If some of the articles are large, sheets for example, the total weight of the load should be decreased in order to insure free motion of the articles in the washer.

5. A prewash or a presoak will usually be helpful when entire articles are quite soiled, as may be true of jeans or denim shorts and gar- dening clothes. The prewash preferably uses soap or syndet and warm, not hot, water.

6. The controls for some automatic washers with a maximum washing time of 10 minutes can be reset to increase the washing time without adding or removing wash water. In home washers a wash time of about 15 minutes is the maximum that should be used for cottons, linens, and the like. If the cotton-linen load is not clean in 15 minutes, the water should be extracted and

the load washed again. On the other hand, many synthetic fabrics need to be washed for only a few minutes.

7. To get the *cleanest* washed fabrics, the best wash water temperature for the soaps and syndets commonly available as this book is written appears to be at least 135 F for white and colorfast cottons, white nylons, Dacrons, and Orlons, and for some white and colorfast rayons.[1] Certain materials—such as wools, silks, some acetates, and all materials that are not colorfast—should be washed at "warm" temperatures, which might range from 100 F for wool to 110 F to 120 F for some colored materials. Solution-dyed acetates can be washed at higher temperatures, provided a label on the material so indicates.

It is pertinent to note the water heater ther-mostat will usually have to be set at 145 F to 155 F to obtain a temperature in the washer of 135 F for the first wash load. After one load is washed, the washer may be sufficiently warm so that the temperature differential between the water in it and that in the water heater will be less than 20 F.

8. A rinse water temperature of 90 F to 105 F is usual, but some washers provide settings for cold rinses. These actually are likely to be slightly warmer than the cold tap water because clothes and washtub will be warm when the rinse water enters the tub. Up to this time, experimental work has not been reported on the relative effectiveness of 100 F versus cold rinses, though Williams[2] found no significant difference for a 100 F versus a 140 F rinse for cotton washed in soft and hard (25-grain) water at a wash water temperature of 140 F.

[1] Experimental work on laundering cotton treated with a radioactive soil at wash-water temperatures of 120 F, 140 F, and 160 F is discussed in an article by Ehrenkranz and Jebe entitled "Carbon-14 Method Tests Home Laundering Procedures," *Nucleonics,* March, 1956.

[2] Velma L. Williams, "Removal of Soil from Fabrics Laundered in Home Washers. I. Soft and Hard Water; Number of Rinses and Temperature of Rinse Water," unpublished master's thesis, Iowa State College Library, 1951.

D. Experiments

Experiment 1. *Inspection of Washers*

Steps 1 through 6 apply to both wringer-type washers and automatics. Step 7 applies to wringer-type washers only and step 8 to automatics only.

1. Is the nameplate accessible? Does it give manufacturer's name and address, model number, serial number, voltage rating, horsepower rating of motor, other information? Does the washer have the Underwriters Laboratories seal of approval?
2. Are the controls easy to use?
3. What are the overall dimensions when the lid is raised or the door opened?
4. Does the washer appear to be well constructed? Would disassembly for servicing be reasonably easy? If the washer has an agitator, can it be removed from its shaft by the user?
5. Are instructions in the user's booklet on use and care of the washer clear?
6. Precisely what does the manufacturer's warranty promise the purchaser about the appliance?
7. Check the following points for wringer-type washers.
   a. Can the washer be moved easily and are locks provided for the casters?
   b. Is the safety release easy to operate and can the wringer be reassembled easily after the rolls have been separated?

    c. Check the following points with a specification sheet or user's manual.

       1) Characteristics of interior and exterior surfaces with respect to rust resistance.

       2) Gallon capacity of the tub.

       3) Is a motor-overload protective device provided?

       4) Special features.

8. Check the following points for automatics.

    a. If the machine is a front-opening type, does the door close easily and tightly?

    b. Is the toe space adequate?

    c. Check the following points with a specification sheet or user's manual:

       1) Characteristics of interior and exterior surfaces with respect to rust resistance.

       2) Gallon capacity of the tub. Total water consumption per cycle for normal and for partial fills, if partial fills are provided. Hot water consumption.

       3) Type of drain needed with the washer.

       4) Method of controlling fill. Is it timed or not? If timed, can an adjustment be made on the washer by the service man to increase or decrease the time of fill?

       5) Is a motor-overload protective device provided? How is the washer grounded?

       6) What provision is made for sediment in the wash and rinse waters?

       7) Characteristics of cycle such as rinse time, kind of rinses, spinning time, total time of cycle for a 10-minute wash.

       8) In what parts of the cycle, if any, does the washer stop automatically when the lid is raised?

       9) Special cycle for delicate fabrics, partial-fill provisions, controls for different wash- and rinse-water temperatures, provision for automatic injection of packaged water softener in rinse part of cycle, lint filter, other special features.

    Additional Experiments　The most significant additional experiment would be a test of the effectiveness of different washers in washing clothes clean. Unfortunately, such an experiment performed in one or two laboratory periods might give unreliable data and lead to misleading conclusions. Research on home laundering methods attests to the fact that experiments on the effectiveness of washers have to be repeated several times before valid conclusions can be drawn.

Experiment 2. *Wrinkling of Washed Clothes for Different Washers, Different Wash Water Temperatures, and Different Fabrics*

Because of the numerous "drip-dry" fabrics now on the market an experiment on wrinkling is of practical importance. Some of these fabrics may have a few wrinkles if washed in a washer but not if washed by hand.

If the effect of the washer alone is to be observed at a given wash water temperature and for a particular fabric, the washed fabric must be dried on a line or a wooden horse. Wrinkling of fabrics washed in a washer and dried in a dryer would be a separate experiment.

The experiments should be carried out two or more times before conclusions are drawn on washers, water temperatures, or fabrics.[3]

[3] Experiment 3, Chapter 21, describes a procedure for measuring the amount of water added to dry loads in washers and the amount removed in different drying times in dryers.

Dryers, Combination Washer-Dryers, Irons, and Ironers

A. Dryers

Both gas and electric dryers are available and they have many similar parts. Some of their interior components can be seen by looking through openings in the front, top, and back. The cabinet consists of a lid assembly, a wrap-a-round section, and a back panel, or a lid assembly and front, side, and back panels. The panels are fastened to a welded steel frame by screws. The perforated or partially perforated rotatable dryer drum, mounted in the drum housing, has three to six interior vanes. It rotates at a speed of approximately 50 revolutions per minute. Details of the mechanical support of the drum vary in different models. For the one shown in Figure 21–1, the rear surface of the drum is mounted on a hub

shaft and the front is supported by two rubber-covered rollers.

The gas burner or electric heating unit is usually located near the top of the dryer in a heater housing that forms part of the drum housing. In some models, the heating unit is located below the drum.

A motor furnishes power to the drum through pulleys and also drives the blower or exhaust fan that provides the forced air circulation within the dryer. The temperature of the air inside the dryer is controlled by a cycling thermostat or thermostats and a safety thermostat.

For many models, drying time is controlled by a timer set by the user, but for a few it is

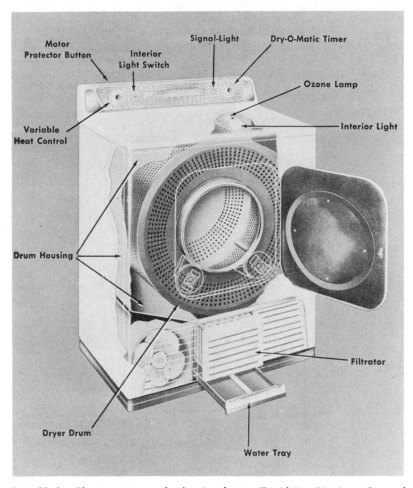

Fig. 21–1. Phantom view of electric dryer. (Frigidaire Division, General Motors Corporation)

controlled according to the fabric load, for example, delicate, heavy, medium. The user sets the dial for the type of fabric load and the dryer turns off automatically when the load is dry.

Fabrics dry by tumbling in a current of warm air in the rotating drum. Except for a few models of electric dryers that have water cooling, operation of a dryer consists simply in the following: the exhaust fan or blower causes air to enter the dryer cabinet through an inlet grille or grilles and pass over the burner or heating unit. This heated air is then drawn through perforations in the drum of an exhaust duct which has a vent or port at either the front or rear of the dryer.

In electric dryers with water cooling, the drum housing is sealed to prevent air from entering or leaving it during the drying cycle. A cold-water spray in a condensation chamber cools the heated, moisture-laden air and condenses the moisture from it (Fig. 21–2). A pump expels the spray water and that condensed from the hot air through a drain hose. The air is then reheated and recirculated; and the process repeats.

Dryers that are not water-cooled have a lint trap located near the bottom of the dryer below an opening in the drum housing or a mesh bag located in the upper part of the

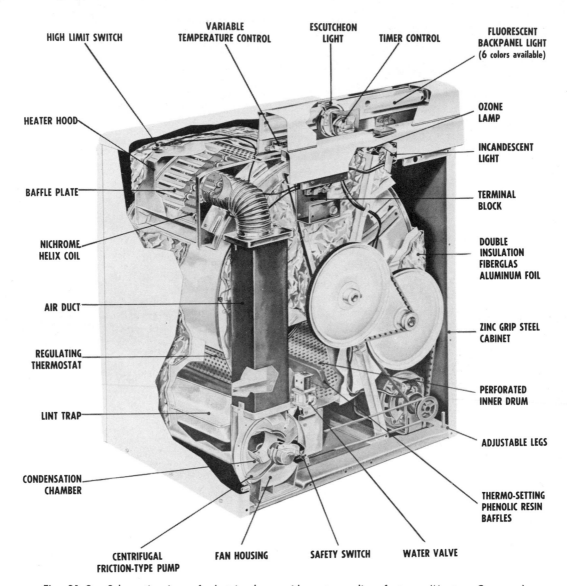

HIGH LIMIT SWITCH

VARIABLE
TEMPERATURE CONTROL

ESCUTCHEON
LIGHT

TIMER CONTROL

FLUORESCENT
BACKPANEL LIGHT
(6 colors available)

HEATER HOOD

OZONE
LAMP

INCANDESCENT
LIGHT

BAFFLE PLATE

TERMINAL
BLOCK

NICHROME
HELIX COIL

DOUBLE
INSULATION
FIBERGLAS
ALUMINUM FOIL

AIR DUCT

ZINC GRIP STEEL
CABINET

REGULATING
THERMOSTAT

PERFORATED
INNER DRUM

LINT TRAP

ADJUSTABLE LEGS

CONDENSATION
CHAMBER

THERMO-SETTING
PHENOLIC RESIN
BAFFLES

CENTRIFUGAL
FRICTION-TYPE PUMP

FAN HOUSING

SAFETY SWITCH

WATER VALVE

Fig. 21–2. Schematic view of electric dryer with water-cooling feature. (Maytag Company)

cabinet (Figs. 21–3 and 21–4). Some water-cooled electric dryers have no lint trap; instead the lint is carried down the house drain with the cold water.

21–1. CONSTRUCTION CHARACTERISTICS

The dry-clothes capacity of different dryers is 8 to 10 pounds; in other words, one washer load usually makes one dryer load. For driving the fan and drum, gas and electric dryers use a motor rated at 115 volts and $\frac{1}{6}$ to $\frac{1}{3}$ horsepower. The burner capacity of gas dryers is usually about 18,000 Btu's per hour, but a higher British thermal unit capacity is possible. Gas dryers are available for different types of gas supply: namely, natural gas, bottled gas, and manufactured gas. The main burner orifice in the dryer *must* have an opening appropriate for the type of gas used.

The heating unit of most electric dryers uses approximately 4200 to 5000 watts at 230 volts. Many electric dryers are designed for use at either 115 or 230 volts. The wattage rating for 115 volts is of the order of 1400 to 1650 watts. The drying time at 115 volts is likely to be three or more times as long as at 230 volts.

Nameplate wattage ratings are of course maximum values. Electric dryers with temperature selector switches may have two or more resistance elements which are connected in different ways, according to the setting of the temperature selector switch. One model uses 4500 watts for heating at high setting, 3375 at medium, 2250 at low, 1125 at warm, and zero watts at "tumble." (The tumble setting is used to fluff articles without heat.)

High-speed models have been introduced that use 8000 or 9000 watts at 230 volts. Such models may require special house wiring.

Blower capacities in cubic feet of air per minute vary for different dryers. Capacities of the order of 60 to 80 cubic feet per minute are usual; one combination electric washer-dryer, however, uses a blower with a capacity of 200 cubic feet per minute.

Outdoor venting of either a gas dryer or an electric dryer without water cooling is desirable when the machine is installed in a poorly ventilated room, in order to avoid excessive humidity in the room. Manufacturers of both these types of dryers supply accessories for such outside venting. Electric dryers with the water-cooling feature do not add excessive humidity to the room, because the moisture in the hot air of the dryer is condensed and goes down the house drain.

Outdoor venting of gas dryers is sometimes required by local ordinance for the following reason: When gas dryers are vented to the outside, the products of combustion of the gas, as well as the moisture and some lint from the clothes, pass to the outside rather than to the

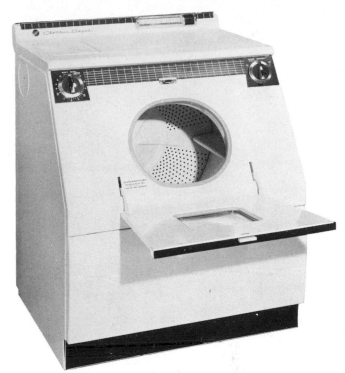

Fig. 21–3. Electric dryer with nylon lint trap in upper left part of housing. (Courtesy Westinghouse Electric Corporation)

room in which the dryer is installed. If a gas dryer is installed in a small room, such as a bathroom, outside venting of the products of the gas combustion is necessary as a safety measure for persons using the room. On the other hand, if the dryer is installed in a space equivalent to a room of conventional size, outside venting is not necessary as a safety measure.

21–2. HEATING CHARACTERISTICS AND SAFETY FEATURES

For gas and electric dryers, a safety thermostat or equivalent safety device and a cycling thermostat are used. In some models with several heat settings, more than one cycling thermostat may be used. The safety device is usually mounted in the drum housing; ordi-

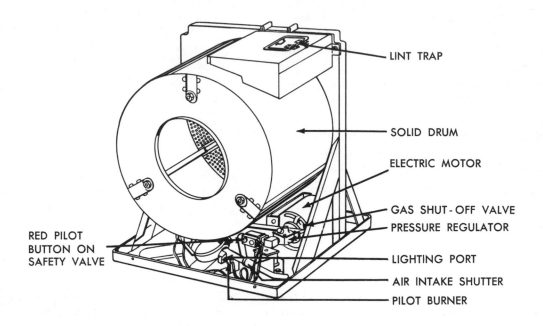

LINT TRAP

SOLID DRUM

ELECTRIC MOTOR

GAS SHUT-OFF VALVE
PRESSURE REGULATOR

RED PILOT
BUTTON ON
SAFETY VALVE

LIGHTING PORT

AIR INTAKE SHUTTER

PILOT BURNER

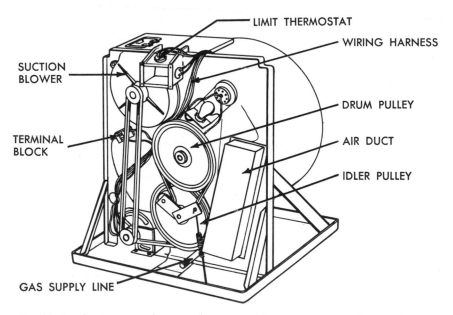

LIMIT THERMOSTAT

WIRING HARNESS

SUCTION
BLOWER

DRUM PULLEY

AIR DUCT

TERMINAL
BLOCK

IDLER PULLEY

GAS SUPPLY LINE

Fig. 21–4. Construction of a gas dryer. (Franklin Manufacturing Company)

narily it will function only if the cycling thermostat misfunctions. The cycling thermostat or thermostats may be mounted either in the drum housing or in the exhaust duct. The cycling thermostat or thermostats thus actually are responsive to either the temperature of the drum housing or the air in the exhaust duct. However, the temperatures of both the drum housing and the exhaust air are partly dependent on the temperature of the air in the drum.

A cycling thermostat of a gas dryer controls flow of gas to the burner by one or the other of two heating control mechanisms. In one, the flow of gas to the main burner is interrupted, that is, stopped completely, when operating temperature is reached, and only a pilot burns; if the temperature then falls below a preset value, gas will flow again. In the other, the flow of gas to the main burner is decreased when operating temperature is reached and only a small so-called by-pass flame and the pilot continue to burn. In this control mechanism the flow of gas increases if the temperature falls sufficiently.

A cycling thermostat in an electric dryer makes and breaks the circuit to the heating unit.

Temperatures in the dryer are not the same for all models. In fact, a manufacturer may adjust the cycling thermostat so that there are two different temperatures for the same setting, such as "medium," in two different models! But some standardization probably will be achieved. An example is the "wrinkle-free" setting introduced on some deluxe 1958 models. This setting is supposed to provide a maximum temperature of 140 to 160 F for drying articles made of nylon, Dacron and Orlon.

Both gas and electric dryers should have door switches to stop rotation of the drum and shut off production of heat when the door is opened.

21–3. INSTALLATION, USE, AND CARE

For convenience in use, a dryer should be installed as near the washer as possible and preferably immediately alongside it. The dryer should be installed level. As indicated previously, rear venting to the outdoors is desirable, whether required by local ordinance or not, when an electric dryer without water cooling or a gas dryer is installed in a room with inadequate ventilation from open doors and windows. The duct from the exterior of the dryer to the outside of the house should be as short as possible and should have a minimum number of 90-degree bends, preferably not more than one or two. The efficiency of the dryer is reduced when a long duct is used or one with several sharp bends.

Occasionally an ill-informed home owner vents a gas dryer through a chimney, to avoid having a duct extend through a house wall. Such an installation is likely to prove unsatisfactory. When outdoor venting is not possible, a small ventilating fan in the room will be helpful.

Gas dryers require a 115-volt, 60-cycle current to operate the motor. The electric circuit to the gas dryer should be fused with a 15-ampere fuse or a 20-ampere circuit breaker. Gas connections are made in accordance with local regulations. Usually, semirigid tubing or approved pipe with a half-inch interior diameter is used between the gas supply line and the dryer. Again as indicated previously, the orifice of the main burner of the dryer must be appropriate for the British thermal unit rating or heating value of the gas supplied. Some manufacturers provide a blank orifice, to be drilled to the correct size before or during installation, in accordance with a chart that gives orifice sizes for different ratings (British thermal units per cubic foot) of the gas supply.

Installation of electric dryers should conform to the National Electrical Code and such local regulations as may apply. For 115/230-volt installations, the individual-equipment circuit for the dryer should be a three-wire circuit fused for 30 amperes at the distribution panel. No. 10 wires should be used in the circuit, except when the local electrical code specifies a different size. The dryer cabinet should be grounded to the neutral of the electrical supply or to a cold water pipe, in accordance with local regulations.

For 115-volt operation of the dryer, when only such operation is to be used, the dryer should be installed in a two-wire, individual-equipment circuit fused for 15 or 20 amperes. Wire size should be No. 12.

In the case of water-cooled electric dryers, facilities must be provided for supplying cold water to the dryer and for draining it away.

a. Use and Care

A protective wax finish, of a type recommended by the dryer manufacturer, may be applied to the exterior of the cabinet to maintain its appearance. After drying a load that has excessive lint and after every three loads or so for fabric with normal amounts of lint, most lint traps should be cleaned with the brush provided. Lint traps on dryers with partially perforated drums need to be emptied less frequently. Specific recommendations are given in user's booklets.

The interior of the drum, the door opening of the cabinet, and the inside surface of the door should be wiped with a damp cloth to remove excess lint. After starched articles have been dried, the interior of the drum should be washed with a cloth dampened in sudsy water and rinsed with a damp cloth. In addition to regular emptying of the lint trap, some user's booklets suggest cleaning the interior of the drum and the space occupied by the lint trap once a month with the crevice attachment of a vacuum cleaner. When a vacuum cleaner is used for such cleaning the dryer should be disconnected from the electrical supply so two electrical appliances will not be handled at the same time.

Though most models require no lubrication by the user, some may require infrequent (once a year or so) lubrication. Again, instructions are given in the user's booklet.

Articles cleaned with any dry-cleaning solvent should *not* be dried in a household dryer. The general rule is that only articles washed in water should be dried in a dryer.

In a load with small and large articles, such as pillowcases and sheets, and smooth and absorbent fabrics, such as place mats and turkish towels, the larger articles will not be completely dry when the smaller ones are, and the absorbent fabrics will not be dry as soon as the smooth ones. This is not of great practical importance. For example, sheets that are slightly damp in spots when removed from the dryer will be ready for storage after smoothing and folding on top of the dryer. If enough washer loads are done in a single work period, it may be convenient to make up a separate dryer load of turkish towels.

Fabrics should not be dried to the bone-dry stage, as this promotes wrinkles. Synthetic fabrics usually can be dried safely at any temperature setting, *provided* they are removed while still containing a little moisture. If such fabrics are dried with cottons, little special watching is necessary. *But* check for dryness every few minutes when a small load consisting only of synthetic fabrics is dried in a dryer that does not have a special setting. To check, remove an article from the dryer, because in the moisture-laden air in the dryer your hand "feels" the moisture in the air as well as that in the article and this tends to be misleading.

A bonus feature of dryers is that the tumbling of articles in warm air makes ironing easier, if they have not been overdried. Also, articles not to be ironed, such as turkish towels, that are dried completely, though not bone-dry, have a nice fluffy appearance and "hand."

21–4. AVERAGE DRYING TIME, KILOWATT-HOURS, AND CUBIC FEET OF GAS

Experiments have been carried out with different types of loads (mixed cottons, towels, heavy work clothes, etc.) wetted and extracted in different washers and dried in both gas and electric dryers.[1] The average drying time for the several types of loads extracted in several washers was approximately 40 minutes. During this average drying time, the electric dryer used 2.7 kilowatt-hours and the gas dryer used

10.9 cubic feet of natural gas having a heating value of 1000 Btu's per cubic foot.

21–5. AMERICAN STANDARDS ASSOCIATION STANDARD

Requirements for safe and durable construction and acceptable performance of domestic gas dryers have been sponsored by the American Gas Association and approved by the American Standards Association.[2] Gas dryers that meet the approval requirements carry the American Gas Association blue seal of approval.

No standard has as yet been approved for domestic electric dryers.

B. Combination Washer-Dryers

A combination washer-dryer is a single appliance that washes and dries fabrics. Both gas and electric models are available. The combination appliance has two definite advantages: (1) The user does not need to transfer wash loads from a washer to a dryer. (2) The space required for the combination appliance is less than that required for two separate appliances. Indeed, the space required by some combination models is no greater than that required by a washer alone or a dryer alone.

The combination appliances available at this time incorporate a front-loading, cylinder-type washer. If desired, the appliance may be used for washing only or for drying only. One load is handled at a time; that is, a single load is either washed or dried at one time. Combination gas models require a 115-volt, 60-cycle electric supply for operating the drum during washing and drum and fan during drying, and a gas supply for the burner that

operates during the drying part of the cycle. Combination electric models require a three-wire, 115/230-volt, 60-cycle supply of electric power.

One electric combination washer-dryer is shown in Figure 21–5. Below the rotating drum is a 3-gallon water tank with a 4200-watt, immersion-type heating element inside it. The heating element is thermostatically controlled to insure a water temperature of at least 120 F for the warm setting. The washing action is somewhat different from that of standard cylinder automatics. In the fill part of the wash cycle, water saturates the clothes and fills the tank to the 3-gallon level. During the remainder of the wash period the clothes are sprayed with recirculated, detergent-laden water. The clothes are also rinsed by sprayed water. Three rinses are provided, and the complete cycle uses 12 gallons of water plus the amount needed to saturate the clothes.

Three controls are used with the combina-

[1] Nada D. Poole, "Use of Different Combinations of Laundry Appliances. I. Dryer and Conventional Washer for Weekly Family Laundry," unpublished master's thesis, Iowa State College Library, 1951. Also, unpublished work of the senior author.

[2] Z21.5, *American Standard Approval Requirements for Domestic Gas Clothes Dryers,* American Standards Association, 1956.

Fig. 21–5. Electric combination washer-dryer. (RCA Whirlpool, Whirlpool-Seeger Corporation)

ture of 97 F, the medium setting a water temperature of 120 F, and the hot setting a water temperature that corresponds to the temperature of the hot water supply, unless this is below 120 F. If the hot water supply is lower than 120 F and the hot setting is used, the timer motor will not run. (3) The drying temperature control has five marked settings from "high" (195 F) down to "air" or room temperature.

Several other features of this particular combination appliance are worthy of note. Some help give more satisfactory washing results; others are convenience features. A water filter, located behind the bottom panel door, removes lint and foreign objects, such as safety pins, from the water. A lint trap, located in the upper surface (right-rear corner) under a small hinged door, catches the lint given off by the clothes as they dry. A bleach dispenser is also provided under the small hinged door.

Combination washer-dryers are also available with other sets of features. For example, another electric model provides water cooling during the drying part of the complete cycle and dries clothes to the storage-dry stage without the user's setting a dial to a definite number of minutes or to a type of fabric load. This drying feature is achieved by using thermostats that cycle on and off according to rate of water evaporation from the load.

tion appliance illustrated. (1) A two-dial timer controls the minutes of washing time and minutes of drying time. (2) The water-temperature control is marked for three settings. The warm setting gives a water tempera-

C. Irons, Ironers, and Ironing

21–6. ELECTRIC HAND IRONS

Electric hand irons, sometimes called flat-irons, include dry irons, combination dry and steam irons, and steam irons. Travel irons, both dry and combination, are available. These weigh less than regular-size irons and have handles that fold to make a compact package (Figs. 21–6 and 21–7).

All electric irons have a single heating ele-

ment mounted above or in the sole plate. This is either nichrome ribbon wrapped on mica sheets or tubular-type. Most regular-size electric irons are thermostatically controlled to give different temperatures of the sole plate according to dial setting. They are usually rated 1000 to 1150 watts and are designed for use with 110–120-volt alternating current. Regular irons without thermostatic control are rated about 600 watts. Travel irons are not usually

Convenient plaid
zipper carrying case.

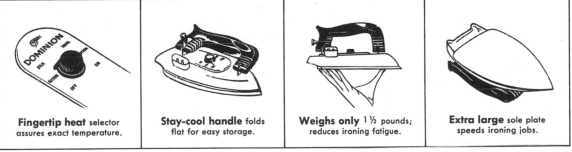

Fingertip heat selector
assures exact temperature.

Stay-cool handle folds
flat for easy storage.

Weighs only 1 ½ pounds;
reduces ironing fatigue.

Extra large sole plate
speeds ironing jobs.

Fig. 21–6.   Travel iron with thermostatic control. (Dominion Electric Corporation)

thermostatically controlled, but they may be, as in the two models illustrated. Nonthermostatically controlled models are usually rated about 500 watts or less.

Combination dry and steam irons and steam irons are either kettle-type or flash-boiler type. Kettle models have a water chamber inside the iron (Fig. 21–8). The heating element in the iron heats the sole plate and the entire mass of water. After the water vaporizes, the pressure of the steam inside the iron increases, and steam is emitted through vents in the sole plate.

Flash-boiler models have either a water chamber in the iron or in a container that is separate from the iron, but connected with it (Fig. 21–9). With either type of water reser-voir, only a small quantity of water is heated at a time to form steam, though steam is generated continuously as long as there is water in the reservoir.

Flash-boiler combination irons may be converted almost instantly from dry to steam or vice versa by flipping a lever. Kettle combination irons convert from steam to dry almost instantly, but in converting from dry to steam an appreciable mass of water must be heated and vaporized before steam is generated.

a. Construction Characteristics

The sole plate of any iron must be smooth and made of a rust-resistant material—or at least have a rust-resistant finish. Aluminum alloys, stainless steel, and chrome-plated steel

Fig. 21–7. Thermostatically controlled, combination dry and steam travel iron that operates on alternating or direct current. (General Electric Company)

are used for sole plates on different models. Lighter-weight models sometimes have aluminum sole plates. The edges of the sole plate are beveled and button nooks may be provided. The nose is usually pointed for ironing into gathers.

A few models, particularly travel models, have indicators that show approximate temperature or fabric range, instead of thermostats. Indicators do not control the temperature of the sole plate; they merely tell the user when to turn the iron on or off while ironing.

As stated earlier, however, most irons have thermostats and are designed for use with alternating current, though they can be designed for use with either alternating or direct current.[3] The thermostat dial should be made

---

[3] If thermostatically controlled irons designed only for alternating current are used on a direct current supply, the "points" of the thermostat switch that open and close the electric circuit are likely to fuse together and thus make the thermostat inoperative. A direct current supply is not usual in the United States, but it is used by some hotels in large cities. So, check before you plug an iron into an outlet in a hotel room. It may be worth noting also that irons designed for 110–120 volts should not be used on 220 volts, which is the characteristic electric supply in many foreign countries.

of a material that is a poor heat conductor and it should be so located that it can be turned easily without hazard of burning one's fingers.

An especially important characteristic for ease in use is the fit of the iron to the hand of the user, which depends partly on the handle. Handles are made of Bakelite or other materials that are poor heat conductors. A new trend is toward open handles (Fig. 21–10). The balance of an iron in the hand is different for different women, and a prospective purchaser should lift an iron to determine whether it feels right in her hand.

Most regular irons now have permanently attached cords. If a cordminder is used, to hold most of the cord above the iron, the place of attachment of the cord to the iron (rear, right, or left side) is of little importance (Fig. 21–11). Otherwise, a cord attached at the rear or on the right side of the iron is best for ironing from right to left with either hand. One attached at the rear or the left side is best for ironing from left to right with the left hand. (Women who are motion-conscious transfer an iron from one hand to the other while ironing.)

Models are available in different weights. Currently, regular-size models usually weigh between 2½ and 4 pounds. Travel irons may weigh as little as 1½ pounds. The best weight is largely a matter of personal preference and habit.

Weights of combination irons and steam irons given on specification sheets are usually exclusive of the weight of the added water. Combination irons with interior water reservoirs usually hold about 6 ounces (¾ cup) of water; at least one model holds 7½ ounces. Steam irons vary in the amount of water they hold; one model holds approximately a pound.

Most irons can be tilted to one side or to the rear to raise the sole plate off the fabric as needed.

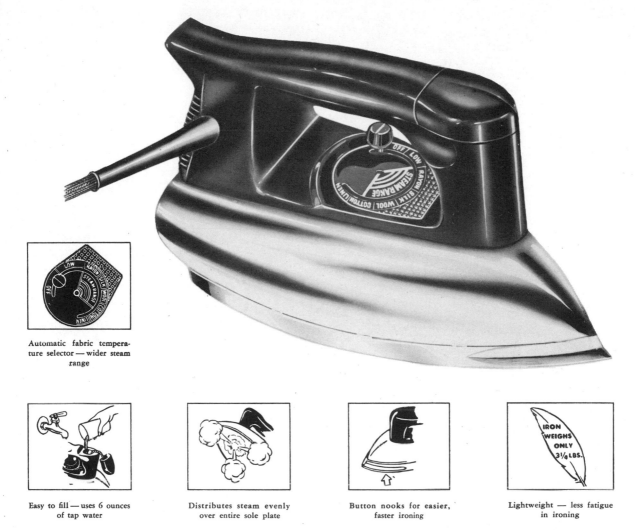

Automatic fabric temperature selector — wider steam range

Easy to fill — uses 6 ounces of tap water

Distributes steam evenly over entire sole plate

Button nooks for easier, faster ironing

Lightweight — less fatigue in ironing

Fig. 21–8. Kettle-type, combination dry and steam iron. (Dominion Electric Corporation)

b. Care

Actually, little care of irons is necessary. They should be used in small-appliance circuits whenever possible. Abrasives should not be used on the sole plate. A cloth dipped in sudsy water or beeswax helps remove starch from the sole plate; clean when the iron is only moderately warm. Let it cool before storing it. Wind the cord loosely around the iron for storage.

Steam and combination irons with interior water reservoirs should be disconnected when they are filled at the start of ironing or during ironing, and again when they are emptied. They should be emptied of any remaining water while still hot to insure maximum removal of moisture.

For some models the manufacturers state that tap water can be used. But steam irons and the steam feature of combination irons will last longer if only distilled or demineralized water is used in them. Small demineralizers are sold in hardware stores.

Fig. 21–9. Flash-boiler, combination dry and steam iron. (Sunbeam Corporation)

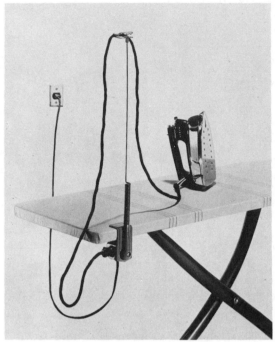

Fig. 21–11. "Mary Proctor" steam and dry iron, cordminder, hi-lo ironing table. (Proctor Electric Company)

Fig. 21–10. Dry iron with open handle. (Sunbeam Corporation, Copyright © 1954)

Mechanically softened water contains minerals and therefore is not recommended for use with steam or combination irons.

21–7. IRONING WITH A HAND IRON

Loosely woven and lightweight washable fabrics and many woolens can be steam-ironed when dry, but a steam iron should not be used on silks and rayons that water-spot.

Materials laundered with a vegetable starch, most linens, heavy cottons, and some medium and heavyweight rayons iron better when they have been dampened. Logically, dampened articles are dry-ironed—that is, ironed with a dry iron.

Follow instructions on labels for nylons, Orlons, etc., and for materials with special finishes. When instructions are not given on labels, experiment with a small test patch to see whether steam or dry ironing is better.

In both dry and steam ironing, do first the articles made of fabrics that require the lower heat settings. This saves time because it takes less time to heat an iron from a low to a high setting than to cool it from a high to a low setting.

Ease and speed in ironing depend on appropriate moisture content of the articles to be ironed. (See Experiment 6 at the end of this chapter, p. 300.) A well-padded ironing board makes ironing easier. Correct height of the board either for stand-up or sit-down ironing is desirable. Ironing boards are available that are adjustable to different sitting and standing heights.

There are a few practical techniques for making ironing easier:

1. As far as possible, utilize the full length of the ironing board. Use long, rhythmical strokes and transfer the iron from one hand to the other on the return stroke—for example, on skirts.

2. Do not rearrange the article unnecessarily.

As far as possible utilize the full width of the board.

3. Iron each part of an article dry before proceeding to another part. (An ironed part that is not dry is likely to acquire creases and wrinkles while other parts of the article are being ironed!)

21–8. ELECTRIC IRONERS

Models that are being manufactured at this time have a motor-operated roll and a shoe curved to fit the roll. They are dry type. One or two insulated and thermostatically controlled resistance elements are mounted inside

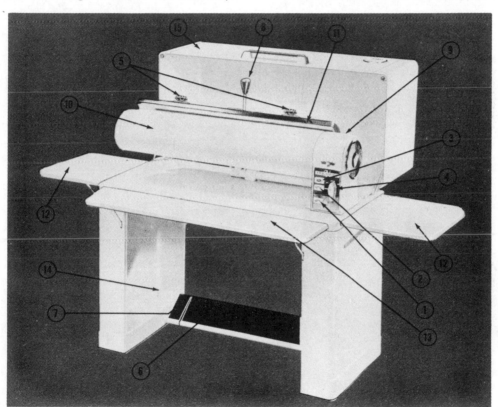

Fig. 21–12. Ironer with parts labeled. (Frigidaire Division, General Motors Corporation)

1. Motor switch
2. Heat switch
3. Signal light
4. Speed selector
5. Thermostatic heat controls
6. Foot control
7. *Press* toe switch
8. Release lever
9. Roll drive mechanism
10. Roll
11. Shoe
12. End Shelves
13. Lap tray
14. Adjustable casters
15. Cabinet top

or under the shoe assembly, which is mounted above or below the roll. The small motor that drives the roll is mounted at the side of the roll for the type of ironer shown in Figures 21–12 and 21–13, and behind the roll for the type of ironer shown in Figure 21–14.

In operation, the article being ironed is carried around on the roll and the shoe fits against the article.

A manually operated release lever is always provided to bring shoe and roll near, but not next to, each other and to separate shoe and roll. For models that have the shoe on top, the shoe is moved near the roll; where the shoe is on the bottom, the roll is moved near the shoe.

The release lever is used to separate shoe and roll when the ironer is preheating, when it is cooling before it is put away, and when a power outage occurs. After the release lever has been used to separate roll and shoe, it must be operated again to bring the two parts near each other before ironing can be started.

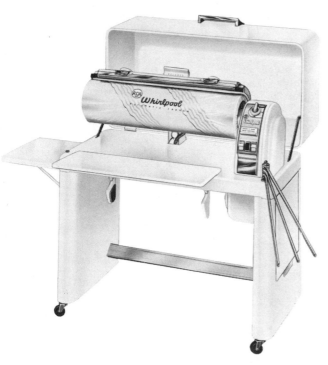

Fig. 21–13. Ironer with shoe above roll. (RCA Whirlpool, Whirlpool-Seeger Corporation)

Usually, a heat switch is provided, separate from the thermostat or thermostats, to close and open the electric circuit to the resistance element or elements. In addition, most models have both a finger-operated and a toe- or knee-operated switch for starting and stopping the roll and for pressing. In normal operation the toe or knee switch is used rather than the finger switch.

Some ironers have a three-position speed switch for press and for high- and low-speed rotation of the roll. When the switch is at press, the shoe moves against and away from the roll and repeats, or the roll moves against the shoe and away and repeats. The high-speed setting is used most of the time. Low speed is used for very damp articles; also, new owners use the low-speed setting at first.

To iron, the ironer is first preheated. Then the article to be ironed is arranged on the roll and the release lever is operated to bring shoe and roll near each other; this does *not* bring the two parts into contact with each other. Operation of the switch for starting brings shoe and roll into snug fit and starts the roll rotating. Once the roll is started, it keeps on rotating until the user operates the switch for stop or press. Thus ironing with an ironer consists chiefly in arranging and rearranging an article on the roll with the hands and operating a switch with one leg or foot.

a. Use and Care

Ironers use 1000 to 1500 watts at 115 volts, the exact wattage depending on the model. An ironer therefore should be used in a small-appliance circuit.

Just as for an iron, little care is required. The principal rules to observe are these:

1. After ironing, release the shoe from the roll with the release lever.

2. Clean the ironing surface of the shoe with a soft cloth wrung out in sudsy water. Occasionally wax the ironing surface with a small amount of beeswax or paraffin while the shoe is

warm; then polish with a dry cloth to remove excess wax.

3. Keep the padding on the roll in a soft and fluffy condition by removing the pad occasionally and shaking it.

4. Follow instructions in the user's booklet on adjusting pressure between shoe and roll and on periodic lubrication by a service man. For some models the pressure is adjusted permanently at the factory; others have a wheel the user can turn to increase pressure after the ironer has been used for some time. Some models require lubrication once in four years or so by a service man; others are factory-lubricated for the life of the ironer.

5. Maintain the appearance of the ironer by waxing the cabinet occasionally.

It takes practice to acquire skill in using an ironer, but the reward is real. The senior author has seen a blindfolded professional demonstrator do a man's shirt acceptably in two minutes! To acquire skill, follow these steps: (1) Observe carefully how a professional demonstrator uses an ironer. (2) Read the instructions in the user's booklet on how to iron different types of articles. (3) Following the instructions, use the ironer at first for flat pieces. (4) After some skill has been acquired, observe a professional demonstrator again. (5) Again following instructions in the user's booklet, use the ironer for articles made of several parts, such as shirts. Handle the parts, sleeves for example, as though they were flat pieces.

Some owners of ironers never acquire real speed. However, very early in one's use of an ironer one can develop enough skill to experience enjoyment in the use of the appliance.

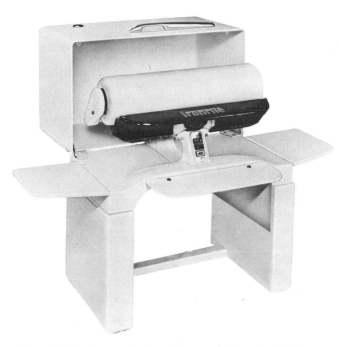

Fig. 21–14.   Ironer wih shoe below roll. (Ironrite, Inc.)

D. Experiments

Experiment 1. *Inspection of Dryers*

1. Is the namplate accessible? Does it give manufacturer's name and address, model number, serial number, voltage rating or ratings, wattage rating for electric dryers, British thermal unit input per hour for gas dryers? Does the dryer have the Underwriters Laboratories seal of approval? If it is a gas model, does it have the American Gas Association seal?
2. Do you understand how the controls operate? Are they easy to use?
3. What are the overall dimensions when the door is open? Is the dryer so constructed that flush-with-wall installation is possible?
4. Does the dryer appear to be well constructed? Does the door close easily and tightly? Does operation of the dryer stop when the door is opened?

5. Check the following points with a specification sheet or user's manual:
   a. Safety features in addition to stoppage when the door is opened.
   b. Characteristics of interior and exterior surfaces with respect to rust resistance.
   c. Rating in pounds of dry clothes.
   d. Does the drum continue to rotate for five minutes or longer after the heat goes off? (This feature is ordinarily desirable, unless other means are provided to insure that clothes are not too hot to handle at the end of the cycle.)
   e. If the dryer is a water-cooled model, how much cold water is used in an average drying time of 40 minutes? Is any type of house drain for the water satisfactory?
6. What special features are provided? These may include several heat settings, special "wrinkle-free" setting, special lint trap characteristics, ozone or other "freshener" device, sprinkler device, weighing scale in door. Electric ignition in a gas dryer is a special and, for many users, desirable feature.
7. Are instructions in the user's booklet on use and care of the dryer clear?
8. Precisely what does the manufacturer's warranty promise the purchaser about the appliance?

Experiment 2. *Inspection of Combination Washer-Dryers*

Inspect for the points given in the inspection experiments for washers and for dryers. Check manufacturers' literature for average drying times.

Experiment 3. *Water Added to Loads by Washers and Water Removed by Dryers*

1. Assemble four dry loads that weigh approximately 6 pounds each of the following materials: (1) terrycloth towels, (2) medium-weight cottons, such as blouses, uniforms, and dresses, (3) heavy cottons, such as denim jeans and work shirts, and (4) synthetic fabrics such as nylons, Dacrons, Orlons.
2. Wash the loads separately, without soap or syndet, in warm water (100 F or the warm setting of an automatic.) For automatics, use the complete cycle with a 10-minute wash. For wringer washers, also use a 10-minute wash and remove the water from the load by passing the load through the wringer. Then use one 5-minute rinse in the wringer washer and again remove water from the load by passing it through the wringer.
3. Weigh the loads after the cycle is completed in automatic washers or after the loads have been wrung in wringer washers. If a combination washer-dryer is used, remove the load before the dry part of the cycle starts. (It is convenient to weigh the loads in a plastic bag or on a sheet of freezer paper.)
4. Dry the loads separately in dryers for 15 minutes. Weigh again. Caution: use a low heat setting, if one is provided, for the load of synthetic fabrics. Check dryness after 5 minutes and 8 minutes and remove from dryer if load is dry.

5. Repeat steps 2, 3, and 4, except this time dry for 20 minutes and do not dry the load of nylons, Dacrons, and Orlons.

6. Again repeat steps 2, 3, and 4, except this time dry for 30 minutes and do not dry the load of nylons, Dacrons, and Orlons. (When a load is removed from a dryer for weighing, some water evaporates. This is the reason for rewashing before drying for another length of time.)

How do the washers compare in percentage of water added to the clothes? What percentage of water is removed from the different types of loads in 15, 20, and 30 minutes? What conclusions can you draw on factors that determine how much water is removed from loads dried in dryers for the times used?

Experiment 4. *Inspection of Electric Irons*

1. What are voltage and wattage or voltage and amperage ratings? Note particularly whether alternating current only is specified on the nameplate. Is a model or catalogue number specified? Are manufacturer's name and address given? Does the iron carry the Underwriters Laboratories seal of approval?

2. Observe overall construction features.
   a. Is the handle easy to grasp?
   b. Is the thermostat dial operated easily? Is the dial located so that the user will not touch the hot iron when turning the dial?
   c. Lift the iron by the handle. Does it balance well in the hand or does it tip forward or backward?
   d. Is it convenient to tilt the iron?
   e. How many pounds does the iron weigh?
   f. Is the cord attached at a convenient location for your ironing habits? Is a protector provided at the place of attachment of the cord? Is the cord plug large enough to grasp easily when the iron is connected or disconnected from the power supply?
   g. If the iron is a combination or steam type, how is water added? If possible, add water to determine how easy or difficult it is to do this. Notice the pattern of the steam openings in the sole plate. Is it such that the front third or half of the iron will probably be covered with steam during ironing?

3. Estimate the area of the sole plate by making a tracing. (Usually the area is between 29 and 32 square inches.)

4. What kind of warranty is provided?

Experiment 5. *Inspection of Electric Ironers*

1. Are the following data marked on the ironer: manufacturer's name and address, model number, serial number, voltage rating, wattage rating? Does the ironer carry the Underwriters Laboratories seal of approval?

2. Does the user's booklet explain clearly how the controls operate? Are they easy to use?

3. What are the overall dimensions when the ironer is closed? When the ironer is opened and the side shelves and lap shelf are in the extended positions? Is it easy to open and close the ironer?
4. Observe the following overall construction features:
   a. Is the ironer easy to move? Are lock-type casters provided?
   b. Is the height of the work surface adjustable?
   c. What are the length and diameter of the roll?
   d. Sit at the ironer and operate it with heat off. Can you adjust articles on the roll easily without hazard of touching the shoe? Does the shoe seem to fit evenly to the roll?
   e. Is a convenient storage place provided for the cord of the ironer?
5. Are illustrations and instructions in the user's booklet clear to you?
6. What does the warranty promise the purchaser?

Experiment 6. *Optimum Moisture Content for "Dry" Ironing*

1. Weigh three, similar, dry cotton shirts and three similar sheets or pillowcases.
2. Compute the amounts of water that must be added to the articles to give them moisture contents of 15, 25, and 30 percent, respectively.
3. Use a sprinkler with warm water and wet the articles as follows: one shirt and one sheet or pillowcase to a moisture content of 15 percent; one shirt and one sheet or case to a moisture content of 25 percent; one shirt and one sheet or case to a moisture content of 30 percent. (For convenience, water added to the sprinkler may be measured in a graduate rather than weighed, since 1 milliliter of water weighs 1 gram.)
4. Store each set of two articles with the same moisture content in a separate plastic bag for 24 or 48 hours.
5. Iron with an iron or ironer.
6. Which moisture content is associated with the best final product? With the most ease in ironing?
7. Repeat the experiment to determine whether your answer or answers on best moisture content change as your skill in ironing these articles increases.

It may be necessary or desirable to wet portions of the articles with a damp sponge as you iron.

Index